BY THE SAME AUTHOR

The Naturalized Animals of the British Isles
Naturalized Mammals of the World
Naturalized Birds of the World
Evolution of Domesticated Animals (contrib.)
The Mandarin Duck
The New Atlas of Breeding Birds in Britain and Ireland (contrib.)

THEY DINED ON ELAND

THEY DINED ON ELAND

The Story of the Acclimatisation Societies

Christopher Lever

QUILLER PRESS
London

First published 1992 by Quiller Press Ltd
46 Lillie Road, London SW6 1TN

Text copyright © 1992 Sir Christopher Lever Bt

ISBN 1 870948 59 9

Produced by Hugh Tempest-Radford *Book Producers*
Typeset by Galleon Photosetting, Ipswich
Printed in Great Britain by St Edmundsbury Press

Contents

Preface   vii
Acknowledgements   x
Introduction   xiii
1. La Société Zoologique d'Acclimatation   1
2. Menageries and Aviaries in Eighteenth-century England   11
3. Frank Buckland and The Acclimatisation Society of the
    United Kingdom   20
4. The Society in 1860–1861   33
5. The Society in 1861–1862   38
6. The Society in 1862–1863   44
7. The Society in 1863–1864   52
8. The Society in 1864–1865   64
9. The Society's Questionnaire   74
10. The Acclimatisation Society of Great Britain and The
    Ornithological Society of London in 1865–1866   80
11. The Acclimatisation and Ornithological Society of London in
    1866–1867   87
12. What Did the Society Achieve?   94
13. Acclimatisation Societies in Australia   99
14. Acclimatisation Societies in New Zealand   130
15. The Imperial Russian Society for the Acclimatisation of
    Animals and Plants   172
16. Acclimatisation Societies in the United States and the
    Hawaiian Islands   183
17. Is there a Rôle for Exotic Species?   191

Appendix:
  Chronological List of Principal Acclimatisation Societies   193
Bibliography   195
Notes   202
Index   213

Plates   *between pages* 112–13

Preface

THE definition of the term 'acclimatisation' (or acclimation) has altered much during the past hundred and thirty years. In the year of the foundation of the Acclimatisation Society of the United Kingdom (1860), the *Saturday Review* magazine defined 'the acclimatisation of animals . . . [as] the reduction into a state of domestication of wild species and their addition to the domestic stock'. Half a century later, *The Encyclopaedia Britannica*[1] described acclimatisation as 'the process of adaptation by which animals and plants are gradually rendered capable of surviving and flourishing in countries remote from their original habitats, or under meteorological conditions different from those which they have usually to endure, and at first injurious to them.' A further half-century on, Fitter, in his seminal work, wrote: 'I shall use . . . *acclimatised* to mean that [the animal in question] can live in the open air but either has not succeeded in breeding or still has to be fed at some season of the year, usually winter.'[2] Eighteen years later, I defined acclimatised as meaning 'able to survive in the wild only with the support of man.'[3] Eight years on, I elaborated on this by describing acclimatised as ' "grown or become habituated to a new climate".[4] Used to describe an exotic species living in the wild in an alien environment or climate with the support of and dependent (e.g. for food) on man.'[5] More recently still, *The Encyclopaedia Britannica*[6] defined acclimatisation as 'any of the numerous gradual, long-term responses of an organism to changes in its environment.' What might be called a sub-meaning of the term acclimatisation today is the pre-release conditioning of a captive-bred species about to be reintroduced into the wild for the purpose of conservation.

These changes of nuance and variations in meaning need to be borne in mind when discussing the subject of acclimatisation throughout the world, especially since acclimatisation societies in some countries had totally different aims and objectives from those in others, and were founded by quite different types of people. Furthermore, those societies still surviving today have fundamentally different purposes to the ones for which they were founded; the *Société Zoologique d'Acclimatation*, for example, formed in 1854, is now one of the leading nature conservation and preservation groups in France, while Australian and New Zealand societies, which are likewise heavily involved in nature conservation, now largely cater for shooting and fishing interests.

When, as Fitter points out, a species clearly alien to Britain has been introduced before living memory, natural historians have as often as not ascribed its presence to the Romans, or in some cases even to the Phoenicians. There is, however, no evidence to suggest that any of the exotic animals which the Romans (or Phoenicians) may have acclimatised (in the current sense of the word) in Britain (such as the edible dormouse and possibly the common pheasant, the European rabbit, the common carp, and perhaps the allied crucian carp) and which may subsequently have become naturalised[7], survived the Middle Ages to become the progenitors of current naturalised populations; these are all descended from later—in some cases much later—introductions. A possible exception is the fallow deer, which was probably introduced and acclimatised by the Phoenicians around 1000 BC, and subsequently became naturalised; it was certainly well established in the wild in Britain by the Roman period.

Three domestic animals, the wild goat, the Soay sheep, and the domestic cat—introduced respectively in the Late Stone Age or Early Bronze Age, the Viking or pre-Viking period (c. 300–800 AD), and before about 1000 AD—all became acclimatised and later feral[8] in Britain during the Middle Ages.

Early attempts deliberately to acclimatise exotic animals in Britain were originally the exclusive domain of royalty; later, the nobility, aristocracy and landed gentry took up the running (see chapter 2), and it was from them and through their activities that the Society for the Acclimatisation of Animals, Birds, Fishes, Insects and Vegetables within the United Kingdom was formed. Although, as Fitter rightly says, the Society appears to have had no more direct effect on the fauna and flora of Britain than did the Romans before it ('we still lack our troops of eland and kudu galloping over the green-sward'), it undoubtedly had a considerable indirect effect through encouraging numerous private experiments in the acclimatisation of exotic species.

These experiments were carried out by individual landowners, only some of whom were members of the Society but all of whom were, to a greater or lesser extent, influenced by its activities or the events leading up to its formation. They included such men as James Duff (1776–1857), the fourth Earl of Fife, a Spanish general and MP for Banffshire in 1818, at Mar Lodge in Aberdeenshire in the 1820s; Charles Waterton (1782–1865), the eccentric squire of Walton Hall in Yorkshire, where in the 1820s and 1830s he created what was probably the first bird sanctuary in the world; Sir Thomas Fowell Buxton, Bt, of Northrepps and Cromer Halls in Norfolk, also in the 1820s and 1830s; the Marquess of Breadalbane, at Taymouth Castle, Perthshire, in the 1830s and 1840s; Mervyn, Viscount Powerscourt, an original council member of the

Society, at Powerscourt, County Wicklow; Mr J. H. Gurney of Northrepps, and the Earl of Leicester at Holkham Hall, Norfolk, in the middle of the century; Colonel Edward Cooper of Markree Castle, County Sligo, Lieutenant-Colonel E. G. B. Meade-Waldo at Stonewall Park, Kent, and the distinguished ornithologist Thomas Littleton Powys (1833–96), 4th Baron Lilford, towards the end of the century: and the Dukes of Bedford of Woburn Abbey, Bedfordshire, from the 1890s. Their experiments were continued during the present century by, among many others, Alfred Ezra of Foxwarren Park near Cobham in Surrey; Captain Henry Brocklehurst of Roaches House near Leek in Staffordshire; the Hon. Walter (later Lord) Rothschild at Tring in Hertfordshire; Viscount Grey of Fallodon in Northumberland; Mr F. R. S. Balfour of Dawyck Park, Stobo, Peeblesshire; the Earl of Iveagh at Elveden Hall near Thetford, Norfolk; Sir Giles and Sir Edmund Loder, Bts, at Leonardslee Park near Horsham, Sussex; and the Duke of Portland at Welbeck Abbey, Nottinghamshire.

After the First—and even more so after the Second—World War, fewer landowners could afford major experiments in the acclimatisation of exotic species, many of which escaped from private menageries into the countryside, where some of them became naturalised. With the passing in 1981 of the Wildlife and Countryside Act, whereby under Section 14 it became an offence 'to release or to allow to escape into the wild any animal which is of a kind which is not ordinarily resident in and is not a regular visitor to Great Britain in a wild state', legal attempts to acclimatise or naturalise new exotic species in Britain finally came to an end.

Acknowledgements

ONCE again I am indebted to a host of correspondents, principally in Britain, the United States, Australia and New Zealand, who have patiently and generously answered my many requests for help, and without whose cooperation this book would have been very much the poorer.

One of the few who failed to respond to my enquiries was *The Field* magazine, which was one of the main sponsors and supporters of the Acclimatisation Society of the United Kingdom in the 1860s.

My special thanks are due to the librarians and staff of the various institutions in which I carried out much of my research, in particular the British Museum (Natural History), the British Library, the Linnean Society of London, and the London Library. Others to whom I extend my grateful thanks are:

Mr D. G. C. Allan (Curator-Historian, Royal Society of Arts, London, UK); Mr N. Altenbernd (Massachusetts Institute of Technology, USA).

Mrs R. Balmford (Australia); Dr A. J. Berger (Hawaiian Islands); Mr F. Brightman (Editor, *Natural History Book Reviews*, UK); Mr J. W. Brown (Government of Western Australia); Mr J. A. Burton (UK).

The Earl of Caithness (Minister of State for the Environment, UK); Miss M. Calhoun (Field Museum of Natural History, USA); Mrs B. Carroll-Horrocks (American Philosophical Society, USA); Miss P. Chapman (British Library, UK); Miss E. Clark (Chicago Historical Society, USA); Mr K. Cooper (British Library, UK).

Miss B. J. Dawson (Cincinnati Historical Society, USA); Dr W. A. Deiss (Smithsonian Institution, USA); Mr J. DeJose (Perth Zoo, Australia); Miss G. Douglas (Librarian, Linnean Society of London, UK); Mrs B. S. Duggan (Southland Acclimatisation Society, NZ); Professor T. R. Dunlap (Virginia Polytechnic Institute and State University, USA).

Mr D. C. Emmett (Auckland Acclimatisation Society, NZ).

Mrs S. Festing (UK); Miss D. Finegan (Monash University, Australia); Mr R. Fish (Librarian, Zoological Society of London, UK); Mr F. E. E. Fox (UK).

Miss L. Geckler (Johns Hopkins University, USA); Dr L. R. Gillbank (University of Melbourne, Australia); Mr R. E. Goodman (American Philosophical Society, USA).

Mr E. G. Hancock (Glasgow Museum & Art Gallery, UK); Mr

A. Howell (Guernsey Museum & Art Gallery, UK); Mr K. H. Hyatt (London Natural History Society, UK).

Mr C. F. H. Jenkins (Australia); Mr B. Johnson (National Executive of Acclimatisation Societies, NZ).

Mr J. W. Kirby (Taranaki Acclimatisation Society, NZ).

Mr H. M. Lander (Australian Fresh Water Fishermen's Assembly); Mr A. Lewis (Institute of Marine & Terrestrial Ecology, Canada); Dr D. N. Livingstone (Queen's University of Belfast, UK); Mr K. Lomax (Oregon Historical Society, USA); Mr J. H. Long (Agriculture Protection Board of Western Australia).

Mr E. G. McCrae (Tasmania Acclimatisation Society, Australia); Dr R. M. McDowall (Freshwater Fisheries Centre, NZ); Mrs G. H. McFarlane (Glasgow University Library, UK); Mr N. O. Munns (Emu Farmers of Australia).

Mr G. Naylor (Monaro Acclimatisation Society, Australia); New York Public Library, USA; Miss B. Newlands (Australia).

Mr H. V. Ormond (Tauranga Acclimatisation Society, NZ); Dr M. A. Osborne (University of California, USA); Professor J. D. Ovington (Australian National Parks and Wildlife Service).

Mr B. Parkes (National Executive of Acclimatisation Societies, NZ); Madame V. Plocq (Scientific Committee on Problems of the Environment, France); Mr W. Pugh (New England Trout Acclimatisation Society, Australia).

Lord Quinton (British Library, UK).

Mrs B. Reardon (University Microfilms International, UK); Mr J. G. Ritchie (NZ); Professor H. Ritvo (Massachusetts Institute of Technology, USA); Mr M. A. Rodway (Southland Acclimatisation Society, NZ).

Mr A. L. Savage (Nelson Acclimatisation Society, NZ); Mr G. S. Shofter (Royal Melbourne Zoological Gardens, Australia); Dr E. Stellar (American Philosophical Society, USA); Mr B. H. Strange (Ashburton Acclimatisation Society, NZ); Mr R. Sutton (Wellington Acclimatisation Society, NZ); Mr H. M. Swinburn (Hawke's Bay Acclimatisation Society, NZ).

Mr W. G. Teagle (UK); Mr J. Thackray (Society for the History of Natural History, UK); Mr J. Thomas (Ohio Historical Society, USA).

Mr T. Vaughan (Oregon Historical Society, USA).

Dr R. M. Warnake (Department of Conservation, Forests & Lands, Australia); Mr B. Welsh (North Canterbury Acclimatisation Society, NZ); Professor D. R. Weiner (University of Arizona, USA); Mrs V. Wheat (American Museum of Natural History, USA); Mr G. A. Wheeldon (Department of the Environment, UK); Dr M. J. Williams (Department of Conservation, NZ); Mr R. Wilson (Audubon Society of Portland, USA).

Dr M. N. Yavercovski (Société Nationale de Protection de la Nature et d'Acclimatation de France).

Finally, my especial thanks are once again due to Mrs R. Rugman for her patience in deciphering and typing my almost-illegible manuscript.

Christopher Lever
Winkfield, Berkshire

Introduction

THE term acclimatisation[1] is all too frequently confused with domestication or naturalisation[2], or even with the designation feral[3], but all four words have in fact clearly distinct meanings. A domesticated animal or a cultivar need not necessarily be acclimatised (let alone naturalised)—i.e. it need not be capable of surviving severe weather even with artificial protection provided by man. A naturalised exotic species, on the other hand, must, by definition, be as able to endure unprotected the climatic and environmental conditions of its adopted home as an indigene. In many, if not in most, instances of naturalisation, there is no evidence of a gradual adaptation to alien conditions, which is a prerequisite of the theory of acclimatisation. Indeed, many naturalised species of both animals and plants, in an alien environment and climate, frequently increase and spread so rapidly and to such an extent as to overwhelm native competitors. In none of these instances is acclimatisation a forerunner of naturalisation. On the other hand, an acclimatised species may well fail to become naturalised, since inter-specific competition is an equally—indeed, some would say more—efficient means of controlling the success of an alien species as climate or habitat.

Animals and plants differ materially in their ability to adapt to new climatic conditions. Most tropical and semi-tropical plants are unable to survive unprotected in a temperate climate, and indeed many species become seriously stunted if moved only a few degrees of latitude north or south of their natural range. This is because, unlike most animals, plants have no inbuilt means of temperature control. That animals, especially mammals and birds, are much less affected by changes in temperature, is shown by the widespread distribution from north to south of many species. Although most terrestrial animals are confined to countries which do not have wide ranges in temperature or a greatly varying climate, this is largely the result of the presence of predators and/or competitors and a restricted supply of suitable foods.

Thus, whereas most (especially tropical and semi-tropical) plants and some—in particular cold-blooded—animals are basically restricted to countries having climates and temperatures similar to those of their natural range, some non-tropical or semi-tropical plants and a considerable number of warm-blooded animals are not confined by their constitution to their natural range alone, but are able to survive, increase and spread in differing climatic conditions and temperatures.

To domesticate or naturalise species in the latter group, in countries possessing temperatures and climates which do not differ materially from those pertaining in their native range, acclimatisation is not normally required; for species in the former group however, acclimatisation is an essential prelude to domestication or naturalisation—if, indeed, it is even feasible.

Acclimatisation, if it is to take place, can occur either through adaptation or modification of the physiology and/or morphology of an individual or, far more commonly, through inherited variation of its descendants, which are better adapted than their parents to cope with alien conditions. In some cases little perceptible alteration in a species' form or structure takes place, but in others it can be quite marked. Although many of these modifications may be due to other than climatic causes, they show how local conditions can affect the form and structure of both animals and plants, and make it likely that morphological and/or physiological changes are continually occurring.

It is thus apparent that some species of animals and plants, whether domesticated, cultivated or wild, are more or less suited than others to potential acclimatisation in an alien environment. Although climatic conditions may not always be directly responsible for producing variations in a species' offspring, it is clear that such morphological and/or physiological variations do arise, and that some of these variant forms will be better adapted than others to the climatic and environmental conditions of the area. In the wild, harsh winters weed out weak or otherwise inferior individuals, and thus the adaptation of the species to an alien climate is maintained. In domestication and cultivation, man deliberately selects those varieties most suited to local conditions. In order to have the best chance of acclimatising any species, whether animal or plant, in an alien environment and climate in which it is known that it cannot survive unsupported by man, some form of natural (or, in the case of domesticated or cultivated species, what may be termed 'unnatural') selection therefore needs to be practised.

The many rapid changes which elicit speedy short-term responses in an organism through the hormonal or nervous systems, whereby individuals are able to control their internal functions swiftly, so as to survive within the normal range of short-term environmental changes, are not examples of acclimatisation. This accelerated control or homoeostasis (the ability of a biological system to resist alteration and to maintain itself in a stable equilibrium)[4] is confined to a limited range of climatic changes. In most cases, homoeostatic control is unable effectively to combat major environmental alterations outside normal seasonal variations. With the onset of winter in temperate latitudes, some organisms change their physiology and their way of life in order to cope with colder conditions; this gradual bodily adjustment to changing conditions is a form of acclimatisation.

In contrast to homoeostasis, the natural adaptive responses that result in acclimatisation are continual, and are reversible in the event that environmental conditions in which an organism finds itself revert to the *status quo ante*. The genetic make-up of an acclimatised organism is not permanently marked by acclimatisation; the adaptation to changes by populations of organisms which produces evolution through the selection of genetic capability, is a different process to the acclimatisation of an individual. The primary definition of 'acclimatisation' in *The Oxford Dictionary of Natural History* (1985) is the 'reversible, adaptive response that enables animals to tolerate environmental change (e.g. seasonal climatic change). The response is physiological, but may affect behaviour (e.g. when an animal responds physiologically to falling temperature in ways that make hibernation possible, and behaviourally by seeking a nesting site, nesting materials, and food).'

The effects of climate on the life of an organism, so far as it relates to acclimatisation, comprise adaptations to temperature, humidity, light, barometric pressure, salinity, and chemistry. Of these, the most important is temperature. The secondary definition of acclimatisation '(acclimation or hardening)' in *The Oxford Dictionary of Natural History* is 'changes . . . that occur in a plant in response to chilling or freezing temperatures, which protect tissues or confer tolerance to the cold'. Since organisms are limited in their methods of adapting to climatic and environmental variations, they sometimes make use of the same processes to adapt to changes of differing sources.

Because it is possible successfully to acclimatise (or even to naturalise) organisms outside their natural range, it is sometimes claimed that animals and plants do not necessarily flourish to their best advantage in their home latitudes. Whether or not this is so, it is certainly true that an acclimatised species is not always able to exist at its maximum potential. In temperate latitudes in the height of summer, acclimatised (and some naturalised and indigenous) mammals and birds shelter from the sun, while in winter some animals (mostly mammals) hibernate, and plants in general become dormant; in some tropical and semi-tropical regions a number of species aestivate. Any organism *in extremis* may suffer from some natural failing, but in most cases it will survive; if the damage is excessive, the individual has not become adequately acclimatised, and may die.

The adaptations that allow animals and plants to become acclimatised sometimes enable them to live in areas of considerable seasonal climatic variation, and occasionally indeed to exploit entirely new and different environments. McCoy, however, considered that '. . . by far the greater number of important achievements of acclimatisation have been *the bringing together in any one country the various useful or ornamental animals of other countries having the same or nearly the same climate and general conditions of surface.*[5] The individuals of a species that successfully acclimatise produce offspring from which new populations can become established, and in some cases even naturalised. The capability of different species to acclimatise successfully varies considerably; some breeds of domesticated animals and cultivars acclimatise easily and well, while others may be comparatively or even completely unsuccessful.

Under experimental conditions, some insects, plants and microorganisms show a tolerance for much lower or higher temperatures than they are ever likely to meet in the wild; the purpose of this phenomenon is uncertain. Other species seem able to evolve adaptive characteristics for acclimatisation in advance of climatic changes; precisely why and how this is achieved is similarly unknown. We clearly have much still to learn about the science of acclimatisation.

1. La Société Zoologique d'Acclimatation

THE collection and propagation of exotic animals and plants flourished in pre-Revolutionary France as it did elsewhere in continental Europe and in England. As early as the beginning of the seventeenth century, the French government had frequently taken advantage of the scientific expertise of the king's medical staff at the *Jardin des Plantes du Roi* in its search for fresh sources of income. This search was one of the principal reasons why the government was subsequently to sponsor the operations of the *Société Zoologique d'Acclimatation* (the *Société*).[1]

Originally a garden of simples, by the 1630s Guy de la Brosse, the intendant of the *Jardin des Plantes du Roi* from 1626 to 1641, had accumulated a collection of many exotic non-medicinal plants for use in agriculture and commerce. By the end of the seventeenth century, the *Jardin des Plantes du Roi* was distributing plants and seeds among municipal gardens, scientific societies, and private horticulturists at home, and to such colonies as Martinique and the Antilles overseas.

Prior to the Revolution in 1789, the intendants of the *Jardin des Plantes du Roi* had confined its activities almost entirely to the cultivation of exotic plants. The enabling legislation of 1793 that converted the *Jardin des Plantes du Roi* into the *Muséum National d'Histoire Naturelle* (the *Muséum*) both codified the horticultural activities, whose scope and nature increased during the nineteenth century, and also provided for the creation of a menagerie.

Hitherto, the country's largest assemblage of exotic animals had been that of Louis XIV (1638–1715) at Versailles, where the animals were kept mainly for hunting, the table, and entertainment. By the mid-eighteenth century, however, menageries had come to be regarded more as places of scientific research, while the government encouraged agricultural improvement by founding schools of veterinary medicine at Lyons in 1762 and Alfort in 1765 and the *Société Royal d'Agriculture*, and by providing funds for experimenting with exotic animals in the hope of agricultural progress.

Georges Louis Leclerc, Comte de Buffon (1707–88), intendant of the *Jardin des Plantes du Roi* from 1739 until his death, tried unsuccessfully to transfer the menagerie at Versailles to the *Jardin* in Paris. Frustrated in this ambition, Buffon was forced to rely heavily on the Versailles collection and on his own personal menagerie at Montbard (which may well have been the first place in which live wild animals were studied scientifically) for information for his *Histoire Naturelle* (1749–67).

1

Although the *Muséum* menagerie did not actually open until five years after Buffon's death, he deserves much of the credit for its creation.

From the 1780s onwards Louis Jean Marie Daubenton (1716–99) was responsible for the increasing involvement of the *Jardin des Plantes du Roi* in the study of economic zoology, including the acclimatisation of exotic animals for commercial and agricultural purposes, and may rightly be regarded as the father of the acclimatisation movement in France.

The constitution of the *Muséum*, which was approved in June 1793, also provided for the creation of a menagerie; its first director, who was in charge until 1837, was Etienne Geoffroy Saint-Hilaire (1772–1844); he was succeeded in turn by his son Isidore (1805–61).

From the outset of his career, Isidore had envisaged a menagerie as a multi-purpose institution, combining the education and entertainment of the public with serious zoological research. To this end he proposed the creation of two separate branches of the menagerie, in the Bois de Vincennes and—in the Bois de Boulogne—a *Jardin Zoologique d'Acclimatation*. The former failed to get off the ground, but as an institution specialising in the practical utilisation of exotic animals, the latter was to have a significant impact in usurping the *Muséum* menagerie's rôle in acclimatisation studies.

Several factors contributed to the failure of animal acclimatisation at the *Muséum*, which in the mid-nineteenth century was moving slowly towards the creation of an experimental programme, of which the science of acclimatisation came to be regarded as the poor relation and suffered from its association with agriculture and the applied arts. In this, the rôle of Isidore Geoffroy Saint-Hilaire was decisive, and it is ironical, as Osborne (1987) points out, that this scientific zoologist, who made a detailed study of animal acclimatisation, should have been responsible for both a revival of Daubenton's early experimental work on the acclimatisation of exotic animals, and also for a reduction of this activity within the *Muséum*.

On 20 January 1854 a group of French savants held a preliminary meeting to discuss the formation of a society for acclimatisation (the *Société*), under the chairmanship of Isidore Geoffroy Saint-Hilaire, who addressed them thus:

> Nous serons plus heureux que nos devanciers, nous aurons ce qui a manqué jusqu'à a ce jour l'ésprit d'initiation uni à l'ésprit de suite, l'effort individuel, l'action passagère de chacun, unis à l'action collective et durable de tous. Voilà où est nôtre force. Que petit chacun de nous? Presque rien. Tous ensemble nous pouvons et nous ferons.

['We shall be more successful than our predecessors because we shall possess what has hitherto been lacking, a spirit of initiative linked to one of continuity of individual effort, the transitory actions of each individual being joined to the collective and continuing work of us all. That will be our strength. What can we achieve alone? Virtually nothing. Collectively, we can [succeed] and we shall.']

The society would be formed, Geoffroy Saint-Hilaire continued, of agriculturalists, naturalists, landowners and scientists, not only from France but from the whole of the civilised world. The principal object of the society was to stock fields, forests and rivers with new species, so as to increase and add variety to the nation's food supply and to benefit the country's economy. Although many exotic vegetables had already been introduced to France, only two alien mammals (the rabbit and goat) and one bird (the common pheasant) had become naturalised in the country.

Similarly, despite the fact that in times past several domestic species of mammals and birds had been brought from abroad, very few had been imported in recent times. Soon after the discovery of North America in 1492, Geoffroy Saint-Hilaire continued, the Spaniards had brought back a few birds from the New World, but none of any domestic value.[2] To the 'many educated people who say that the present variety of domesticated animals satisfies our requirements' and who enquire 'why do we need new conquests?', Geoffroy Saint-Hilaire pointed out that the aim of his embryo society was 'the enrichment and expansion of agriculture, now, as before, the greatest source of national wealth.'

Exotic species, Geoffroy Saint-Hilaire went on, were becoming increasingly important to Europeans as a source of food: potatoes from America, grapes and wheat from Asia, and horses, donkeys, goats, cats, dogs, fowl, pheasants, peacocks and silkworms from Asia or Africa for food or other purposes, were all of undeniable value. 'There are', Geoffroy Saint-Hilaire claimed sententiously, 'no "insignificant" discoveries in the field of agriculture. To introduce and develop a variety, to make a wild animal useful in some way—for food or for work', was of inestimable benefit to the whole of mankind, and not only for the present but for the future as well. In part, these benefits were economic, since the domestication of new animals and plants brought their own financial rewards, and thus further emphasised the value to agriculturalists of successful acclimatisation, as well as having a more direct and immediate scientific relevance.

Of the total of 140,000 animals then known to science, only forty-three had so far been domesticated, and of these ten were absent from western Europe. In European colonisation of the unknown world, acclimatisation had been exclusively a one-way outward bound traffic. 'We have given the sheep to Australia; why have we not taken in exchange the kangaroo—a most edible and productive creature?' 'New conquests of animals and plants', Geoffroy Saint-Hilaire declared, 'will serve as new sources of wealth.'

Thus exhorted, the *Société*—which was officially founded on 10 February 1854, and can justly lay claim to be the senior such society in the world[3]—opened its doors to scientific academics, agronomists, agriculturalists, biologists, botanists, landowners and zoologists, and to all 'friends of human progress' generally. Its declared intentions were principally 'The introduction, acclimatisation, and domestication of animals, whether useful or ornamental. The perfecting and multiplication of races newly introduced or domesticated. The introduction and cultivation of useful vegetables'. While its primary objective was the enrichment of the food supply and economy of France, it wished similarly to benefit other countries as well.

The impact of the infant *Société* was such that in 1855, in only the second year of its existence, a report was laid before the members stating that in other parts of France a desire had arisen to form similar organisations, which wished to become affiliated to the parent body; the first of these, the *Société Zoologique d'Acclimatation pour la Région des Alpes* in Grenoble, was quickly followed by the *Société Régionale d'Acclimatation d'Encouragement et de Progrès* in Nancy, and various provincial agricultural societies were elected corresponding members. By 1862–3, no fewer than thirty-nine French metropolitan scientific institutions, five colonial acclimatisation societies (in Algeria, French Guyana, Réunion, Martinique and Guadeloupe), and twenty-four foreign associations (but excluding the United Kingdom society) had come under the Parisian society's umbrella.

In 1857 the *Société* offered a series of medals, each worth between £20 and £80, for the introduction and successful domestication or acclimatisation of, among others, the alpaca from South America; the kiang, 'a valuable beast of burden, of great power and swiftness, which belongs to Thibet'; the 'peetsi' or quagga from South Africa (now extinct); the eastern and western grey kangaroos from Australia, and the emu, greater rhea, ostrich and great bustard from, respectively, Australia, South America, Africa and Europe. Awards were also offered for the acclimatisation or domestication of game birds, edible fish, silkworms, a 'wax-producing insect, not a bee', a new variety of Chinese yam, and quinine.

It was subsequently recorded that the government of Peru, 'wishing to give a proof of its devotion to that of the Emperor of the French . . . had relaxed a prohibition, and had permitted the exportation of a dozen alpacas and a dozen llamas, animals whose worth for improving the quality of wool is inestimable.' A lengthy discourse was provided on the best means of cultivating and acclimatising the Chinese yam, which was judged 'worthy to be employed in fine soups, and as garnish to certain *ragoûts*, and as the basis for several sweet *entremêts'*.

The wide variety of species suggested for acclimatisation or domestication gives some indication of the eclectic field of the operations of the *Société*. Among the first recipients of medals in 1857–8 were Queen Isabella II of Spain for the introduction of alpacas, and Major Henry C. Wayne for introducing Arabian camels or dromedaries as beasts of burden for the United States army. The Emperor of France, Napoleon III (1808–73), was commended for the introduction of the rock partridge, the formation of coastal oyster beds, and for the creation of a fish hatchery at Huningue near Basel. The Minister of Marine had arranged for the establishment of acclimatisation gardens for exotic plants in all the French overseas colonies, and the War Department had taken the same step in Algeria. The King of Würtemburg had agreed to experiment with the domestication of angora goats, and the Emperor Dom Pedro had volunteered to do likewise with camels in Brazil, 'the vast, arid, sandy regions of which render the service of that animal so invaluable'.

Less exalted members of the *Société* also achieved considerable success. The distinguished traveller, writer, naturalist and diplomat, Louis-Charles Nicolas Maximilien de Montigny (1805–68) had imported from China the 'Sorgho grass . . . which abounds in sugar, and which will probably supersede the cultivation of beetroot [sugar-beet] in that country as a sugar-producing plant . . . alcohol may be distilled from it, and the refuse makes excellent food for cattle'; it had been successfully cultivated in Kaylie in Algeria, and in the French departments of Provence, Isère, Loiret and Maine-et-Loire, and even in the environs of Paris. Good-quality paper and wine had been extracted from it, and it was regarded as 'the first conquest' of the *Société*. Several new species of silkworm had been added to those already being propagated in southern France, and a number of mammals, birds and fish had also been introduced from abroad.

Elected an honorary member of the *Société* at its inauguration in 1854, de Montigny worked tirelessly, during the decade or so he spent as a diplomat in the Far East, to send back to France plants (including cotton, bamboo and yams), seeds, medicinal products, and animals (including silkworm eggs, domestic fowl and yaks from Tibet), and any other natural objects or artefacts that he considered might have scientific interest or commercial potential for France.

In 1859 the *Société* acquired a splendid garden and vivarium—the *Jardin Zoologique d'Acclimatation* (the *Jardin*)—in 'a section of the Bois du Boulogne, comprehending nearly forty acres of salubrious soil . . .' according to one account,[4] and described elsewhere[5] as 'a space of not less than thirty English acres, situated in the best part of that favoured locality, with an unlimited supply of water and many other "priviliges" ' (thrice the extent of the Zoological Society of London's gardens in Regent's Park) 'with every convenience and appliance for carrying out its principles'; the first director of the *Jardin* in 1859 was Mr David W. Mitchell, lately secretary of the Zoological Society of London.

By 1860, when it was corresponding with more than thirty scientific institutions throughout the world and was publishing monthly reports, the membership of the *Société* had risen to over two thousand, including thirty-five members of royal families such as Friedrich-Wilhelm of Prussia and the Emir of Khartoum, and ranging from 'the Emperor of the French to the King of Siam, from the Sovereign Pontiff to the Emperor of Brazil'.

The *Société* took an active interest in the agricultural development and European settlement of its colonies overseas, of which by far the most important was Algeria. As well as being employed for the acclimatisation of exotic plants in its own right, Algeria was also useful as a trial ground for the subsequent introduction to France of plants from tropical and semi-tropical climates. By way of North Africa came various edible tuberous roots from Siam; 'oleaginous peas' from China; via Egypt no less than fourteen varieties of dry Javanese rice; the gum-producing *Astrogalus verus* and *A. cereus* from the Middle East; several Chinese plants which produce lac and varnish; the fruits *Arrona charniolia* and *A. muricata* from Peru and the Antilles; bamboos from Madagascar and other African islands, India and China; a variety of Syrian peach; some twenty varieties of nuts from Egypt; and the ornamental tree or shrub *Araucaria* from Brazil.

Charles-Victor Naudin, director of the agronomic institute in Antibes and assistant naturalist at the *Jardin Zoologique de Marseilles*, achieved a significant *coup* by successfully acclimatising in southern France palm trees from Natal in South Africa, and had suggested that date palms from Algeria and palmettos from Louisiana[6] in the United States might similarly be established.

As a result of the ravages of the potato blight in France, which had been as serious as in the United Kingdom and Ireland, a new variety was introduced from Australia, in the hope that it would regenerate the old stock, and plans were afoot to obtain others from the uplands of South America.

Among animals, one of the most potentially valuable importations made by the *Société* was that of the Chinese silkworm, whose silk produces a strong and durable fabric. Considerable progress was also made with the artificial propagation of fish, using ova and spawn from the government hatchery at Huningue.

Some 20,000 rock partridge eggs were imported into France, in some parts of which the species was now said to be abundant, and the indigenous capercaillie was successfully transplanted within France outside its natural range. Ostriches and cassowaries were bred

with sufficient success to suggest that the medals offered for their acclimatisation would not long remain unclaimed, and *The Field* magazine
proclaimed that 'the society is to be congratulated upon the prospects
of the valuable feathers, savoury flesh, and delicious eggs promised by
these monster additions to the domestic poultry-yard.'

Taking an early conservationist position, the *Société* inveighed against
the wholesale slaughter 'by ignorant rustics' of insectivorous songbirds
which, as it rightly pointed out, were really the farmer's and horticul-
turist's best friends, and ought to be strictly preserved.

Turning to the acclimatisation of alien animals in French colonies and
in foreign countries, the *Société* believed that the establishment of some
animal capable of combating snakes in Martinique in the West Indies
should be considered; for this purpose European hedgehogs, the small
Indian mongoose, and the secretary bird were suggested. Eventually,
in the 1880s or 1890s, mongooses were successfully introduced to Martinique, among many other West Indian islands, where they succeeded
in controlling the venomous pit viper or *Fer-de-lance* of tropical South
America.[7]

For the improvement of domestic pigs in Cayenne (French Guyana),
it was suggested that tapirs from Central and South America should be
introduced, as well as agoutis from the same area and acuchis from the
Amazon basin.

The group of savants who founded the *Société* in 1854 were motivated
by a desire to place science at the service of agriculture and commerce,
and in this capacity they began (especially after the formation of the
Jardin Zoologique d'Acclimatation in 1859) to encroach upon the access
of the *Muséum* to exotic animals, and on its rôle as a source of zoological
information.[8] As president of the *Société* and also director of the
Muséum menagerie (both of which also had a large number of members
in common), Isidore Geoffroy Saint-Hilaire acted as a mediator between
the two organisations. His intention was for the *Jardin* to specialise in
the useful application of zoological theory, while the *Muséum* would
retain its position as the country's centre of theoretical zoology, and col-
laborate with the *Jardin* in the selection of potentially useful species. In
the problems arising from domestication and acclimatisation, Geoffroy
Saint-Hilaire saw an opportunity of studying the degree of variation in
domestic species. The unfortunate tendency of many people to treat
naturalisation, acclimatisation and domestication as a single subject,
and the even more deplorable propensity (then as now) to use the
terms synonymously, prevented the evolvement of a consensus, let
alone a synthesis, on acclimatisation.

Osborne (1987) distinguishes three distinct phases in the relation-
ship between the *Société* and the *Muséum* during the Second Empire

(1851–70). The period between 1854 and 1859 was characterised by amicable interaction and mutual collaboration: after the opening of the *Jardin* in 1860, there arose in the two organisations a mood of resentment and competition for both animals and resources: finally, the election as professor of mammals at the *Jardin* of Henri Milne-Edwards (1800–85), marked a period of overt hostility and almost total estrangement which was to last throughout much of the period of the Third Republic (1870–1909).

As Osborne observes, the three main achievements of the *Société* were firstly the formation of a menagerie in Paris, secondly the development of crops in colonial Algeria and, thirdly, in rural metropolitan France. Of these, the first named was undoubtedly the best-known project of the *Société*.

Permitted under its constitution to exhibit solely species considered 'of public utility', the founders of the *Jardin Zoologique d'Acclimatation* intended that the requirements of practicality and public exhibition should be the menagerie's guidelines. A fashionable attraction in the 1860s, the *Jardin* combined commercialism with popular scientific education and, as Osborne says, it soon became a popular resort of the *demi-monde*, families, and schoolchildren.

Visitors to the *Jardin* were able to see the largest collection of exotic domestic animals in Europe, could attend lectures on the practical and scientific aspects of modern animal husbandry and plant cultivation—i.e. acclimatisation—and witness demonstrations of the latest agricultural implements. Although it initially received governmental and private and public funding, the *Jardin* soon ran into financial difficulties. In the late 1860s attendances started to fall, and increasing fiscal problems forced it to sponsor commercial ventures such as plays, operas, concerts and other non-scientific enterprises. Direct government subsidies began to dwindle, and the revenue derived from the exhibition, breeding and sale of exotic species was insufficient for self-maintenance.

Created and sustained with direct imperial patronage, the apogee of the *Jardin* occurred during the years of the Second Empire. Despite the provision of financial assistance by foreign and French organisations following the disastrous Franco-Prussian War of 1870–71, the fortunes of the *Jardin* continued to decline. At the expense of its principal scientific objective of the acclimatisation of animals, in 1882 the statutes of the *Jardin* were amended in a desperate attempt to achieve financial stability. Following its reorganisation, additional stock was issued and several loans were floated. Isidore Geoffroy Saint-Hilaire's son, Albert, who had been director of the *Jardin* since 1865, resigned from his position in 1893 when the corporation was on the verge of bankruptcy. He left behind an organisation beset by debts and virtually divorced from its parent *Société*, which was finally declared insolvent in 1901.

The second of the main achievements of the *Société* was the development of agricultural and horticultural crops in Algeria—the largest and geographically closest and most important of France's colonies.

Algeria, which held a privileged position within the French Empire, was consistently allocated the major proportion of the mother country's colonial budget, and Algeria's scientific institutions—especially the important *Comité d'Acclimatation de l'Algérie* (founded in 1859) and the *Jardin d'Essai* in Algiers—greatly benefited from this liberality. Although the attitude of the French public towards the colonies, particularly prior to the Franco-Prussian War, was generally apathetic, a number of scientists and administrators—mainly members of the parent *Société* in Paris—were committed to the overseas colonies in general and to Algeria in particular. The *Société* acted as the French government's consultant on agriculture and horticulture in Algeria, on the economics of which was based European settlement of the colony. In an attempt to define and manage the country's economic development, the government and the *Société* became joint sponsors of several scientific delegations to Algeria, the reports of which until the early 1860s invariably favoured protectionist economic policies that supported metropolitan interests.

By the mid-to-late 1860s the activities of the *Société* in Algeria—combined experiments with governmental organisations, inspections by *Société* representatives, and the recruitment of new members—started to decline as the French Empire entered the era of free trade, and Algeria prepared itself for non-military government. The resulting changes in high-ranking personnel—especially the departure of those in accord with the objectives of the *Société*—and increasing financial difficulties, led to a decline in the ability of the *Société* to continue its colonial administration.

A number of factors complicated the European settlement of Algeria. The government of France changed hands four times between August 1830, when Algiers was taken by the French army, and the end of the Franco-Prussian War in February 1871. Three major conflicts, an exceptionally unhealthy climate, and a number of uprisings combined to discourage European settlement, while the development of a consistent economic policy in Algeria was further complicated by internecine squabbles among the military forces, Parisian land developers, and the resident civil authorities. The *Société*, which was loyal to the French army but claimed to be on the side of European settlers, actively supported Napoleon III's policy of *petite culture*, which was the principal method of land tenure in the 1850s and 1860s.

Turning now to the third of Osborne's list of the principal achievements of the *Société*—the development of crops in rural metropolitan

France—we find that the economic histories of the Lorraine and Dauphiné in eastern France during the Second Empire are remarkably similar. The principal cities, Nancy in the department of Meurthe-et-Moselle and Grenoble in that of Isère, were centres of both agriculture and commerce. The railhead, which arrived in both cities in the 1850s, served to join commercial and industrial resources to national and international markets. Prior to the Franco-Prussian War the remnants of the previous economy remained, but thereafter the peasants' polyculture subsistence small-holding type of farming gave way to agricultural monoculture on large commercial farms.

Within a few years of its foundation, the *Société Zoologique d'Acclimatation* had become the acknowledged international centre of the acclimatisation movement. As such, it was the inspiration for the formation of similar societies in various countries throughout the world (all the European ones, with the exception of that of the United Kingdom, being formally affiliated to the *Société*), including Switzerland (five), Italy, Sicily (in Palermo in 1861), Spain (in Madrid), Prussia (the *Akklimatisations-verein* in Berlin, founded in 1858, and Cologne), Holland, Madeira, Egypt, Natal (South Africa), India (at Lahore and Calcutta), Ceylon (Sri Lanka), China, Australia, New Zealand, the United States of America, Russia—and England.

2. Menageries and Aviaries in Eighteenth-century England

SINCE early times—indeed, since the biblical days of Noah and his Ark—exotic wild animals have been recognised as prestigious presents and symbols of political power, and have been maintained in private collections by royalty and the nobility throughout the world—especially in ancient Egypt, China, India and Rome.[1] The earliest recorded zoos or menageries were to be found in Egypt around 1400 BC, when various exotic beasts were regarded as appurtenances to places of worship, and in China in the twelfth century BC, where the first ruler of the Chou dynasty maintained what he referred to as 'a garden of intelligence'. King Solomon of Israel (c. 1015–977 BC) had a collection of apes and peafowl, and King Nebuchadnessar II of Babylon (d. 562 BC) kept captive lions.

Julius Caesar (100 BC–44 BC) mentions in his *Commentaries* that in Roman times wealthy English landowners possessed parks in which they kept such domestic animals as hares, geese and fowl, not for the table but as 'companions' or 'pets' or for ornamental purposes. The Norman aristocracy who invaded Britain in 1066 with William the Conqueror (1027–87) commandeered these parks for their own use, which they stocked with deer for hunting.

Originally, however, the emphasis in collections of exotic animals was on spectacle rather than utility. Blunt (1976) states that on one occasion a nobleman received a bear for his park from William II ('Rufus'; reigned 1087–1100), and the English chronicler, William of Malmesbury (c. 1090–1143), records that Henry I (1068–1135) maintained at Woodstock, near Oxford, a collection of camels, leopards, lions, lynxes and other animals, including 'a remarkable owl' and a porcupine which had been given to him by William of Montpellier.[2]

In 1235, according to Festing (1988), or in 1252, as Blunt maintains, in the reign of Henry III (1207–72), or, as Ritvo (1987) says, during the reign of Henry IV (1367–1413), the royal menagerie was transferred from Woodstock (where it had been established since, or before, the time of William the Conqueror) to the Tower of London, where it remained until in 1830–1 it was presented by William IV (1765–1837) to the recently formed Zoological Society of London. Henry III kept in his menagerie a polar bear, for whose maintenance at the Tower the sheriffs of the City were made responsible; they were obliged to furnish

11

it with a muzzle and chain, and a rope on which to tether it when it was taken down to the Thames to bathe and catch fish. In 1254, Henry was presented by his son-in-law, Louis IX of France, with what is believed to have been the first elephant to be seen in England, the maintenance of which again fell on the unfortunate sheriffs.

From the late fifteenth century onwards, eight acres of medicinal gardens in Magdalen College, Oxford, on the site of the present deer park, provided space for a collection of exotic animals among the flowers, vegetables, orchards, dovecote and ornamental fish ponds. In 1494, Henry VII (1456–1509) received a gift of some marmosets from the college, and a decade later returned the compliment with the 'extraordinary present' of a female bear.[3] In 1611 Frederick II, King of Denmark, sent some fallow deer from Norway or Sweden to Dalkeith Palace, Midlothian, as a gift to James I (1566–1625) and his Danish-born wife Anne. Charles I (1600–49) stocked the royal parks with wild boar from Europe, while his son, Charles II (1630–85), maintained a large collection of acclimatised exotic waterfowl in St James's Park in London, including Canada geese and Egyptian geese, both of which subsequently became naturalised in Britain. The Swiss historian, Jacob Burckhardt (1818–97), believed that private menageries and aviaries were part of the appurtenances of a prince of the Renaissance.[4]

Travellers returning from abroad served to whet the appetite of the home-bound for the acquisition of exotic creatures. While in Holland in 1634, the parliamentary commander, Sir William Brereton (1604–61),[5] remarked in his diary on 'all manner of dainty fowl' he saw in the Hague, and Sir Henry Wotton (1568–1639), the poet and diplomat, commented on the 'rare beasts, birds and fishes' he observed while on the continent, 'of which noble kind of creatures we ought not childishly to despise the contemplation, for in all things natural there is ever something that is admirable'.[6]

The diarist John Evelyn (1620–1706) reported on a beautiful aviary he saw on a visit to the Doria palace overlooking the Italian port of Genoa, 'wherein grow trees of more than two foote diameter, besides cypresses, myrtils, lentiscus and other rare shrubs, which serve to nestle and perch all kinds of birds who have ayre and place enough under their ayrie canopy'.[7] Vivaria, Evelyn continued, should be 'green and shady places . . . where wild beasts are kept', which were 'by the Greeks call'd Paradises'. Gardens for animals ought ideally to include enclosures constructed of 'wales partitions and accommodations', like those he had seen in Brussels. He complimented the Turks for the manner in which they kept 'Bears, Wolves, Leopards and the fiercest Lyons and Panthers', and concluded, rather tamely, by suggesting that squirrels and tortoises might similarly be kept in Britain.[8]

Francis Bacon (1561–1626) advocated naturalistic rather than artificial aviaries which, he said, should be large enough to cover with turf and provide sufficient space for nesting so that 'no foulness appear in the floor of the aviary'.[9]

It was not until the late seventeenth century, however, when Britain became physically and culturally less isolated from much of the rest of the world, that the maintenance of collections of wild animals ceased to be regarded as solely a royal prerogative. The exploration of Africa, North America and the Caribbean resulted in the introduction to Britain of many exotic species of animals and plants. The curiosity of the general public and the aesthetic appeal of foreign animals in the parks of great country houses owned by the aristocracy were important reasons for the new fashion. The visual attraction of wandering herds of cattle, antelope and deer, and flights of waterfowl, complemented the informal 'natural' landscapes of such men as Lancelot ('Capability') Brown (1715–83), and species unsuitable for keeping 'in the wild' were housed in appropriate buildings.

From the end of the seventeenth century—when magnificent collections in 'romantic' settings were to be found on the continent, especially in Holland and France—private individuals who were unable to afford their own menageries could see for themselves some of the fruits of overseas exploration and the increase in foreign trade by visiting the public collections resulting from such activities. Advertisements for these displays frequently made much of the uniqueness of their exhibits; thus around 1795 one showman offered 'a most stupendous elephant' which was alleged to be 'the only animal of the kind seen in this Kingdom for upwards of TWENTY YEARS'. In 1805, a Peruvian llama exhibited in London's Haymarket was described as 'the first that has ever been offered to the inspection of a British Public'. One Thomas Shore offered a reward of no less than £500 to 'any Person who ever saw in any other Travelling Menagerie, a Black Tyger, His being the ONLY ONE in Europe'. In 1770 the noted equestrian and entrepreneur, Philip Astley (1742–1814), introduced the public to the 'joys' of the (now happily ailing) modern circus, when he opened an establishment at the Halfpenny Hatch on London's Westminster Bridge Road.

Well into the nineteenth century, visitors to the capital would flock to see sufficiently unusual individual animals, such as the so-called 'bonasus' (probably a European bison) which was much admired by Queen Caroline and billed by its promoters as 'the only one that was ever imported into this Kingdom—*the sight of which instantly impressed every beholder with that magnificent idea of wonder which no words can describe.*' Kendrick's Menagerie boasted 'Two Surprising Nylghaws [nilgai]', while a French showman crossed the Channel with a wildebeest or gnu which he not inaccurately described as 'one of the most Extraordinary Productions of Nature!'

Later in the nineteenth century, collections of different species began to supplant the display of individual animals. Encouraged by his successful exhibition of two boa constrictors in 1804, in the following year George Wombwell (1779–1850), a cordwainer (bootmaker) of Soho, formed what was the first major travelling menagerie in Britain. When Wombwell acquired a pair of rhinoceroses, he advertised them as 'Those Rare and Wonderful Animals, the . . . Unicorns of Scripture . . . and the Largest Quadruped in the World', with below, in much smaller type, 'the Elephant excepted'. His success inspired others, and by 1825 London's annual Bartholomew Fair in Smithfield Market offered two large menageries in addition to Wombwell's.

The principal private early-nineteenth century collection of wild animals in London, however, was the Exeter Change Menagerie, which had started life in the eighteenth century as Pidcock's Exhibition of Wild Beasts, later becoming Polito's Royal Menagerie, before coming under the management of Mr Edward Cross. It was originally kept in a commercial warehouse off the Strand in central London, and in 1812 included two tigers, a lion, a panther, a hyaena, a leopard, two sloths, a camel, a large number of monkeys, and a tapir. In 1829 it transferred to the King's Mews, on the site of the present National Gallery, and thence to the grounds of the Manor House in Wandsworth, where Cross established the Surrey Zoological and Botanical Society. In spite of gross overcrowding, one visitor praised Cross for what he delicately referred to as 'the extreme attention bestowed on the removal of everything offensive'.

Londoners, however, were not alone in their desire to view captive animals and, to satisfy demand from the provinces, travelling menageries regularly toured the length and breadth of the country. In 1783, for example, 'all Admirers of the Wonderful Productions of Nature' in and near the city of Norwich were invited to an inn-yard near the market-place to see a lion, a 'hunting tiger' (probably a cheetah), a porcupine, a wolf, 'an Astonishing Animal called, The MOON ACT', which bore 'A strong Resemblance of the Human Species', 'A Beautiful Creature, called, The WANDEROO [? Wallaroo], Being the only one of that Species ever seen in Europe', and 'A FEMALE SATYR or Aethiopian Savage'. In 1806 a 'noble Lion and Lioness, Panthers, Leopards, Hyaena, Lynx, Kangaroo, Ostrichs, and upwards of a hundred other animals and birds' were to be seen in the city of Exeter. The principal attractions of a travelling menagerie which visited that city six years later were a lion (alleged, improbably, to be 'absolutely the only one travelling this Kingdom'), a lioness, a pair of tigers, a zebra, a spotted and a striped hyaena, and a pair of kangaroos.

In the late seventeenth century the Duke of Chandos was purchasing in the markets of Long Acre in London such exotic species as canaries, monkeys and parakeets, and by the 1720s was introducing alien animals from all over the world to stock his huge private menagerie and aviary at Cannons, near Edgeware. By 1740 the Duchess of Portland had established free-ranging pheasants from China and an East Indian bull[10] at Bulstrode Park, and by the second half of the eighteenth century private menageries and aviaries had become commonplace among the aristocracy.

The following is a chronological list[11] of the more important private menageries and aviaries in England of the eighteenth century.

Date	Owner	Location
1485–1894	Magdalen College	Oxford
1670–83 (–1697)	Bess Dysart, Duchess of Lauderdale	Ham House, Richmond, Surrey
c. 1680 (or earlier)	William III	Hampton Court
1712	'Mr Mansell'	Cosgrave, Northamptonshire
c. 1720	Earl of Lichfield	Ditchley Park, Oxfordshire
1720s–1744	James Brydges, Duke of Chandos	Cannons, Edgeware
1720s	Lord Oxford	Wimpole Hall, Cambridgeshire
1725–1773	Dukes of Richmond	Goodwood House, Sussex
1730s	Lord Fortescue	Castle Hill, Filleigh, Devon
1730s	Viscount Weymouth	Longleat, Wiltshire
Before 1736–after 1784	Lord Burlington	Chiswick
1740s–1785	Margaret Cavendish Bentinck, Duchess of Portland	Bulstrode Park
Before 1745	Horace Walpole	Strawberry Hill
1750s	Mary, Mrs Patrick Delany	Delville, Co. Antrim, Ireland
1750s	Lord Halifax	Horton, Northamptonshire
1750s	Lord Orford	Houghton, Norfolk
1750–1788	Sarah, Mrs Robert Child	Osterley Park, Middlesex
1760	Earl Strafford	Wentworth Castle
1760–1840s	Princess Augusta and Queen Charlotte	Kew, Surrey
1760s	Mary Blount, Duchess of Norfolk	Worksop Manor, Nottinghamshire
1760s	Queen Charlotte	Richmond, Surrey
1760s–1774	Earl of Northampton	Castle Ashby, Northamptonshire
1760s & 1770s	Lord & Lady Ossory	Amphill Park, Bedfordshire
1761	Lord Sackville	Knowle, Kent
1762	Queen Charlotte	Buckingham Gate, London
c. 1762–?1781	Lord Shelburne	Bowood, Wiltshire
Before 1763	Mr Philip Southcote	Woburn Farm, Surrey
1763	Lord Sandwich	Hinchingbrooke, Huntingdonshire

1764–1831	Duke of Cumberland	Windsor, Berkshire
1765–1793	Mr John Hunter	Earls Court, London
1771	Marquess of Rockingham	Wentworth Woodhouse, Yorkshire
1772–1775	Earl of Craven	Benham Park, Berkshire
1773–1777	Lord & Lady Clive	Claremont
1777–1782	Sir Thomas Wentworth	Bretton Hall, Yorkshire
1781	Lord Cobham	Stowe, Buckinghamshire
1783–1787 (–1850)	Sir Richard Hill	Hawkstone Park, Shropshire
1787	Duke of Marlborough	Blenheim Palace, Oxfordshire
1788	Lady Ailesbury	Park Place, Richmond, Surrey
c. 1790	Frederica, Duchess of York	Oatlands, Weybridge, Surrey
1796	Lord Harewood	Harewood, Yorkshire
c. 1796	Lord Stamford	Enville, Staffordshire
c. 1800	Lady Brigit Galway	Bawtrey Hall, Yorkshire

At Ham House, the Duchess of Lauderdale converted one of the bedrooms into an aviary for 'outlandish birds', which she could feed from her own room next door.[12]

The contents of the Duke of Chandos's menagerie and aviary, set in no less than 83 acres at Cannons, near Edgeware, were drawn from the four quarters of the globe. It included 'Barbary hens from Portugal; Tortoises from Minorca; storks from Rotterdam; Barrow ducks from Holland; wild geese from Barbados; whistling duck and flamingo from Antigua; sea fowl from Cornwall; ostriches; blue macaws; geese; Muscovy ducks; Virginia fowls and songbirds; a red bird from the Gold Coast; powsies and parakeets from Barbados; an eagle; a crown bird; a Virginia buck and doe; a deer from Wydah; mocking-birds from Virginia; a tiger'.[13]

The first mention of an exotic animal at Goodwood, seat of the Dukes of Richmond and the best-known menagerie of its day, is to a 'coat for a monkey' in 1725. Three years later the Duke's collection contained 'wolves, tygerrs, lepers, sived cat, tyger cat, foxes, Jack all, Greenland dogs, vulturs, eagles, kite, owls, bears, white bear, large monkey, Woman tygerr, Raccoons, small monkeys, armadilla, pecaverre, caseawarris', leopard, martins, manligo, hochs, sow, wild boar'. His menagerie was a source of great pleasure to the second Duke, who had fortnightly reports on it sent to him whenever he was abroad. In 1770, in the time of the third Duke, the collection acquired the first bull moose to be seen in England.[14]

At Longleat in the 1730s, Lord Weymouth had in his menagerie a pair of leopards, a bear, some wolves, a parrot, an eagle, and pairs of bustards and vultures.

The first Duke of Portland constructed a number of aviaries at Bulstrode for his wife, but all the birds died from the cold before her arrival in 1734. The cold, predators and thieves were a constant problem at Bulstrode, where many of the mammals, though still artificially fed, were allowed to range free in the park, where they were seen and depicted by Mrs Delany (see below) and where they remained until the Duchess's death in 1785. The collection included 'Porcupine; East Indian bull [zebu]; deer; buffalo; moufflon; Java hare; squirrels; peacock-pheasant; Chinese pheasant; silver pheasant; gold pheasant; pied pheasant; red-legged partridges; black and red game; curlew; Numidian crane; widgeon; bantams; parrots; peacocks; guinea fowl; curasson; stork; macaws; crown birds; bustards; ducks and drakes; teal; tumblers; yellow paraquets; loretta bluebirds; waxbills; Java sparrows; Virginia nightingales; widow birds'.[15]

At Horton in Northamptonshire, Lord Halifax maintained a collection that included 'storks; raccons [believed by Horace Walpole to be the first in England]; large and white-headed eagles; 2 hogs from the Havannah "with navels on their backs"; 2 young tigers; 2 uncommon martins; does from Guadaloupe, "brown with blue heads and a white streak crossing their cheeks"; an ermine, "sandy with many spots" '.[16]

Lord Orford's collection at Houghton was said to be 'curiously and infinitely stocked with every original in beast and fowl of almost every country from the African bull to the pelican of the wilderness'.[17]

According to Lady Beauchamp Proctor, Osterley Park was 'fill'd with all curious and scarce Birds and Fowles'. These included the following species:

> Archer; Alexandrine Parrakeet; Amadavad; Baltimore Oriole; Bantam Cock; Barbary Partridge; Black Bullfinch; Black-faced Bunting; Black-capped Lory; Blue-bellied Finch; Blue-headed Parrot; Blue and Yellow Macaw; Blue-headed Turtle [Dove]; Blue Grose-Beak; Brazilian Finch; Cardinal; Cass-More; Cocatoo; Chinese Crane; Chinese Duck; Crane; Crowned African Crane; Curasso; Cushew; Erne [white-tailed sea eagle]; Ghillham-Sparrow; Gold-Pheasant; Great Bustard; Great Crowned Indian Pigeon; Great Red-Crested Cockatoo; Grenadier Grosbeak; Grosse-Bee from the Isle of Bourbon; Humming-Bird from the Cape [a sunbird]; Java Grosbeak; Java Sparrow; King of the Vultures; Minor Grackle; Numidian Crane; Pada; Painted Pheasant; Paradise Tanager; Pensilled Chinese Pheasant; Purple Gallinule; Rock-Pigeon from Jamaica; Red-breasted long-tailed Finch; Rose-headed Ring Parrakeet; Short-tailed Whidah; Silver Pheasant; Tourago, Variagated Bunting; Virginian Eared Owl; Warwowen; Waterhen from China; Waxbill; Waxen Chaterer; White Stork; Yellow Goldfinch; Yellow Finch.[18]

At Queen Charlotte's menagerie in Buckingham Gate, George Stubbs in 1762–3 painted from life the first zebra to be seen in England.[19] At Kew, Princess Augusta and Queen Charlotte kept 'Kangaroos; a fine blue nylghau [nilgai] from India; Algiers cows; a hog like a porcupine in skin; with navel on its back [a peccary]; Chinese pheasants; Tartary pheasants; many small exotic birds and gold fish'.[20] At Bowood, in 1769, Lord Shelburne received a wild boar from Count Lippe, and Jeremy Bentham (1748–1832), who presented him with a 'white fox' from Archangel, refers to a tiger at Bowood in 1781. Lord Shelburne's collection is also known to have included a lion and an orang-utan.[21]

According to an auctioneer's catalogue of a sale held on behalf of the eighth Earl of Northampton on 30 May 1774, the collection at Castle Ashby in Northamptonshire included:

> drake; ducks; hens; bantams; white rabbits; turkeys; swans; Canada geese; sea pies [oyster catchers]; Spanish cock; gold pheasants; grey curasson; hare; partridges; Virginia Nightingales; Chinese pheasants; white pheasants; Comon [sic] pheasants; pied pheasants; parrots; cockatoo; mackaws; Cape geese; shell duck; Muscovy duck; canary birds; red dove; turtle dove; paroquots; blue birds; widow birds; waxbills; osterlins; mesel-toe thrush; yellow bird; linnets; chaffinches; bullfinches; blackbird; goldfinches; doves; quails; linnet; Newfoundland dog cub; white shag dog; eagles; Angola [Angora] goats; geese; peafowl.[22]

At Amphill Park in Bedfordshire in 1767, Lord Ossory received from Churchill Fort in Manitoba, via the Hudson's Bay Company, what was probably the first or second female moose to be seen in England.[23] Three years later, the naturalist Thomas Pennant (1726–98) saw another female moose in the Marquess of Rockingham's menagerie at Wentworth Woodhouse in Yorkshire.[24]

Immediately after Lord Clive's death in 1774, an inventory of the menagerie at Claremont revealed the presence of a 'Zebra and foal; small cows; spotted deer; antelopes; hog deer; African bull; goats, Cape geese, white Spanish geese; Poland geese; swans; Newfoundland geese; wild ducks; summer drakes [? Carolina or wood ducks]; turkeys; guinea fowl; Chinese pencil'd pheasants; pea fowl; curaso birds'.[25]

The diarist Thomas Raikes (1777–1848), who visited Oatlands on a number of occasions in the 1790s, referred to the presence of several eagles and a troop of monkeys. Each monkey had its own pole, and on meeting a monkey on the lawn with long white hair (possibly a black-and-white colobus) the first Lord Erskine, who was appointed Lord Chancellor in 1806, raised his hat and, bowing thrice, said, 'Sir, I sincerely wish you joy—you wear your wig for life.' The menagerie and aviary at Oatlands also contained parrots, cockatoos, an ostrich, a Brahmin bull, wallabies, goats, fowl, peafowl, macaws, and Somali sheep.[26]

At Hawkstone in 1802 there were various species of eagles, monkeys, and parrots, 'a mackaw', and some rabbits.

The majority of these eighteenth-century and earlier private menageries and aviaries were kept solely for the aesthetic gratification of their owners. Although a few, such as the Dukes of Richmond and Chandos, the Duchesses of Portland and York, Lady Ailesbury, Sarah Child, and Queen Charlotte were, in varying degrees, serious ornithologists and zoologists, little thought was given until the nineteenth century to improvements in animal husbandry or scientific research, let alone experiments with acclimatisation.

In 1824 Sir Stamford Raffles (1781–1826) returned to England after a lifetime of colonial service in the East Indies, where in his spare time he had made a study of the fauna and flora of the region. In the following year he began to solicit subscriptions for what he described as 'a grand Zoological collection in the metropolis'. His application met with a response so enthusiastic that within a year he had obtained nearly two hundred subscribers to the 'Zoological Society of London', for which the government provided a plot of land in Regent's Park, where the society opened its gardens in 1828. In its first year, the zoo was visited by no fewer than 112,226 people.

These visitors, however, were not of the same ilk as those who flocked to view public menageries. Admission was confined solely to members and to people personally introduced by them, and was thus closed to the general public. The interest of members and visitors was invariably described as 'scientific', which served both to distance them from visitors to public menageries and also lent them an appearance of respectability. At the same time, the society described its own institutional purpose not as a place of entertainment but as primarily scientific. 'It has long been a matter of deep regret to the cultivators of Natural History', the society's prospectus of 1826 claimed, 'that we possess no great scientific establishments either for teaching or elucidating Zoology, and no public menageries or collections of living animals where their nature, properties or habits may be studied.' It was not until 1846, when the society was in dire financial straits, that the newly appointed secretary, Mr D. W. Mitchell, persuaded the council to grant admission to anyone willing to pay the entry fee.

The earliest collector of exotic animals in England who attempted their acclimatisation was Lord Stanley (1775–1851; from 1834 the thirteenth Earl of Derby), whose menagerie at Knowsley Hall near Liverpool, described by a contemporary as 'the largest private collection of modern times', was pre-eminent. Stanley despatched collectors to Central and North America, India, Singapore, Norway and Lapland in search of animals, and subsidised expeditions to West Africa over a period of some fifteen years: he may well be called the father of the acclimatisation movement in Britain.

3. Frank Buckland and The Acclimatisation Society of the United Kingdom

I F Isidore Geoffroy Saint-Hilaire can be regarded as the founding father of the *Société Zoologique d'Acclimatation* in France, so the prime influence behind the Acclimatisation Society of the United Kingdom (which owed its foundation directly to the success of the French *Société*), was Francis Trevelyan Buckland (1826–80).

Frank Buckland (as he was invariably known) was the eldest of nine children of the Very Revd William Buckland, DD, Dean of Westminster, and his wife Mary Morland; he was born on 17 December 1826 in Christ Church, Oxford, where his father was at the time Canon.

As he later recorded:[1]

> I am told that soon after I was hatched out, my father and my godfather, the late Sir Francis Chantrey,[2] weighed me in the kitchen scales against a leg of mutton, and that I was heavier than the joint provided for the family dinner that day. In honour of my arrival my father and Sir Francis then went into the garden and planted a birch tree. I know the taste of the twigs of that birch tree well. One of my earliest offences in life was eating the end of a carriage candle. For this, the birch rod not being handy, my father put me into a furze bush, and therein I did penance for ten minutes. A furze bush does not make a pleasant lounge when only very thin summer garments are worn.

From an early age the young Frank Buckland, encouraged by his parents, exhibited a precocious interest in natural history beyond his years, and was clearly possessed of a retentive memory and an inquisitive mind. His father, himself a keen amateur naturalist and geologist, was obviously at pains to explain things to him from his youth, for Bompas records how 'a clergyman travelled from Devonshire to Oxford, to bring Dr Buckland some "very curious fossils". When he produced his treasures Dr Buckland called his son . . . "Frankie, what are these?" "They are the vertebrae of an ichthyosaurus," lisped the child, who could not yet speak plain. The dumbfounded clergyman returned home crestfallen.'

In *Curiosities of Natural History* (1868)[3], Frank Buckland recorded that:

> In November 1829 met in the High Street, Oxford, Black Will—who was then a celebrated coachman, and drove the 'Defiance'—carrying, not a coachman's whip, but tugging along in each hand a crocodile about four

20

feet in length. Will had bought them on speculation in London, and my
father purchased them from him. . . . Both the crocodiles were put into
hot water: one died in the water, and the other lived but a few hours. . . .
My father and the late Dr Kidd . . . tasted a little bit of the crocodile. . . .
Many persons assisted at this feast, and the flesh was pronounced to be
excellent, much resembling sturgeon or tunny.

On another occasion, Frank Buckland records:[4]

a live turtle was sent down from London, to be dressed for the banquet in
Christ Church Hall. My father tied a long rope round the turtle's fin, and
let him have a swim in 'Mercury', the ornamental water in the middle of
the Christ Church 'Quad', while I held the string. I recollect, too, that my
father made me stand on the back of the turtle while he held me on . . .
and I had a ride for a few yards as it swam round and round the pond.
As a treat, I was allowed to assist the cook to cut off the turtle's head in
the college kitchen. The head, after it was separated, nipped the finger of
one of the kitchen boys who was opening the beast's mouth. This same
head is now in my museum.

The Buckland household was clearly of an unconventional, not to say
eccentric, nature. The furniture and floors were permanently covered
with a profusion of books, papers and geological and natural history
specimens, and a visitor was once enjoined to be careful where he sat
down, as there was a boa constrictor under his chair. Burgess records
how even some of the furniture itself testified to its owner's interest;
one table was made entirely from coprolites '(fossilised saurian faeces)',
and 'was often much admired by persons who had not the least idea
of what they were looking at'.[5] The candlesticks were formed from the
vertebrae of an ichthyosaurus.

The food consumed by the Buckland family, and even offered to
their guests, was no less peculiar than their furniture. Hedgehog, while
not exactly commonplace even on a countryman's menu, is not entirely
unknown; puppies, crocodiles and garden snails, on the other hand, are
distinctly unusual. Frank once complained to a fellow undergraduate
at Oxford that earwigs were 'so horribly bitter'.[6] The distinguished
naturalist and anatomist, Richard Owen (1804–92), and his wife, who
were close friends of the Bucklands, once dined with them on roast
ostrich, which Caroline Owen described in her diary as 'very much like
a bit of coarse turkey'. Her husband afterwards spent an uncomfortable
night.[7]

John Ruskin (1819–1900), however, 'always regretted a day of un-
lucky engagement on which I missed a delicate toast of mice; and
remembered with delight being waited upon one hot summer morning
by two graceful and polite little Caroline lizards, which kept off the
flies'.[8] Ruskin might have regretted a previous engagement less, had
he been invited to share with Dr Buckland a portion of the embalmed

heart of Louis XIV, owned by Buckland's friend Lord Harcourt. 'I have eaten many strange things,' the good doctor afterwards commented, 'but have never eaten the heart of a king before.' The eccentric Charles Waterton would undoubtedly have envied him the experience! William Buckland was wont to say that the worst-tasting animal he had ever eaten was mole; he later changed his mind, and said that a bluebottle fly was even worse. Years later, guests at Frank Buckland's house in Albany Street would be regaled on occasion with panther (dug up after being buried for several days and pronounced 'not very good'), elephant trunk soup or roast giraffe, acquired from the London zoo.

William and Frank Buckland once visited a foreign Catholic cathedral, 'where was exhibited a martyr's blood—dark spots on the pavement ever fresh and ineradicable'. Dr Buckland dropped on his hands and knees, and touched the spots with his tongue. 'I can tell you what it is,' announced the Protestant divine unequivocally, 'it is bat's urine'![9]

The love of, and interest in, animals was part and parcel of the Buckland family. Not for them were their pets solely the mundane variety of cats, dogs, rabbits and guinea pigs; they also owned more interesting ones, such as monkeys, snakes, green frogs, foxes, ferrets, hawks, owls, magpies, jackdaws, tortoises, toads and a bear—some, it is true, confined to the stables and outbuildings, but many allowed the run of the house; not least the family pony which, having entered the house from the garden, would nose open the dining room door and canter round the table with three laughing children on his back, before retiring through the front door and continuing his course round Tom Quad.

In November 1838, Caroline Owen recorded in her diary: 'A visit from Dr and Mrs Buckland and their two eldest boys, a friend, and a couple of live marmots . . . the Doctor sat on the sofa with the two marmots and his bag on his lap. They were all going to Drury Lane. I don't know whether the marmots are going too!'[10]

This, then, was the happy and contented household in which the young Frank Buckland grew up. William Buckland was a stern but kindly and devoted father, who regarded only idleness as a cardinal sin. He was a firm believer in communication between parents and children, and ensured that his offspring met the many distinguished and learned visitors who came to see him at Oxford, and at mealtimes encouraged them to listen to and participate in his guests' conversations. Every evening he would have an interesting anecdote or story to relate, and expected his children to play their part by some intelligent comment or query. Their mother, Mary, too, was firm but loving, and saw to it that her children were seldom unoccupied.

It was against this background that in August 1839, at the age of twelve, Frank Buckland went as a scholar to Winchester. One final anecdote of his early years is worth recording:

> . . . I went from Oxford to Winchester in a four-horse coach. . . . Soon after we had driven over Folly Bridge on our road to Winchester . . . the rest of the passengers began to complain about a nasty unpleasant smell, which apparently proceeded from the luggage on the top of the coach. A bluebottle fly first appeared . . . then another, until a perfect swarm of flies soon followed the coach, hovering and buzzing over the luggage. The passengers were mostly Oxford boys, going to Winchester, and there was a strong idea among them that somehow or other *I* knew from whence this odour proceeded. I knew perfectly well the cause of the smell, but I said nothing. The 'governor' . . . had kept a haunch of venison for me to take as a present to the head master, Dr Moberly; he had kept it so long hanging up in the larder at Christ Church that it had become very 'exalted' indeed; nevertheless he packed it up, thinking to make it last anyhow as far as Winchester. His experiment failed, and the other boys punched my head on the top of the coach, and were very near throwing me and my venison overboard altogether.

From Winchester, in October 1844 Buckland went up as a Commoner to Christ Church, where he graduated as a Bachelor of Arts in 1848. After training as a surgeon at St George's Hospital in London (where his decapitation of the turtle at Christ Church doubtless stood him in good stead), in August 1854 he was gazetted Assistant-Surgeon to the Second Life Guards, resigning his commission some nine years later.

Buckland's first book, *Curiosities of Natural History*—a collection of articles (not all of a zoological nature) which had previously appeared in the *St James's Medley* and *Bentley's Miscellany*—was published in 1857. It was generally well reviewed, met with instant success, and was followed by further volumes that were equally applauded. The titles of some of the essays make interesting reading, and give an insight into the eclecticism of their author's interests: 'A queer mode of dislodging a Newt from a Man's stomach'; 'Foot Tracks of wooden-legged people'; 'The Head of a Poacher Shot-Dead'; 'Barnacles on Drain-Pipes at Brighton'; 'The Hungerford Market Mermaid and The Spitalfields Merman'; and 'The Author poisoned by a Cobra di Capello: a Narrow Escape'. A few months after its publication, Buckland received an offer from *The Field* magazine, which had first been published in 1853, to reply to readers' queries on natural history. In 1859 he entered into a formal contract with the magazine, whose business manager was John Crockford, later one of Buckland's closest friends. He was also much in demand for his ability as a lecturer—a facility inherited from his father.

At the time of Buckland's birth, Britain was still suffering from the consequences of the Napoleonic Wars of 1792–1815 and the increasing effects of the Industrial Revolution. The corn harvests between 1792 and 1813 were exceptionally poor; the wars hindered the importation of corn from abroad, and the price of food soon rose dramatically. To make matters worse, the population increased at an unprecedented rate, and although some went to seek their fortune in the New World, the rising labour pool helped to lower industrial wage rates. The danger of mass starvation was averted in the short term by the notorious so-called 'Speenhamland Act' of 1795; this supplemented workers' wages out of the parish rates, but in the long term perpetuated and even exacerbated the situation, which was further aggravated by the infamous 'Waterloo' Corn Law of 1815; this prohibited the importation of foreign grain until the price of wheat rose above eighty shillings a quarter, which curbed overseas trade while maintaining the price of corn artificially high, and caused much suffering—and in years of grave shortage, even starvation—in town and country alike. Landowners and industrialists were at loggerheads, and acts of violence such as rick-burning and the wanton destruction of property among their workforces were manifestations of an almost universal discontent.

These problems persisted into and beyond the middle of the nineteenth century. Meat, for which Britain was almost entirely dependent on home-reared stock, was an expensive luxury, and more intensive methods of cultivation resulted in the increasing spread of diseases and pests in crops; in particular, the potato blight of the 1840s continued to reappear.

It was against this background that Frank Buckland began to develop his interest in 'acclimatisation', 'a term which may be said to comprehend the art of discovering animals, beasts, birds, fishes, insects, plants, and other natural products, and utilizing them in places where they were unknown before.'[12] This idea was by no means new. In a preliminary circular of the Zoological Society of London, founded in 1826, one of its declared intentions had been stated to be 'to attempt the introduction of new races of Quadrupeds, Birds, Fishes, etc., applicable to purposes of utility, either in our Farm Yards, Gardens, Woods, Waters, Lakes or Rivers.'[13] This was later amended to 'introducing and domesticating new Breeds or Varieties of Animals, such as Quadrupeds, Birds or Fishes, likely to be useful in Common Life.'[14] 'When it is considered', the prospectus continued,[15]

> how few amongst the immense variety of animated beings have been hitherto applied to the uses of Man, and that most of those which have been domesticated or subdued belong to the early periods of society, and to the efforts of savage or uncultivated nations, it is impossible not to hope for many new, brilliant and useful results in the same field, by the

application of the wealth, ingenuity, and varied resources of a civilized people.

An American historian, Harriet Ritvo, in *The Animal Estate: the English and other creatures in the Victorian age* (1987), maintains that the keeping of exotic wild animals in captivity in Victorian Britain

> was a compelling symbol of human power . . . physical domination and confinement was only the first stage in a process that would eventually overcome the animals' wild nature altogether . . . the ultimate goal was domestication—ostensibly so that they could serve pragmatic human ends, but actually as a crowning metaphorical demonstration of human ascendancy. Most of those involved in organized efforts to domesticate exotic animals were either scientists with a professional interest in illustrating the power of human intellect over nature, or magnates and officials with a social or political interest in emphasizing their dominion over other people. . . . Complete domestication [and successful breeding] embodied the most powerful possible symbol of possession and control. Wild animals were to be raised as livestock, not because their flesh would improve the national food supply, but because those with the wealth and skill to breed them wished also to appropriate them as completely as possible. . . . Thus acclimatisation offered the very powerful a figurative reenactment of their commanding positions. . . . private menagerists used their ability to confine, produce, and ingest wild animals within their own domains to celebrate their own splendid preeminence among their fellow humans and their dominion over nature.[16]

This is a philosophy that is hard to accept; it shows a lack of appreciation of certain of the social problems prevailing in Britain at the time, and does both scientists and 'magnates and officials' (actually altruistic—if misguided—country landowners and naturalists) a grave injustice.

In December 1847, the Zoological Society presented medals to Sir Roderick Impey Murchison (1792–1871), later to become a patron of the Acclimatisation Society, and M. Dimitri de Dolmatoff for their joint efforts in introducing to Britain the European bison or wisent. Murchison had been employed as a geologist by Tsar Nicholas I, who presented him with a pair of bison as a reward for his services, and a further pair was captured by de Dolmatoff while he held the post of Master of the Imperial Forests in the government of Grodno, one of the Lithuanian governments of western Russia. Unfortunately, all four bison (incorrectly referred to in *The Saturday Review* (1860) as 'aurochs (*Bison urus*)' died shortly after their arrival in England from 'a murrain' (pleuroneumonia) which decimated the zoo's cattle.

When the Earl of Derby, who had been president of the Zoological

Society for more than twenty years, died in 1851, *The Edinburgh Review* (1860) reported that he

> directed that whatever group of animals [from his collection of 345 of ninety-four species] should be considered most eligible, for the purpose of acclimatization, at the time of his death, should be transferred from the Knowsley collection in its entirety to the Society's possession. By the advice of Mr Mitchell [the Society's secretary] the elands were most judiciously chosen.

The animals flourished and increased to such an extent that a number were presented to the Marquess of Breadalbane at Taymouth Castle in Perthshire, to Lord Egerton at Tatton, and to Viscount Hill at Hawkstone near Shrewsbury.

The columns of *The Field* of the time contained innumerable references both to the activities of the *Société Zoologique d'Acclimatation* in France and to the progress of the elands in England and Scotland. Frank Buckland's interest was apparently aroused when he was invited to attend a special 'eland dinner' at the London Tavern, of which he wrote as follows:

> On 22nd January, 1860, I had the good fortune to be invited to a dinner, which will, I trust, hereafter form the date of an epoch in natural history—I mean the now celebrated Eland dinner, when for the first time the freshly-killed haunch of an African beast was placed on the table of the Aldersgate Tavern.
>
> The savoury smell of the roasted beast seemed to have pervaded the naturalist world, for a goodly company were assembled all eager for the experiment. At the head of the table sat Professor Owen himself, his scalpel turned into a carving-knife; and his gustatory 'apparatus' in full working order.
>
> It was indeed a Zoological dinner, to which each of the four points of the compass had sent its contribution. We had a large pike from the west, American partridges (shot but a few days ago in the dense woods of the transatlantic east), a wild Goose (probably a young bean-goose) from the north, and an Eland from the south. The assembled company—the ardent lovers of nature in all her works—most of them distinguished in their individual departments.
>
> The gastronomic trial over, we next enjoyed an intellectual feast in hearing from the Professor his satisfaction at having been present at the inauguration festival of a new epoch in natural history. He put forth the benefits which would accrue to us by naturalizing animals from foreign parts—animals good for food, as well as ornamental to the park. The glades of South Africa have been described by numerous travellers as reminding them forcibly of the scenery of many of our English parks; and here were the first fruits of the experiment as to whether the indigenous animals of these distant climes would do well in our own latitudes. The experiment was entirely successful, and he hoped would lead to more, and that we might one day see troops of elands

gracefully galloping over our green sward, and herds of Koodoos, and other representatives of the antelope family, which are so numerous in Africa, not only enjoying their existence in English parks, but added to the list of food good for the inhabitants of not only England, but Europe in general. The Vice-Chairman, the late Mr Mitchell, then instanced the case of the Indian pheasants already in course of naturalization at several points in England, and expressed his conviction that the American partridges we had just partaken of, as well as the European Gelinotte, would thrive well in our woods and copses, particularly in Kent, and that there could not be any great difficulty in getting them over from America for this purpose. Elands, since the present experiment had become public, had been found to answer every expectation; 'they had risen in the market;' the demand much exceeded the supply, and there were numerous applicants for them, whose demands, he was sorry to say, the Zoological Society could not now satisfy. There were, however, plenty more elands in South Africa to be had for the trouble of importing them. A fresh supply was much wanted, and he trusted that this subject might be taken up by those who had convenient pasture ground for them in England, and who would be patriotic enough to further the important cause of the acclimatisation of useful exotic animals in English parks and homesteads.[17]

In a letter to *The Times* on 21 January following this dinner, Owen wrote of the eland that

The meat was of a bright colour and of a close, fine texture, but without any fat mixed with the lean. . . . After hanging 10 days the joint was simply roasted . . . the meat . . . presented the colour of pork. . . . The finest, closest, most tender, and masticable of any meat. . . . In taste . . . it was compared with veal, with capon . . . *mammalian* meat with a soupçon of pheasant flavour. The committee rose with the conviction that a new and superior kind of animal food had been added to the restricted choice available in Europe.

Owen followed up this letter by saying[18] that

It is not too much to expect that in twenty years eland venison will be at least an attainable article of food: and seeing the rapidity with which it arrives at maturity, its weight, and its capacity for feeding, it is quite possible that before the expiration of the century it may be removed from the category of animals of luxury to the more solid and useful list of the farm.

Although, as Burgess (1967) says, the idea of herds of eland galloping across the pastures of Britain nowadays seems slightly ridiculous, many people in the mid-nineteenth century genuinely saw it not only as an easy and original way of increasing the supply and variety of food for the poor, but also as requiring little effort to make it a commercial success.

Owen's views, taken in conjunction with those of Mitchell and Sclater published in *The Edinburgh Review*, greatly impressed Buckland, 'for they showed us how science, even in her gravest moods, tends to utility, and that there was a grand uncultivated field open to those who would take up the subject in earnest.'

Buckland, as we have seen, was not averse to trying any new article of food that might become available, and Owen, too, was clearly prepared to indulge in the same experiment. 'I have just received from a friend in Canada', he wrote to Buckland on New Year's Eve 1859, 'a steak cut from a fine Moose-deer which he had shot. Perhaps he wished me to compare it with "Eland". . . . I mean to have the steak for luncheon; and if you could run down on the 1.30 p.m. train to Mortlake, you would find it on the table . . . about ½ past 2.'[19]

Buckland adopted the idea of acclimatisation with characteristic energy and enthusiasm. On 19 April 1860, with the cooperation and agreement of Mr Edward William Cox, proprietor of *The Field*, John Crockford and the Hon. George Charles Grantley F. Berkeley, sixth son of the fifth Earl of Berkeley, he placed the following announcement in the columns of that magazine:[20]

Society for the Acclimatisation of Animals in the United Kingdom.

A number of gentlemen interested in the Acclimatisation of Foreign Animals and Birds in the United Kingdom, have determined to form themselves into a Society under the above title. Further particulars will shortly be announced. The following noblemen and gentlemen have expressed their approval of the object and have consented to be enrolled as patrons.

Marquis of Conyngham
Marquis of Clanricarde
Marquis of Breadalbane
Earl of Malmesbury
Earl of Craven
Viscount Uffington
Viscount Somerton
Hon. Grantley Berkeley
Andrew Drummond Esq. of Cadland
T. Pilkington Dawson Esq., Groton House
Thomas Blackwell Esq., Engineer, of the Grand Trunk Railway of Canada

Communications and suggestions from all interested in the subject are invited, and the names of those who are desirous of becoming members and supporters of the Association will be received by

F. T. Buckland, M.A.
(2nd Life Guards)

At a meeting held in the offices of *The Field* in London at 346 Strand on 26 June 1860, the Marquess of Breadalbane was elected President of the embryo Society, Grantley Berkeley became Vice-President, and Buckland was appointed Honorary Secretary. The objects of the Society were declared to be:

1. The introduction, acclimatisation and domestication of all innoxious animals, birds, fishes, insects, and vegetables, whether useful or ornamental.
2. The perfection, propagation, and hybridization of races newly introduced or already domesticated.
3. The spread of indigenous animals, &c., from parts of the United Kingdom where they are already known, to other localities where they are not known.
4. The procuration, whether by purchase, gift, or exchange, of animals, &c. from British Colonies and foreign countries.
5. The transmission of animals, &c., from England to her Colonies and foreign parts, in exchange for others sent thence to the Society.
6. The holding of periodical meetings, and the publication of reports and transactions for the purpose of spreading knowledge of acclimatisation, and inquiry into the causes of success or failure. . . . It will be the endeavour of the Society to attempt to acclimatise and cultivate those animals, birds, &c., which will be useful and suitable to the park, the moorland, the plain, the woodland, the farm, the poultry-yard, as well as those which will increase the resources of our sea shores, rivers, ponds, and gardens.

Five months later, before the Society of Arts, Buckland delivered a seminal lecture 'On the Acclimatisation of Animals' at which, after describing the celebrated 'Eland Dinner', the formation of the *Société Zoologique d'Acclimatation*, and other events which culminated in the founding of the Acclimatisation Society of the United Kingdom, he described some of the animals which he deemed could most profitably be acclimatised in Britain. Today, his list makes bizarre reading.

Not surprisingly, he started off with the eland—'the most noble, the largest, the heaviest, and the most useful of the deer tribe [*sic*]'— which Mitchell had described as 'the *gibier par excellence* of the South African wilderness; his brisket is "the dainty bit they set before the King". Every travelling sportsman in Caffraria [South Africa] agrees upon the fine quality of this meat.'

The first steps towards the acclimatisation of the eland in Britain, Buckland claimed, had been made some twelve years earlier by the Earl of Derby. At Derby's death in 1851 his herd of two bulls and three cows had been acquired by the Zoological Society of London, in whose care they had flourished and increased. Other herds 'of this noble antelope' had been established by Viscount Hill at Hawkstone, by the Marquess of Breadalbane at Taymouth, and by Lord Egerton at

Tatton. 'Nothing can be more stately', said *The Edinburgh Review* (1860)

> than the eland, leading out his family along the lovely slopes of Hawk-
> stone, where a great rocky ridge rises in the midst of the park, and
> stretches nearly through it, affording every variety of shelter. There the
> pale tawny flanks of the antelope glisten in the morning light; infinitely
> surpassing the dun deer in colour, while they rival them in grace, and
> their great size makes them immediate objects of attention. Their clean,
> small legs, full of power, push them over hill and dale at a tremendous
> pace; and if an obstacle opposes, their faculty of leaping is almost
> incredible compared with their weight.[21]

Other antelopes from Africa which Buckland suggested for possible
acclimatisation in Britain included the Arabian oryx; the gnu or wildebeest; and especially the 'koodoo' (kudu), which 'combines extraordinary quality of flesh with rapid growth, fecundity, and hardiness. . . .'

Of the many species of deer in the world, Buckland pointed out,
Britain possessed but three, the red, the fallow, and the roe.[22] Could
not, he suggested, experiments in acclimatisation be made with such
species as the wapiti from North America; the barasingha or swamp
deer from India; the Virginia or white-tailed deer from North and South
America; the sambar and the chital, spotted or axis deer from India; the
reindeer from northern Europe 'which recommends itself to the owners
of parks and deer forests';[23] and the moose or elk from northern Europe
and North America.

Other mammals which Buckland believed might advantageously
be acclimatised in Britain included the American bison 'which carries
a hump on its shoulders, a taste of which would be quite sufficient to
impress on the minds of our *gourmets* the necessity of becoming a convert to the acclimatisation of animals'; 'in a magnificent park [on Lord
Breadalbane's estate in Perthshire] we may see the shaggy monster of
the prairies cropping Scottish grass, and watched by Scottish keepers,
and thriving well . . . upon the fat of our favoured land.' The 'nylgau'
(nilgai) of India, the aurochs of Europe and western Asia—the ancestor
of domestic cattle, the yak, and the Eurasian beaver—an erstwhile
native of Britain—could also be experimentally introduced, as might
Bennett's wallaby from Australia and Tasmania, 'which is extremely
hardy, and much the best calculated for acclimatisation in an English
park . . . with very little attention it would rapidly increase in any of the
Midland or southern counties . . .',[24] together with the guanaco, llama,
alpaca, and vicugna from South America.

If the list of mammals that Buckland would have liked to see acclimatised in the British countryside is bizarre, the imagination boggles at his
inventory of birds.

Among game-birds were included the cheer pheasant, the Himalayan monal pheasant, the Japanese pheasant, the ring-necked pheasant, the kalij pheasant, the snow partridge, peacock-pheasants, curassows, the ocellated turkey from Central America, the California quail, the crested guinea fowl from West Africa, Australian brush turkeys, and the once-indigenous great bustard.

Various species of Australia parrots and parakeets—including the budgerigar—whose name in Aboriginal means 'good to eat'—were considered by Buckland to be suitable for acclimatisation, as was the wonga pigeon and the crested dove.

Among wildfowl and other waterbirds approved as potential candidates for acclimatisation in Britain, Buckland listed magpie geese from northern Australia, African red-billed ducks, North American Carolina or wood ducks, ashy-headed geese from Chile and Argentina, and Magellan or upland geese from the Falkland Islands, Hawaiian geese or nenes, cereopsis geese from islands in Bass Strait off southern Australia, bean geese, snow geese, black swans from Australia, black-necked swans from southern South America, Stanley cranes from southern Africa, white storks, Manchurian cranes, the brolga from Australia (also delightfully known as the 'Native Companion', 'from the docility with which it accommodates itself to the society of man'), and the laughing kookaburra. Lest it be wondered for what purpose this last-named species was to be introduced (for, be it remembered, all attempts at acclimatisation had to be made with a definite purpose in mind), it 'is excessively adroit in catching mice, and will wait as patiently as a cat at a hole whence he expects one to emerge'!

After a dissertation on the value of pisciculture in acclimatisation and the possibility of reintroducing Atlantic salmon to the Thames, Buckland went on to mention some of the animals which had been suggested for acclimatisation since the Society had been founded. In a letter to *The Times* on 22 September 1860, Mr Edward Wilson (later the founder of the Victoria Acclimatisation Society in Australia) had suggested the common wombat from Australia, though, as Buckland remarked, 'there would be some difficulty in getting it generally adopted as an article of food, for prejudice would be in the way'. Other species which had been recommended included the Purik sheep from the Himalayas, prairie chickens from North America, and the 'Lucid Perca or Sander' (the pike-perch or zander) from central Europe.

There followed what was clearly a lively discussion on Buckland's lecture which was opened by Mr Chief Justice Temple, who suggested the importation of such morsels as armadillos, which in Honduras 'were esteemed one of the greatest delicacies of the table', curassows, 'gibonets', and 'Indian rabbits'. Subsequent speakers were more cautious, pointing out that animals removed from one set of climatic conditions

to another all too often degenerated, and that some previous introductions, such as that of the red-legged or French partridge to England
in about 1770,[25] had been neither universally popular nor particularly
successful. Furthermore, as one speaker pointed out,

> They had an increasing population, and the extensive plains and com-
> mons which these animals would inhabit were gradually disappearing,
> and were being appropriated to agricultural purposes; therefore, it was
> useless to think of introducing these large animals to be kept in the
> wild state. He would very much like to see some of the animals spoken
> of ranging in parks and meadows, but he questioned whether anyone
> present would venture to intrude his person where there was a herd of
> elands at liberty.[26]

In summing up, the chairman, Professor Richard Owen, stated his
belief in the value of acclimatisation as a branch of science, and in the
Acclimatisation Society

> as being a centre for giving and obtaining information and promoting
> the views of private individuals, and forming also a central body for
> turning to account the materials and information obtained . . . they had
> succeeded, as far as they had yet gone, in the introduction of the eland
> . . . and with that animal they were likely to have the same success as
> they had had with the fallow deer. The eland might be naturalized by
> the same means . . . the establishment of a Society for promoting the
> Acclimatisation of Animals would form a central machinery for stimulat-
> ing individuals having conveniences for these experiments, and might be
> the means of furnishing the specimens in the first instance.

The subsequent activities of the Acclimatisation Society of the United
Kingdom are described in the following chapters.

4. The Society in 1860–1861

THE first annual report of the Acclimatisation Society was presented by the secretary, Frank Buckland, at the inaugural meeting held in the offices of *The Field* magazine at 346 Strand, London, on 26 March 1861.

After briefly summarising the formation of the Society, Buckland opened the proceedings by acknowledging the debt owed by the Society to one of its members, Miss Burdett Coutts, 'a lady, whose name will for future generations be remembered as one of the great benefactors of all good and useful works in this country, [who] came to our aid, and, by the handsome gift of £500, with a yearly subscription of £10.10s., infused life and animation into the veins of our young and struggling Society.'

'Gentlemen,' Buckland continued. 'It will be asked, what has the Society actually done?' The period of nine months that had elapsed since the formation of the Society had been largely one of consolidation, in which enquiries had been made to try to ascertain which species of animals and plants would be most likely readily to become acclimatised and useful in Britain. To this end, in the autumn of 1860 Buckland had read two papers on acclimatisation before the British Association for the Advancement of Science in Oxford, and at the Society of Arts in London. In the latter, as we have seen, he discussed at some length the various animals and plants which, having already lived and reproduced in zoological and horticultural gardens and private menageries, would be most likely successfully to acclimatise in Britain.

The secretary then reported on the direct offers of practical assistance (which demonstrate the eclecticism of the Society's intentions) that had been received from members and non-members alike, both at home and abroad.

1. M. G. St. HILAIRE, President of the French Imperial Acclimatisation Society—Offers to establish friendly communications and interchange of objects, and to send specimens of Chinese Yam.
2. Mr. Chief Justice TEMPLE, British Honduras—Will procure Curassows, Guans, and farm yard birds; also Seeds of edible Vegetables from Honduras.
3. R. M. BRERETON, Esq. Civil Engineer, G.T.P., Nassich, Bombay, India—Will procure Indian Deer, &c., also living Indian Birds.
4. SAMUEL H. BICIDOR, Esq., Melbourne, Australia—Will send Painted Quail and other Australian birds. Recommends the 'Murray Cod.'
5. Captain HARDY, Royal Artillery, Halifax, Nova Scotia—Promises

living Grouse (Tree and Prairie); also Quail from Nova Scotia. Eggs of these birds also will be sent in the spring.

6. F. J. STEVENSON, Esq., Grand Trunk Railway, Montreal Canada— Game Birds of Canada (Ten Quail already received). Seeds of useful vegetables.

7. T. A. AUSTIN, Stratford, Connecticut, America—Will send Prairie Grouse and Quail, and Ruffled Grouse, if possible.

8. E. CUNARD, Esq., New York, America—Promises Grouse and Quail. Specimens have been received, March and April, 1861.

9. J. MAXTONE, Esq., Perth, Scotland—Will send Pearl-bearing Muscles from the Tay.

10. Captain T. R. THOMSON, Woodville Lodge, Red Hill—Intelligence relative to importation of South African Animals.

11. CHARLES PENRUDDOCKE, Esq., 5, Oxford-row, Bath—Will try any kind of Fish, either pond or river, on his estate.

12. S. GURNEY, Esq., Carshalton—Offers to take charge of Birds.

13. H. C. DEAR, Esq., Milbrook, Southampton—Offers to unship, take charge of, and transmit to destination any Animal or Bird arriving at Southampton.

14. E. W. NIX, Esq., 77, Lombard-street—Has written for Guans.

15. THOMAS GARNETT, Esq., Clitheroe—Will interest himself with Peninsular and Oriental Company, through one of their captains in command between Alexandria and Liverpool. Information relative to Hybrid fish.

16. Viscount POWERSCOURT—Will bring home Jungle Fowl and Seeds of useful Plants from Mysore, India.

17. TATTON SYKES, Jun., Esq., Malton, Yorkshire—Will take charge of Game Birds. (Has received ten Quail already).

18. Sir GEORGE WOMBWELL, Newburgh, Easingwold, Yorkshire— Will take charge of Animals or Birds.

19. Miss BURDETT COUTES—Accepts charge of Diminutive Sheep from Brittany, and also of Seeds.

20. W. E. MORLAND, Esq., The Court Lodge, Lamberhurst—Will undertake management of any Animals—suggests Chinese sheep.

21. Dr. GÜNTHER, British Museum—Will assist in transport of Silurus Glanis from South Europe.

22. Captain S. D. DAMER, M.P.—Will procure Grouse from Norway.

23. The Earl of POMFRET—Will take charge of Birds, Seeds, and Plants.

24. Mrs. LEIGH SOTHEBY—Will take charge of Seeds, and Chinese Sheep.

25. Sir JOHN ORDE—Will take charge of Indian Cattle, &c.

26. W. B. TEGETMEIER, Esq., Secretary of Apiarian Society—Will take charge of any new species of Bees, and is particularly anxious for stingless bees from Demerara, &c.

27. W. MALCOMB, Esq., of Glenmory—Will take charge of Game Birds.

28. W. J. DAVIDSON, Esq., Glasgow—Will procure Animals from Mogadore.

29. HIGFORD BURR, Esq., Aldermaston, Reading—Will take charge of
    birds.
30. E. S. BLYTH, Esq., Asiatic Society, Calcutta—Will send Animals,
    Birds, &c. from India.
31. WILLIAM THOMPSON, Esq., Weymouth—Reports successful
    Experiments in transport of Crawfish, Samphire, &c.
32. W. BLACKBURROW, Esq., Weston-super-Mare, Somersetshire (who
    is about to proceed to Natal, South Africa)—Will procure and send
    such Animals, Birds, Plants, and Seeds, as would be likely to do well
    in this country.

After congratulating the Society on receiving a pledge of support
from M. Isidore Geoffroy St Hilaire, president of the *Société Zoologique
d'Acclimatation* in France, Buckland reported that nearer home a Scottish branch society had been formed in Glasgow in the preceding
August, under the joint patronage of the Dukes of Buccleuch, Argyle
[sic] and Hamilton and the Earl of Buchan.

Although the period since the formation of the Society had largely
been spent in gathering information, some practical action had been
taken. The vice-president, the Hon. Grantley F. Berkeley of Ringwood,
Hampshire, had received 'sixteen live Quail [probably bobwhite quail]
from Mr E. Cunard in Canada', which had been placed in the care of
one of the Society's patrons, the Earl of Malmesbury, at Heron Court
in Hampshire, and 'eight prairie grouse' (presumably prairie chickens)
from North America; of the latter unfortunately only two arrived alive,
'but we have learnt a lesson as regards the future transport of other
specimens'. Thus, of a second consignment of nine 'Canadian Quail',
from Mr F. J. Stevenson of the Grand Trunk Railway, Montreal, all
landed safely.[1]

Among mammals, a pair of 'diminutive sheep from Brittany'—part
of a flock that had been exhibited at the Crystal Palace—was purchased
by the Society and presented to Miss Burdett Coutts, with whom they
were said to be thriving in Highgate, north London; other sheep of the
same breed were acquired by Colonel Howard Vyse, who also reported
them to be doing well.

At a joint meeting of the Society and the Thames Angling Preservation Society it had been determined to establish a 'Fish Hatchery
Apparatus' at Sunbury, and the latter society had agreed to supervise
the introduction of salmon into the river.

In his paper presented to the Society of Arts, Buckland had pointed
out that there were then many people alive who could remember the
time when salmon were still regularly caught in the Thames, and that
quite recently a spawning fish had been taken at Erith. 'We hail the
appearance of this fish with glee. If one comes, why not more? Why
should not we assist nature, and hatch salmon artificially on the chance
of restoring them to the Thames. . . ?'[2]

After considerable discussion and correspondence about the transportation and possible acclimatisation of a new species of fish, 'Lucio Perca' (the zander or pike-perch), it had been unanimously decided not to introduce this fish, 'as it would appear to be too voracious in its habits and might prove detrimental to our waters'.[3]

Among plants, 'specimens of the Chinese yam, the Dioscorea Batatas, and of the West Indian sweet potatoe [sic]' had been acquired by one of the Society's members, 'with a view to their being cultivated, if not out of doors, yet in our hothouses'. It was hoped that a further supply of yams, partially acclimatised by several years' growth in France, would shortly arrive from the Société Zoologique d'Acclimatation in Paris. Seeds of an 'edible bean' from British Honduras, presented to the Society by the Hon. Chief Justice Temple, had been distributed among various members, as also had seeds of 'elephant beans, red beans [which] the Djour plant around their fences [and] beans from the Mandar tribe [which are] excellent food . . .', received from Mr J. Petherick, HM Consul in Khartoum.

The secretary concluded his first annual report by saying that the Society had three principal objectives in view; firstly, the introduction of a new species of mammal, of which the most likely and potentially useful appeared to be a small breed of sheep, such as those to be found in Aden, India '(the purik)', and China. Small herds of eland had already been more or less successfully acclimatised by two of the Society's patrons, the Marquess of Breadalbane in Scotland and Viscount Hill in England, and by a council member, Viscount Powerscourt, in Ireland, and several members had expressed an interest in emulating them.

The second objective of the Society was the acquisition of a new species of bird; the Society had been promised the eggs and young of various North American grouse, and of guans and curassows, 'as farm-yard birds', by the Hon. Chief Justice Temple in British Honduras. Also promised 'by a gentleman living in the jungles of Central India', Mr R. M. Brereton, were some game fowl, while a council member, Captain S. Dawson Damer, MP, offered to procure some grouse from Norway.

Thirdly, the Society wished to import 'a good new Pond Fish'. Dr A. Günther of the British Musuem had confirmed the Council's prescience in deciding not to introduce the 'Lucio Perca' ('and this shows the value of not being in a hurry, in chosing objects for Acclimatisation'), but instead suggested the wels or European catfish[4] and the 'Guaramier, Osphrohemus Olfax, which is pronounced to be the very best fresh water fish in the world', which had been successfully introduced from Jamaica to Mauritius.

Finally, the secretary reported that it was hoped shortly to establish communications—through the good offices of the Duke of Newcastle, one of the Society's patrons and Secretary for the Colonies—between the Society and the governors of British colonies throughout the world.

In its issue of 11 May 1861, *The Field* summed up the activities of the Society to date as follows:

> The Acclimatisation Society may now be fairly said to be at work. It has completed the first year of its existence; ever the most critical one, with societies as with individuals. Its promoters have gone the right way to work by not attempting too much until the ground for action had been prepared by a strong and perfect organisation. That organisation is now secured. It has an active working committee in London, and already are secured correspondents and agents in every quarter of the globe. Under the active superintendence of Mr Wilson, a branch of the society has been started at Melbourne, Australia, from which the most valuable co-operation may be expected; and a branch society has also been established at Glasgow by some of the most influential men in the West of Scotland. Even during the past year (when the society might have been excused had it confined itself to preliminary arrangements) much has been done. . . . This next year will, no doubt, see much more accomplished. . . . From these proofs of energetic action we draw an inference which cannot be otherwise than satisfactory to the great body of the subscribers; namely, that it is the intention of the Society to make utility the principal object in view. The cultivation of birds of game may be a very pleasant diversion in its way . . . but if the Society is to command the general respect and support of the public it must be by importations calculated to increase and agreeably vary the natural products of the country, and above all the food of the people.

5. The Society in 1861–1862

THE second annual meeting of the Acclimatisation Society was held in the Society's new offices at 3 Duke Street, Adelphi, on 25 March 1862. Buckland and James Lowe (the latter having been appointed joint-secretary with the former) were able to announce that, after a satisfactory opening year, the number of life members had risen from eighteen to twenty-four, and that of annual members from thirty-nine to forty-eight.

Following personal letters from the Duke of Newcastle to the governors of British colonies requesting their cooperation in the Society's objectives, favourable responses had been received from Sir George Bowen of Queensland, Australia, and from the governors of New Brunswick and Prince Edward Island, Canada. Mr W. J. Stephens of Sydney, Australia, had written to announce the formation of the Acclimatisation Society of New South Wales, while Mr Edmund Thing, honorary secretary of the Auckland Acclimatisation Society of New Zealand, had communicated that society's desire to establish friendly relations with the parent body in England. Mr W. E. Blackburrow had written offering, in a private capacity, to try to furnish the Society with antelopes, bustards and 'young Elands at about £5 per head' from South Africa in exchange for alpacas which, 'as they do so well in Australia, I have no doubt would succeed here.'

In his reply to the Duke of Newcastle, Sir George Bowen offered to form a branch society in Queensland, and to this end suggested that the Society should write to a number of prominent Queenslanders seeking their cooperation. Bowen also suggested, as suitable candidates for acclimatising in Britain, kangaroos, geese, ducks, quail, and especially 'the Bustard or Wild Turkey', 'the *Talegalla* or Mound-building Turkey' (the brush turkey) and 'the *Wonga*, the Queen of the Pigeon tribe', all of which

> afford *delicious eating*. The *Wonga*, in particular, combines, in the most delicate proportion, the flavour of the Pheasant and of the Goose. I enter into these details, because I perceive from its First Annual Report, that the Acclimatisation Society expects 'to command the general respect and support of the public by importations calculated to increase and agreeably vary the natural products of the country, and, *above all the food of the people*'.

In its reply to Bowen, the Society accepted his offers of bustards, brush turkeys and wonga pigeons, 'with any other Birds, Animals, or Vegetables which would be likely to be of service to the Society', promising to reciprocate with the Queensland Society when formed.

The successful establishment of a branch society in Glasgow in the previous year had prompted the formation, under the patronage of the Lieutenant-Governor, General Slade, and the presidentship of the Bailiff, Mr Peter Stafford Carey, of a similar association on Guernsey in the Channel Islands where, 'having regard to the mildness of the climate . . . the Council is satisfied that Guernsey will prove of most important assistance . . . by serving as a sort of acclimatising ladder to aid the more tender Animals and Vegetables of still warmer latitudes on their way to our shores.'

Having given a résumé of the Society's communications with individuals and groups around the world, the joint-secretaries then outlined the various importations of animals and plants that the Society had made.

The sum of £150 had been earmarked for the importation of Chinese sheep, which had been 'recommended to the Council as extremely fruitful in breeding, excellent for eating [and] hardy in their nature'. With the help of Matheson & Co, the 'eminent Merchants', two lots, each consisting of half-a-dozen ewes and two rams, had been purchased in China and shipped to England, at a cost of £42.13s.4d. per lot. Of the first shipment on the *Wagoola* from Shanghai, one ewe died on the voyage, having given birth to triplets, and a second ewe died shortly after being landed. The remaining four ewes—all of which were believed to be in lamb—and the two rams appeared to be in good health and condition. A second consignment of six ewes and two rams on the *Veloz* all arrived safely and in good order. Other lots would follow until the £150 had been expended, and the council confidently expected that within the year 'the permanent and extensive establishment of the Chinese Sheep in England will be an accomplished fact.'

Because of the somewhat precarious state of the Society's finances, which showed a credit balance of only £422.14s.4d., the council had judged it imprudent to take advantage at this stage of Mr Blackburrow's offer of elands, while bearing in mind that 'this animal is to be recommended for its elegance of form and for its utility both as a farm animal and as an article of food. The fact that it is hardy enough to thrive in this country, has been fully established.'

Lord Powerscourt reported that he had been experimenting with the hybridisation of deer at his home at Enniskerry, Co. Wicklow in Ireland, where he had successfully mated sambar from Indonesia with native red deer. He had also imported to Ireland, through the German-born animal-dealer Carl Jamrach, a Japanese sika stag and three hinds.[1] Lord Powerscourt also reported the successful breeding and acclimatisation in his park of the wapiti.

'The introduction of new varieties of edible and ornamental Poultry', reported Buckland and Lowe, 'has been an object foremost in the consideration of the Council . . . the testimony of Travellers and Sportsmen establishes beyond a doubt the fact, that among the Birds found wild in Central America, the Guan (*Penelope cristata*) and the Curassow (*Crax globosa*) offer remarkable advantages in all desirable qualities.'

Despite the only moderate success that had attended previous attempts to breed these species in Britain, Mr Grantley Berkeley had imported four guans—known locally as the 'Turkey of the Woods'—from South America, and a further pair of guans and a single curassow were placed in the care of the Society's treasurer, Mr J. Bush.

To experiment further with these birds, the council had allotted the sum of £50 towards the importation of more guans, and a like amount for curassows. Having 'sought the advice of a mercantile gentleman' who was acquainted with Honduras and adjacent parts of the Gulf of Mexico, the British consul in Belize had been requested to employ lumbermen working on mahogany trees in the interior to bring nests of pullets to Belize for shipment to England, where it was anticipated that both species would be offered to members by the end of the year. Also from Honduras the Society hoped shortly to import a hybrid between the ocellated[2] turkey and the common turkey, the flesh of which was reported to make 'very delicate eating'.

In the preceding May the Society had received as a present from Mr J. Dyce of the Royal Artillery, then stationed in China, seven Pallas's sandgrouse; 'His Royal Highness, the late lamented Prince Consort (who took the greatest interest in the subject of acclimatisation) undertook the charge of these birds, and they are now in the Royal Aviary at Frogmore.'

In the following month a consignment of thirty-seven eggs of the ruffed grouse was received from Captain Hardy of the Royal Artillery, stationed in Halifax, Nova Scotia; these eggs were placed under hens in the royal aviary and in those of three members of the Society, Lord Tredegar in Monmouthshire, Mr Higford Burr in Berkshire and Mr Grantley Berkeley in Hampshire; none, however, hatched successfully.

The last-named member reported that he proposed to cross his prairie chicken cocks, which were 'healthful in form and feather, and very tame', with native black grouse hens from Scotland (sometimes referred to as grey hens), and that he hoped shortly to import more of the former from North America. Berkeley also reported that in the previous spring Lord Malmesbury had experimentally released his entire stock of prairie chickens and bobwhite quail, none of which survived for long. '*It is useless*', Berkeley rightly concluded, '*to turn the imported birds out*. They can only hope to naturalize and locate the young bred from the eggs in aviaries. Reared on the spot, you give to the young birds a local attachment. Old birds turned down have no local attachment but wander about lost and strange.' In confirmation of Berkeley's claim, Mr Tatton Sykes of Yorkshire, who had shared a consignment of bobwhites from Canada with the Earl of Craven in Berkshire, Lady Dorothy Nevill in Hampshire, and the Society's treasurer, Mr John Bush, reported that on release his entire stock too had disappeared.

In pursuance of one of the prime objects of the Society, the provision of a greater variety of palatable meat for the table, Berkeley further reported his successful crossing of a pintail with a mallard, the offspring of which 'forms an excellent variety for the table . . . ducks thus bred from the Pintail may be killed all the year round as excellent for the table, never acquiring the hardness to which the meat of the tame duck is liable when grown to maturity.' It may well have been the announcement of this successful interbreeding that led to the publication of an extract from a hoax annual report of the Society (quoted by Burgess, 1967), which the editor of *The Gardeners' Chronicle* was, somewhat gullibly, deceived into printing:

> In Birds a great success has been obtained by the Hon. Grantley Berkeley who has succeeded in producing a hybrid between his celebrated Pintail Drake and a Thames Rat: the Council considers that this great success alone entitles them to the everlasting gratitude of their countrymen, as this hybrid, both from peculiarity of form and delicacy of flavour (which partakes strongly of the maternal parent) is entirely unique.

Berkeley also announced experimental hybridisation in his aviaries with pochard, scaup, gadwall, Muscovy, and 'Rouen' and 'Buenos-Ayrean' ducks, and the imminent arrival from North America of wood ducks, canvasbacks, and blue-winged teal. In the previous month the Society had purchased a number of 'Dusky Ducks' (probably North American black ducks or their Australian counterparts), with a view to further experiments in hybridisation.

Other experiments in hybridisation had been made by Lord Craven with the black 'Kallagee Pheasant' (the Kalij pheasant of the hills of northern India) which was said to provide 'very good eating', and between the cheer pheasant[3] and the common pheasant.

Finally among birds, Buckland and Lowe reported that they hoped, through the good offices of Mr John Allen and the Revd R. Barnard of Christiana, Norway, shortly to acquire some 'living specimens of the Gelinotte' (the hazel grouse or rock ptarmigan) on behalf of the Society.

Turning to the subject of the acquisition of a new 'Pond Fish', the joint-secretaries announced that, on the recommendation of Mr Edward

Wilson of Melbourne, a number of Murray cod or cod perch had been shipped on the *Lincolnshire* from Australia. Despite the offer of a reward of £10 to the ship's officer in charge of the fish should only half the consignment survive the journey, Buckland and the honorary treasurer, John Bush, 'had the mortification of finding that all the fish had perished during the voyage'. It was considered, however, that this 'untoward result' was a consequence of neglect rather than of any 'insuperable difficulty in the way of transmission', and the council had high hopes of success with future shipments.

The possibility of introducing the '*Lucio Perca*' had been reconsidered by the council, but had again been rejected on the grounds of expense and the uncertainty of the outcome.

One of the objects of the Society being 'The spread of Indigenous and Naturalized Animals, &c., from parts of the United Kingdom where they are already known to other localities where they are not known', some 1100 freshwater crayfish—mostly presented by Mr Henry Early—had been despatched from Oxfordshire to various parts of Scotland, including 400 sent to the Society's president, the Marquess of Breadalbane at Taymouth in Perthshire. Since all the crayfish sent north were gravid, the total of 1100 was only a small percentage of the creatures actually introduced into Scottish waters. In reciprocation, Mr J. Maxtone Graham presented the Society with some pearl mussels from the River Tay, which were distributed among Grantley Berkeley, Lady Dorothy Nevill and Mr Charles Penruddocke in Wiltshire, with all of whom they were said to be 'doing well, and have apparently accommodated themselves to their new habitats.'

The only invertebrate reared by a member of the Society in 1861–2 was some silkworms[4] raised by Lady Dorothy Nevill out of doors on *Ailanthus* bushes at Petersfield in Hampshire: 'I sent samples of my cocoons to the gentleman who buys all the French ones. He pronounced them magnificent, and said he would buy as many as I had.'

> The paramount importance of Vegetable food to the great bulk of the community, and the dangers which, of late years, have menaced the cultivation of the Potato, have directed the attention of the Council to that branch of Acclimatisation. After a careful examination of all the facts that could be distinctly ascertained, it seemed that the Vegetable which gave the best promise of becoming an article of common use was the *Dioscorea batatas*, or Chinese Yam, and to this therefore the Council has paid careful attention.

Many contradictory claims had been received concerning the ease or difficulty of cultivating this vegetable, and of its value as a food. The fact that it had been grown successfully by the *Société Zoologique d'Acclimatation* in France, and by the Guernsey branch of the Society in the Channel Islands, suggested that much depended on climate and the method of cultivation.

In response to a request to the French Society, a box of tubers had been despatched to England in the previous May, some of which were planted in a nursery at Windsor in Berkshire. *The Field* of 16 November following commented that:

> Some of the tubers had been dug up . . . [and] tried both plain boiled, and with white sauce, and were unanimously pronounced to be delicious. In texture and flavour they are excellent and, if one Vegetable can be compared with another, may be said to resemble very good mashed Potatoes. . . . The evidence of gardeners and others acquainted with the plant, leads to the belief that the Chinese Yam is an excellent Vegetable, and with proper cultivation will grow to an enormous size. . . . In the face of the continued failure of the Potatoe, the Secretaries submitted that to encourage the cultivation of the Chinese Yam would be a great national benefit.

Parcels each containing upwards of forty tubers had been sold to a dozen members of the Society at ten shillings each, and it was hoped that recipients would in due course communicate to the council the results of their experiments.

Finally, James Lowe reported the apparently successful acclimatisation of the Brazilian arrowroot by the Sheriff of Guernsey, Mr Peter Martin. Lowe had brought back from Guernsey a few bulbs and one plant, which had been placed in the garden of the Society's treasurer, who reported that they had survived the winter and appeared strong and healthy.

In concluding its second annual report to members, the council noted with regret the recent death of M. Isidore Geoffroy St Hilaire, founder and organiser of the *Société Zoologique d'Acclimatation* in France, and paid due tribute to his contribution to the science of acclimatisation.

6. The Society in 1862–1863

AT the Society's third annual meeting held in their Adelphi offices on 29 April 1863, the secretaries were able to announce an increase in life membership from twenty-four to forty-six, and of annual subscribers from forty-eight to a hundred and thirty-nine. 'So considerable an addition to the ranks of the Society', the Council claimed, 'cannot be regarded otherwise than as a proof that its efforts are appreciated by the Public.' The treasurer reported a corresponding increase in the Society's bank balance to £488.18s.6d.

During the past year the Society's president, the Marquess of Breadalbane, had died; he was succeeded by the Duke of Newcastle, who had been of such service to the Society in securing the cooperation of the governors of British colonies around the world.

In reviewing the events of the past year, the council expressed its satisfaction of the award of two bronze medals to the Society for its exhibit of Chinese sheep and lambs at the Royal Agricultural Society's show at Battersea Park in the preceding June. At the latest annual meeting of the *Société Zoologique d'Acclimatation*, the Society's honorary treasurer, John Bush, had been awarded a silver medal for his husbandry of Chinese sheep, and a bronze medal had been awarded to Lord Powerscourt for his successful breeding of various species of deer.

On 12 July 1862 the Society had held a commemoration dinner, at which, thanks to the cooperation of overseas exhibitors at the Great International Exhibition, the council had been able to serve to the members and their guests 'samples of many natural products which do not often find their way to our tables, and some of which might be advantageously introduced into this country.'

The following is an abridged account of the dinner, taken from *The Field* of 19 July 1862; the menu itself, and the comments thereon, are interesting enough to be worth quoting in full, with Frank Buckland's observations in parentheses:

> The first annual celebration dinner of the Acclimatisation Society was held on Saturday, the 12th July, at Willis's Rooms, King-street, St. James's.
>
> The room was decorated with a variety of interesting objects illustrative of the objects of the Society. The most remarkable of these were the enormous deer-horns belonging to Lord Powerscourt; magnificent heads of the bison, the wild boar, and the eland; stuffed specimens of

the prairie grouse, the ruffed grouse, the guan, and the curassow; some fine stuffed specimens of *Lucioperca*, and a case containing the little swallow[1] which builds the edible birds'-nests, with a specimen of the nest and an egg. This was handed round to the guests when the soup produced from the nests was under discussion, and afforded an interesting corollary to the culinary lesson which the Society was illustrating with plates.

Collecting the majority of suffrages as to the various outlandish dishes offered, we may record the following verdicts:

Birds'-nest Soup. By the most part pronounced to be excellent. The birds'-nest gives a strong gelatinous quality, and the flavour is—what you please. In this case (thanks to Messers Willis's *chef*) it was excellent. ['The nests are built in caves along the rocky coasts of China, Java and Sumatra. The market price of the best nests in China is nearly twice their weight in silver. This soup was the cause of much and dire anxiety to me; at the last moment the gentleman who promised them failed me, and it was only through the great kindness of a friend that we got the soup at all. He gave me four nests, and the cook cleverly made nearly a quart of soup from them; they are formed of a species of gelatine which is soluble in boiling water, the soup therefore tasted gelatinous, but with a very peculiar and not disagreeable flavour'.]

Tripang. The Japanese sea-slug is strong in flavour and excited a divided opinion. Some said it was very unpalatable; others ate it with some delight. We partook of a saucerful, and much enjoyed it. Mr Willis (no mean judge) said that it was very nearly equal to turtle. ['This is a species of *Holothuria*, or sea slug, found in the Chinese and Japanese seas. They are worth about sixpence each in China, and are said to be a most succulent and pleasant food, not at all unlike the green fat of turtle. These Tripangs, too, caused me much anxiety; when I first received them they were as hard and solid as a bit of horse's hoof. I gave them to our regimental mess cook, and they were soaked all day and boiled all night; the next morning when we looked at them—lo and behold!—these dry masses had swollen out into huge, long, black-looking masses amazingly like the common black garden slug. I cut them up into small pieces *instantly*; for if their appearance had *then* been made public, none of our guests, I am sure, would ever have touched them. These bits were boiled and simmered, I am afraid to say how many hours—the cook and I thought they would *never* get soft. However, they *were* soft by the time they were put on the table, and they were—well, if you please, capital; tasting something between a bit of calf's head (as in soup) and the contents of the glue-pot.']

Nerfs de Daim. Soup made of the sinews of the *Axis* deer.[2] High in flavour, and gelatinous. *Laudator ab his; culpatur ab illis.*[3] ['These deer sinews from Cochin China took a monstrous deal of boiling, and they were simmering in the pot an amazingly long time; when served up they were good eating, but glue-like. I am now convinced that the Chinese epicures love gelatinous soups; for all these three soups were from China; and when I have to entertain a Chinaman, I shall certainly give him a gelatinous soup—say sixpennyworth of carpenter's glue, served for appearances' sake in an ordinary soup tureen.']

Semoule. A white soup, thickened with the white flour of the hard wheat grown in South Europe and North Africa. This is the basis of the macaroni of Italy and the Kousccusou of Algeria and Morocco—two of the national and fundamental dishes of the world. ['This soup was more fitted for invalids than for ordinary table soup; but it was very good, and reminded me of the porridge the giant was eating when Jack the giant-slayer killed him.']

Kangaroo steamer. Too highly salted, and not cooked properly; being made up into *croquettes* instead of a stew. Most likely *pour cause*.[4] ['The tin can given me was not over tight, and the consequence was, that the "kangaroo steamer" was a little "gone off", but not bad for all that'.]

Pepper Pot. A mixed stew, deliciously flavoured with cassareep;[5] this dish was in great request. ['. . . everybody wanted "Pepper Pot", and the waiters very nearly quarrelled over it in their anxiety to obtain supplies; and as I was helping it I was obliged to tap their fingers with the spoon, to keep them and their plates out of the way.']

Poulette en Karic à la Siamoise. The peculiarity of this was the curry, which was of Siamese manufacture. It was excellent.

Ris de Veau à l'oseille de Dominique. Here the speciality was the preserved sorrel from St. Domingo, which was of capital flavour.

Chinese Lamb. An entire lamb, of the Society's flock, roasted whole. Very successful, and pronounced to be of admirable flavour. ['Poor lamb, he was very innocent, and also capital eating, for his bones were in ten minutes picked as clean as if a flock of vultures had been at him.']

Kangaroo Ham. Too salt, and not very tender. ['. . . rather dry, (it had not been soaked enough), and very small; but it got as good character, for, by some mistake, the 'Kangaroo ham' cards were placed with the dish containing 'wild boar ham', and many of our guests were eating wild boar's flesh when they thought they had got kangaroo.']

Syrian Pig. A hybrid between the common animal and the wild Syrian boar. It was cooked entire, and was practically approved of by being eaten up.

Canadian Goose and **Guan**. No particular verdict. The *curassow* was not in very good condition; but its flavour was excellent.

The Honourable Grantley Berkeley's Pintail Ducks. The specimens offered were worthy of the *prestige* they already enjoy. They are plump and tender as the domestic duck, and have the gamy flavour of the wild duck.

Honduras Turkey, **Dusky Ducks** and **Brent Geese**. All excellent.

Couple of Leporines. Some *gourmets* pretended to detect the flavour of the hare mingled with that of the rabbit; but we, who reject the theory of the hybrid, believe this to have been an effort of the imagination. ['They are said to be half rabbit, half hare; but as the test of the knife and fork had never been applied to them, I was most anxious that it should be used on this occasion; the verdict from both the roast and boiled specimens being that this animal has 90 per cent of the rabbit in his composition.']⁶

Chinese Yam. Some splendid specimens, sent by Mr Carré, of Guernsey, were served and were much approved of. The flavour is very delicate, and resembles good mashed potato.

Sweet Potatoes. Excellent as dressed for a sweet *entremet*, with sugar and cream.

Sea-weed Jelly. This was made of the *Gracularia confervoides* of the Queensland coasts and other *algae* from Australia. The jelly is fully equal to what can be made with isinglass.

Digby Herring Salad and **Botargo.** Two very appetising *hors d'oeuvres.* The *botargo* is the roe of the red mullet, brought from the Ionian Islands. The *bécasse de mer* grows to great size and perfection in those waters.

There were . . . also some meat biscuits which may be recommended to sportsmen and tourists. The Australian wines were, for the most part, much liked. . . . Of the liquers, the favourites were decidedly the 'Oued Allah' and the 'Nectar de Garibaldi' from Algeria, and some very choice but very powerful rum from Martinique.

'Such feasts', writes Ritvo (1987), 'expressed more than simple culinary flexibility; they enabled those who represented the elites of wealth and knowledge figuratively to reenact their positions at the table.' Again, she fails to appreciate the curiosity—and even eccentricity—of some members of the British aristocracy. The truth is that the participants in this, and other, unusual feasts did so out of simple inquisitiveness to see what the outlandish dishes presented to them would taste like, with perhaps some idea of noting which, if any, might provide a suitable additional source of food for their less fortunate countrymen.

The joint-secretaries reported that in January and March 1862 the Society had received 'from Shanghae (per favour of Messers Matheson & Co.)' a further twenty-one Chinese sheep. Some of these had been retained by the Society, while others had been sold to the honorary treasurer, the French *Société*, Lord Powerscourt, Lord Walsingham in Norfolk, the Revd J. Huyshe in Devon, Mr C. H. Prichard near Bristol, Mrs Leigh Sotheby of Lower Norwood, and Mr David Lumsden of Perth. The total flock of pure-bred Chinese sheep stood at forty-three. In addition, Lord Powerscourt, Lady Dorothy Nevill and some other members had experimentally crossed their Chinese sheep with other breeds (Wexfords, Southdowns, Brittanies and Oxfordshire Downs) to ascertain whether the Chinese animals maintained their fecundity when cross-bred. The results of these experiments, claimed the Society,

clearly show that the fecundity of the Chinese breed belongs at least as much to the ram as to the ewe, and that it is preserved even when crossed

with other breeds usually less fecund. . . . The Council submits . . . that
in the breed of Chinese sheep a solid and valuable acquisition has been
made to the resources of the kingdom.

Lord Powerscourt reported that during the past year he had been
successful in breeding sambar, sika, roe deer, and mouflon, less so
with wapiti, and had failed completely with eland, 'Nylghaie' (Nilgai)
and axis deer. 'I wished', wrote Lord Powerscourt,

> for nothing but animals which would, when established, take care of
> themselves, and not be kept in a glass case. . . . The climate of Ireland
> is, I think, too damp for the Antelope tribe. . . . My experience is, that
> many of these animals will bear a very great amount of dry cold without
> harm, but wet, *continued* wet, as is proverbially the case in Ireland, makes
> it an unfavourable climate for experiments with tropical animals.

Lord Powerscourt concluded his report by saying that he hoped shortly
to acquire some red deer from Prince Lichtenstein's Pohanska Park
estate at Eisgrub near Lundeburg in Austria, where 'the heads I saw
determined me to try the experiment of transporting them'.

A letter recently received from the Acclimatisation Society of Victoria
in Melbourne promised three pairs of Australian wombats, although not
surprisingly 'captains are rather chary of taking these large animals'.

The Council announced that among birds, efforts had been made
chiefly to acclimatise prairie chickens, ocellated turkeys, bobwhite quail
and 'Japanese Poultry'.

Mr Grantley Berkeley reported the successful breeding of prairie
chickens which, he claimed, 'are easily acclimatised'. 'I can now safely
point out', he continued, 'a new game, which . . . will make a splendid
addition to the bag and to the table.' He also reported success in the
rearing of bobwhite quail.

Among wildfowl, Berkeley announced, somewhat surprisingly, that
'with *Brazilian Geese* [the Orinoco Goose] . . . as far as acclimatisation
goes, I have also completely succeeded. . . . I have every reason
to hope that from these lovely little brown and black geese I may
succeed in obtaining eggs.' He also announced that the 'domesticated
Pintailed Duck, bred originally from the wild Pintail Mallard and tame
Duck,' was now well established on the lake at West Wycombe Park in
Buckinghamshire, where there were also two pairs of pintails × North
American 'Dusky Ducks' (the black duck). At his estate in Hamp-
shire, Berkeley reported that pintail × Muscovy duck and Muscovy
× Aylesbury duck crosses were all nesting and were 'excellent for
the table, and perfectly fecundite'. He also had, in good condition, a
pair of North American wood ducks presented to him by the Earl of
Craven, and a Bahama pintail ('this bijou of a bird') given to him by the
Marchioness of Winchester. A scaup drake had recently paired with a

female pochard, though 'what will come of this last attempt at a cross I do not know'.

The Society's treasurer, John Bush, announced that an ocellated turkey in his care at Clapham had hatched nine young from a clutch of twenty eggs, none of which, however, had survived for long, and that he also held, on the Society's behalf, a pair of 'Japanese Fowls', presented by Mr A. D. Bartlett, which were then laying. Lady Dorothy Nevill reported an unsuccessful attempt to cross bobwhite quail with California quail.

In December 1862 Sir George Bowen, Governor of Queensland, had despatched to the Society, on board the *Montmorency*, a pair of *'Talegellas,* or Scrub Turkeys' (brush turkeys). Unfortunately, on boarding the vessel in the London docks to collect the birds, the secretaries found that 'the birds had been washed overboard, during a storm, off Cape Horn'. The council considered that if it were more generally known that they were prepared to offer a financial reward for the safe arrival in this country of animals from abroad, 'the chances of such an accident as this might be rendered more remote'.

Recently, the Society had received, from Mr Robert Marshall of the Royal Mail Steam Packet Company, a pair of 'the *Psopheo Crepitans* Agamia, or Trumpeter Birds' from Central America.

> These fine birds . . . are easily domesticated, and become attached to the human race in a most extraordinary manner. In their own country, they will trustily watch a house, like a dog, and they give warning of danger by . . . giving forth a trumpet-like sound. [They] may also, it is said, be trained to watch a flock of poultry, and even to shepherd a flock of sheep. It possesses great courage, and is beautiful in form and colour.

The Acclimatisation Society in Melbourne had recently shipped to England, on the *Swiftsure*, fourteen bronzewing pigeons, and on the *Moravian* a further six bronzewings and seven wonga pigeons. Finally among birds, it was hoped soon to receive from Norway 'a plentiful supply of the Reiper, or Norway Grouse' (either the rock ptarmigan or hazel grouse) 'a useful and likely bird of game'.

The secretaries announced that, for the introduction of the wels or European catfish, Mr Samuel Gurney MP had offered the use of a lake he owned at Carshalton in Surrey 'extremely well-fitted to harbour the fish', and that 'the arrival of the fish may be expected'. Murray cod or cod-perch had been promised by the Victoria Acclimatisation Society in Australia, and it was also proposed to import some 'Mountain Mullet' from Jamaica (presumably the 'Guaramier' previously referred to), 'of which great expectations may be entertained.'

In pursuance of its policy of experimentally translocating indigenous and naturalised species within the United Kingdom, the Society proposed, through Frank Buckland, to attempt the artificial propagation of salmon, grayling, brown trout, char or 'Ombre Chevalier', 'Danube Salmon', perch, and other species. Buckland had recently discovered, through experiments conducted with the cooperation of the Wenham Lake Ice Company, that salmon ova could be frozen for 135 days without harm; this, the Society suggested, 'seems to solve the problem of how to transport Salmon to Australia and other distant parts of the earth.'

The *Ailanthus* (or *Cynthia*) silkworm successfully raised by Lady Dorothy Nevill in her garden in Hampshire, was the only invertebrate reported on by the Society in its annual report for 1862–3. In the summer of 1862 Lady Dorothy had netted over three dozen *Ailanthus* trees, and had placed on them 500 silkworms which had spun 480 cocoons. The animals, Lady Dorothy reported, seemed impervious to the worst weather, and 'I have no doubt as to their hardiness.' The council concluded that

> These facts seem to establish not only the probability of cultivating the Ailanthus Silkworm in this country, but the ease with which it may be carried out. The shrub . . . delights in poor and sterile soil; and where it lives the worms will live also. The Council cannot but think that the general introduction of this new form of cultivation would be most beneficial, as it could be carried out upon any, even the smallest scale, by every cottager or small landowner. . . . To ladies especially this operation may be recommended by the fact that they may, without the slightest hyperbole, grow their own silk dresses in their own gardens.

Turning to vegetables, the council announced that, as in the previous year, it had received conflicting reports on the success or otherwise of cultivating the *'Dioscorea Batatas*, or Chinese Yam'—the greatest success having been achieved, not surprisingly, by the Guernsey branch of the Society in the milder climate of the Channel Islands.

Regarding the cultivation of the Brazilian arrowroot, the council, 'not having received a single unfavourable report with regard to the Arum, feels itself warranted in pronouncing this experiment to be decidedly successful.' On the other hand, attempts to cultivate the *'Dolichos Unguiculatus*, or Hook-podded Pea, and the *Phaseolus Limensis*, or Lima Bean', sent from Jamaica by Governor Darling, had all failed, due to inclement weather. 'It is to be hoped,' the council claimed with undue optimism, 'that perseverance and more genial seasons will prove that these valuable vegetables may still be added to our gardens.'

Mr Higford Burr announced that he was conducting experiments with bunch grass, a species of *Festuca* imported from the United States, which he considered might be suitable for planting on waste ground and similar marginal habitats. The council had received, from the commissioner for the Tasmanian section of the Great Exhibition, the seeds of some forty species of herbs, shrubs and trees which, like those of Mr Burr's bunch grass, would be distributed to members on application.

Finally, the council was pleased to record that it had established friendly relationships with all the other acclimatisation societies then in existence; the *Société Zoologique d'Acclimatation* in France; the Societies of Melbourne, Hobart, Sidney and Queensland in Australia; New Zealand, and the *Società di Acclimazione* of Palermo in Italy.

Summing up the activities and progress of the Society during the year under review, the council stated that it

cannot but regard the progress of the Society with great satisfaction. . . . The Society appears to be approaching the period when it can safely and prudently embark in the prosecution of experiments upon a larger scale. . . . If the progress of the Society during the past year is to be taken as a precedent, next year will find it in a position considerably to extend the sphere of its operations.

7. The Society in 1863–1864

THE fourth annual report of the Society, presented to members for the year ending 31 May 1864, revealed that during the past year the number of life members had increased from 46 to 81, and that of annual subscribers from 139 to 284. The treasurer reported that cash in hand stood at £438.3s.11d.

From the Society's inception it had been intended, whenever possible, to hold occasional scientific meetings, and the secretaries reported that the first of such meetings had been held in the preceding April at the Society of Arts in Adelphi, when Frank Buckland had delivered a paper entitled 'On the reports from Hong Kong, Labuan, Tasmania and Western Australia relating to fauna and flora suitable for acclimatisation in Britain', James Lowe had spoken on 'Oyster culture', and Mr A. W. Crichton on 'Game-birds and animals of Canada'. The success of this meeting had encouraged the council to express the hope that it might soon be repeated.

One of the most important events of the past year had been the circulation of a questionnaire[1] from the Foreign and Colonial Office (under the auspices of the president, as Secretary of State for the Colonies), addressed to ministers, governors and consuls throughout the world, requesting them to supply to the Society whatever information they might have concerning such of the local fauna and flora 'as are likely to be of use as ornament, whether for domestication or for varying the common food of the people, or for manufacturing, or for any other useful purpose, and whose constitution and habits offer a reasonable prospect of successful cultivation.' Similarly, the Admiralty had issued instructions to the commanding officers of Her Majesty's Ships to afford the Society such assistance as might be within their power, 'upon the distinct understanding that no expense whatever is incurred.'

The joint-secretaries were pleased to be able to report that the council had continued to maintain friendly relationships with other acclimatisation societies throughout the world, especially with the *Société Zoologique d'Acclimatation* in France (which had presented a silver medal to Mr William Bennett for his success in acclimatising and domesticating the 'Emeu'),[2] and those of Queensland and Victoria in Australia. The Acclimatisation Society of Palermo in Sicily had conferred on Frank Buckland its diploma of membership.

The second commemorative dinner of the Society had been held in St James's Hall on 1 July 1863, when 'several dishes were introduced into the bill of fare for the purpose of illustrating the utilitarian purposes of the Society.' One of these was 'White Soup of the Channel Islands' made from the conger eel, 'a creature so despised that the starving Irish have refused to add flavour and nutriment to their potatoes by boiling with them a salted steak of the Conger. . . . It is a curious illustration of the effect of prejudice that whilst the poor reject the Conger Eel, large quantities of the fish are boiled down into stock, to be used in the making of Turtle Soup in London.' The 'White Soup' at this dinner was made, under the supervision of Dr S. Elliott Hoskins, the honorary secretary of the Guernsey branch of the Society, of conger eel with milk and vegetables. According to *The Field*'s report of this dinner, 'in spite of Mr BERNAL OSBORNE'S joking (and what is there that Mr BERNAL OSBORNE will not joke at?) the general opinion was so much in favour of this soup that it was all eaten up.' The *Morning Post's* reporter, following Mr Osborne's lead, denounced it as 'thin gruel'. 'Let us ask this gastronomic critic', continued *The Field*, 'whether it was not much more like very good *Potage à la Reine!*'

On 20 September 1863 The Hon. Grantley F. Berkeley had resigned as a vice-president and member of the Society. The announcement by the secretaries of Berkeley's resignation was made without comment or qualification, but in a letter to the *Dorset Country Chronicle*[3] Berkeley explained that he had withdrawn from the Society because

> it has fallen into the hands of a clique of men always in town, and who, by the monthly meetings, can control its finances and guide its now misconducted interests. . . . It has become evident to me by the late substitution of the *sub-editor of the Field*, a Mr Francis Francis, to the paid position of manager of the fish-culture to the Society, instead of that really clever gentleman Mr F. Buckland, that a clique having a majority in and around *The Field* office has a great deal too much to do with the Society ever to let its interests stand on their own merits.

That Berkeley was a cantankerous, difficult and not universally popular figure, and that his strictures of *The Field* (which had recently refused to continue employing him as a correspondent) may not have been entirely unbiased, is shown by the following contribution, which appeared in *The Field*, under the pseudonym 'A Soldier' on 26 September.

> 'Good heavens! what have they done?' was my exclamation, this morning, when Mr Grantley Berkeley's astounding announcement in *The Times* caught my eye. What a dreadful mistake they have made; why, they will be utterly done for! *I have seen fit to withdraw my name from the Acclimatisation Society in England*, writes Mr Berkeley. Poor unfortunate Society! . . . Of course the Duke of Newcastle will resign, and poor Frank Buckland and James Lowe, the secretaries, will abandon salmon-fishing and take to gudgeons. Before they retire, however, from their responsible

positions, pray let there be light on this horrid matter. Let us insist on the
resignation of the committee, and condign punishment of the secretaries.
What can it be? Can they have been so blind to their duty as to neglect
his paternal advice? Have they winced at the rod so indulgently applied?
Have the secretaries presumed to have opinions of their own? In that case
the sooner those presumptuous persons be removed from their office
the better; or stay!—yes, that must be it. The office of president of the
society was *not* laid at the feet of our honourable, learned, and scientific
friend. This must be seen to, and a new list made out at once. . . . Then
the society is sure to succeed. We shall all be friends, and live happy
ever after.

[Our correspondent, A Soldier, is familiar to the readers of THE
FIELD. . . . It is hardly necessary to say that we agree with him to
the full in his ridicule of Mr Berkeley's eccentricities. Mr Berkeley,
in the drawing-room, is a most agreeable man—upon paper he is
the essence of bigotry and intolerance. . . . As to the Acclimatisation
Society, we . . . do not think the society will suffer by the loss of one of
its vice-presidents.—Ed.]

Although it may very well have been true that 'Mr Berkeley, in the
drawing-room, is a most agreeable man', the Society was no doubt
relieved to be rid of its crabby vice-president.

In this fourth report of the Society is found the first mention of action
taken under one of the purposes in the Society's rules, viz. 'The Transmission of Animals, &c., from England to her Colonies and Foreign parts,
in Exchange for others sent from thence to the Society'. In reciprocation
for the various shipments of mammals and birds received from the
Queensland society, Mr Higford Burr had despatched to Australia on
the *Light of the Age* 'five handsome pied specimens of the Common
Pheasant', only one of which, however, arrived alive. As no relics were
produced for the Queenslanders, they 'very properly refused to pay any
reward to the person who had charge of the birds'. The council recommended that in future 'in all cases where living creatures are shipped
from one place to another for Acclimatisation purposes, some portion
or portions of the creature which unfortunately dies during the voyage
shall be produced on demand'. To make good this loss, Frank Buckland
(now the 'Naturalist Manager') had been instructed by the council to
send out to Queensland as soon as conditions allowed, a consignment
of red deer and fallow deer calves, and also some 'birds of game'.

The council wished to record its debt to the following, for services
rendered:

A. C. MACLEAN, Esq., Haremere Hall, Hurst Green, Sussex, for his
successful experiments in cross-breeding pheasants, and for presenting
the Society with specimens of his crosses.
Rev. W. COLLINGS, Seigneur of Sark, for having undertaken the care
of Wonga pigeons, with a view to breeding them for the Society.

H. O. CARRÉ, Esq., Lieut-Bailiff of Guernsey, for having undertaken the care of Curassows, with the same view.

Dr MILLER, of the Indian Army, for presents of animals, &c.

Dr W. HARTE MILLER, of Victoria, for Bronze-wing Pigeons and eggs.

W. WIENHOLT, Esq., of Reading, for one Fire-back Pheasant (*Euplocamus Mythropthalmus*).

––– HEPBURN, Esq. for the loan of an Emeu.

Dr GENCZIK, of Linz, for his endeavours to obtain *Silurus Glanis*.

G. D. BERNEY, Esq., for presenting Gold Schley [tench].

Col. DENISON, for presenting Jungle Fowl.

J. A. CRAUFORD, Esq. (Bengal Civil Service), Calcutta, for presenting birds from India.

Dr JAGER, of Vienna, for assisting in obtaining *Silurus Glanis*.

THE ACCLIMATISATION SOCIETY OF QUEENSLAND, for presents of Mammals, Bronze-wing and Green-wing Pigeons, Speckled Doves.

JACKSON GILLBANKS, Esq., for his services in introducing Canadian Rice.

HIGFORD BURR, Esq., for his experiments with Pheasants.

JOHN RICE CROWE, Esq., C. B., &c., H.M. Consul, Christiana, Norway, PETER TRONHÜÜS, Gubldenbranstadt, H.M. Vice-Consul, JOHN ALLAN, Esq., Christiansund, for efforts to obtain Jerper.

M. GUERIN-MENEVILLE, Vincennes, Ailanthus Silkworms.

It will be remembered that in the previous report Lord Powerscourt had announced his intention of importing to Ireland some red deer from Prince Lichtenstein's estate in Austria. Six stags and four hinds (the latter all in calf) had been despatched to Powerscourt, near Dublin, of which only seven had reached their destination alive. The method of catching the deer in Pohanska Park, which had a circumference of twenty miles, is of some interest, and was described by Buckland in *The Field* of 6 April 1864 as follows:

It required the services of a hundred men, working day and night, in 24 deg. frost, to drive the deer into a place where they could easily be caught. The portion of the park where the deer are to be found is inclosed by the men, who form themselves into a semi-circle, in the manner [in which] they drive the bears in Norway by means of what are called 'skals'. The men walk some yards apart and carry between them on poles long sheets of canvas some 12 or 14 feet high; they advance in line, and gradually diminish the circle, till at length they drive the deer into a trap, built much in the same way as that into which the natives drive elephants in India. This trap ends in a narrow gangway, where only one deer at a time can enter.

Buckland ends his account by remarking that 'during the driving of the deer two men actually died from the cold and exhaustion'. The seven Austrian deer that reached Powerscourt alive, which were—as indeed they still are—very much larger than their Scottish and Irish counterparts, were all said to be in good health.

Of the other mammals at Powerscourt, a pair of young wapiti, the Japanese sika, the sambar and the mouflon were all reported to be doing well. The eland, no doubt due to the unsuitability of the damp Irish climate, had been transferred into the care of King Victor Emmanuel II of Italy and Sardinia.

After all the praise that had been lavished on the breed of Chinese sheep, in this fourth annual report are found the first discouraging reports. Lord Powerscourt's bailiff commented that the cross-breds yielded small and poor-quality fleeces, that butchers would not buy the carcasses, that they were not prolific breeders, and that they were subject to foot-rot. All but one of the animals in the care of the treasurer, John Bush, despite being housed at night and fed on oilcake, hay and corn, had died, while reports on pure-bred and cross-bred sheep under the care of members of the Society were in general unfavourable to the former, though in some cases favourable to the latter. The council concluded 'that in a wet climate, such as Ireland, the Chinese sheep require great care and tending, careful feeding and housing.' 'There is no reason, however', the council continued somewhat optimistically, 'for believing that in dry localities, and where the animals can be carefully tended, they will not thrive.'

Three common wombats had been purchased by the Society from its Australian counterpart in Victoria; they had become quite tame, and were given the run of John Bush's property in Clapham. 'It has been objected against these animals', said the council, 'that they will do much injury by burrowing, but experience has shown that when in a state of domestication and where a habitation is provided for them they do not burrow, but accommodate themselves to their altered circumstances.'

In June and July 1862 the Society had received through Mr Robert Marshall of the Royal Mail Steam Packet Company, half-a-dozen ocellated turkeys from Honduras. These birds had been handed over to the treasurer, who in the following year had successfully reared sixteen poults; some of these were distributed among Mr John Stone, Sir Charles Rushout, and Mr J. Wingfield Malcolm, 'to breed from on behalf of the Society upon the usual conditions'. What these conditions were we are not told, but under Rule VI of the Society's constitution 'The Council shall have the power of entrusting . . . to Members or other persons, the Animals, Vegetables, or any articles which are the property of the Society, under agreements to be approved of by the Council and signed by the parties.'

In December 1863 a life member, Colonel Denison, presented the

Society with a pair of red jungle fowl from India, but unfortunately both birds died immediately after their arrival. In the following April a further four were despatched on the *Nile* by Colonel Crawford, of which only a pair arrived safely. Although Crawford had described the birds as 'very wild in their habits' they were found on arrival actually to be extremely tame; the hen subsequently laid a clutch of eggs, from which three chicks hatched successfully.

In May 1863 Mr William Wienholt gave the Society a pair of fire-back pheasants (natives of Indonesia and Indochina), of which only the cock arrived alive. In the following August Dr Miller presented a single 'Indian Partridge' (? sp.), for which the Society hoped to be able to find a mate.

The council reported that several hundred beautifully plumaged common pheasant × Japanese pheasant hybrids had been bred by Mr A. C. McLean. It was hoped that 'Indian Pheasants' (? sp.) would shortly be delivered to the Society through the cooperation of Mr Herman Merivale and the Secretary for India, Sir Charles Wood, and Matheson & Co had been requested to supply, through their agent in Japan, a further stock of Japanese pheasants.

Between June 1863 and April 1864 the Society purchased two dozen wonga pigeons—referred to in the annual report as 'Wonga Wongá Pigeons'—from the Acclimatisation Society of Victoria in Australia, which were distributed among the Revd William Collings (the 'Seigneur of Serk'), Lady Dorothy Nevill, Dr Bull of Hereford, Mr Henry Hancock of Bagshot, Surrey and the treasurer, 'to breed from on the usual conditions'. The council announced that in its own aviary the Society now had eight of these beautiful pigeons which, though they had not as yet bred, had overwintered well.

Also between June 1863 and May 1864 the Society had acquired from Australia nineteen bronzewing pigeons and three eggs; the latter were placed under a domestic pigeon, but failed to hatch; from the former, a pair in the care of James Lowe had produced two squabs, and the same pair was currently incubating a further clutch of eggs. All the birds had survived the winter with no protection from the weather apart from the netting of their aviary.

Attempts were continuing to obtain 'living specimens of the Gelinotte or Hjerper' (the hazel grouse or rock ptarmigan) from Switzerland, Prussia or Norway; 'these birds are, however, exceedingly difficult to capture, and do not live very long in confinement.'

Regretfully, the council reported that the Society's pair of common trumpeters had both died, but the 'Native Companions' (brolgas) from Australia—so called because of their affinity to man—were in excellent condition.

In June 1863 a cock brush turkey, a pair of 'small-hawks' and a dingo[4] had arrived from the Acclimatisation Society of Queensland; the dingo dog, together with a bitch owned by the Zoological Society of London, were to be presented to the Dublin zoo in Ireland; the council proposed to give the hawks to the London zoo, and to request that in return the zoo should donate to the Society a brush turkey hen as a mate for the Society's cock, the offspring, if any, to be shared equally between the two societies. Nine months later the Society also received from Queensland three 'Speckled Doves', two 'Greenwing Pigeons', and one 'Emeu', all of which arrived in good condition. The latter was said to be a 'highly amusing and ornamental creature for a gentleman's park or lawn'.

The council was actively pursuing attempts to introduce the wels or European catfish from continental Europe; a pair, packed in wet moss by Professor Jager in Vienna, not surprisingly failed to survive the journey. 'It is highly to be regretted,' the council reported, 'that any attempt was made to transport these fish by a mode so certain of failure as packing them in wet moss.'

The Acclimatisation Society of Victoria had purchased, on behalf of the Society, a quantity of Murray cod or cod-perch; these fish had been caught at the confluence of the Edward and Murray rivers, transported by boat down-river to Echren and from there taken to Melbourne by the Victoria Railway Company. At Melbourne they were loaded onto the *Lincolnshire*, which berthed in the London docks three months later on 21 May 1863. Unfortunately, the 130 or so fingerling fish were all found to be dead on arrival, due, it was believed, to contamination of the water of their container.

Mr G. D. Berney had presented the Society with a number of 'Gold Schley', which had been exhibited at the Society's annual dinner; they were subsequently introduced to a pond on Mr Higford Burr's estate near Reading in Berkshire, where they were believed to be doing well. At least some of the freshwater crayfish which had been presented to Lord Powerscourt were apparently surviving on his estate in Ireland. The joint-secretaries had recently instituted enquiries into the practicality of oyster cultivation, which the council considered could be 'carried on with great advantage to the natural resources of the country', using not native British species but American oysters and 'those found in the Cattegat' (Kattegat) channel between Denmark and Sweden.

For some time the council had been considering embarking on a programme of pisciculture, especially with members of the Salmonidae and with fish imported from abroad. To this end, a separate piscicultural branch of the Society had been formed, and the distinguished icthyologist, Mr Francis Francis, had been commissioned to construct a suitable 'apparatus' at his home on the Thames at Twickenham, together with a stew-pond and 'other conveniences'. Francis's report was presented as an appendix to the Society's annual report.

Francis started by bemoaning the problems that had beset 'the formation of the first public Piscicultural Establishment in this country'. There were no results based on previous experience on which to formulate any plans or operations, and

> The means at my disposal were very limited . . . no skilled attendant . . . could be found, . . . and we have had perhaps the very worst season . . . for a great many years. This necessarily has thrown an immense amount of labour upon my hands—much more, indeed, than I had ever contemplated. Indeed, the anxiety and labour for many months was most trying and incessant.

Despite these difficulties, Francis considered that the results of the first year's operations 'were as fully successful as our most sanguine anticipations could have desired'. Several thousand ova of salmon, common, sea and 'Lake Trout',[5] and char or 'Ombre Chevalier' were laid down, many of which hatched successfully. Only with 'Greyling' had Francis experienced almost total failure when, as a result of a sudden heatwave, many ova that had reached the eyed stage were killed. Some of the salmon and trout ova and fry had been despatched to France, Australia and India, while others had been distributed among members of the Society and non-members who had been of assistance to the piscicultural branch. Francis had also acquired twenty burbot—the only freshwater representative of the cod family to be found in British waters—which he described as 'that most delicious and valuable . . . excellent and curious fish'. Two brace '(as the fish is so little known and distributed, that it is . . . a natural curiosity)' were presented to the Zoological Society of London, the remainder being placed in Mr Samuel Gurney's stews at Carshalton in Surrey.

The council was pleased to report that Lady Dorothy Nevill, the Society's treasurer, John Bush, and other members had had a successful year rearing 'Ailanthus Silkworms'. Furthermore, 'a gentleman (named Mongredian)' had enclosed several acres of virtually waste ground near Bagshot in Surrey for cultivating the species on a large scale. The governor of the Cape of Good Hope and High Commissioner of South Africa, Sir Philip Wodehouse, had asked for some silkworm eggs to be sent out to him, and the council reported that 'means will be taken to supply this *desideratum*'. Lady Dorothy Nevill was experimenting with a new species of silkworm—'viz., the *Bombyx Yama Inai*', which she proposed in due course to exhibit to members.

The council reported that a new supply of seeds of the 'Hook-podded Pea (*Dolichos Unguiculatus*)' had been received via the Foreign Office from Lieutenant-Governor Eyre of Jamaica, and had been distributed among Lord Abinger, the treasurer, Mr Higford Burr, Viscount Gage, Mr Samuel Gurney, James Lowe, Lady Dorothy Nevill, Lord Tredegar and other members of the Society. Seeds of the Canadian rice, presented by Mr Jackson Gillbanks of Cumberland (now Cumbria) had been distributed to Lady Dorothy Nevill, Mr J. Wingfield Malcolm of London and Mr Thomas Chamberlayne of Winchester. Also available for distribution to members were seeds of 'several varieties of Peruvian Maize; the Ebony Tree; a peculiar kind of Chinese Thistle, which produces a fibre capable of being spun into very fine thread; a new kind of Sorglio; a new kind of Turnip, and *Cryptomeria Japonica*', all of which had been given to the Society by M. Pierre Pichot of the French *Société Zoologique d'Acclimatation.*

In concluding their fourth annual report, the joint honorary secretaries stated that since 'the main source of obstacle in the way of the operations and experiments of the Society is the difficulty of enlisting the *zeal* of persons abroad . . . and especially the officers of the vessels which bring over the objects for experiment', the council believed that the award of a medal to those who had been of singular service to the Society might help to solve the problem, and that donations towards the costs of the die (estimated at between £100 and £150) for such a medal would be gratefully received.

Finally, while congratulating members on what the Society had achieved in the short time since its inception, the council wished to impress upon them that much still needed to be done before the Society stood on a sound financial footing. 'It is obvious', the council said, 'that until the number of annual subscribers is greatly increased it is impossible for the Society to carry on its experiments in an independent manner, and upon a proper scale.' It was hoped that within the year the membership would considerably increase, 'so as to place it within the power of the council to have an experimental farm or garden wherein the operations of the Society may be conducted.'

The Guernsey branch of the Society

As an appendix to the parent Society's fourth annual report, an account of the activities of the Guernsey branch during the year past was presented by the honorary secretary, Dr S. Elliott Hoskins, FRS.

James Lowe, on his visit to Guernsey in August 1863, had concluded his address by saying that, with but sixteen members, the financial contribution of the Guernsey branch to the parent Society could never be large, but that

> Blessed as you are with a genial climate and a fertile soil, you may render to England the most important assistance in persuading the natural riches of other climes to accommodate themselves to her shores. . . . The British Islands owe almost every useful animal they can boast to practical Acclimatisation, and it is the object of our Society to increase that stock.

Although the membership in Guernsey was so small, the branch society had not been inactive. The parent body, as we have seen, had entrusted to the care of their compatriots a pair each of crested curassows and wonga pigeons, 'highly ornamental to the lawn and the aviary, and, moreover, choice articles of food'. The former, in the care of the island's Lieutenant-Bailiff, Mr H. O. Carré, had at first caused considerable anxiety through their apparent dislike of all the food offered to them, and because of the cock's propensity to stray. They were now, however, said to be feeding well, had become extremely tame, and the cock had abandoned his previous tendency to roam. The latter, which were being looked after by the Seigneur of Serk (Sark), the Revd W. T. Collings, were reported to be 'thriving, healthy-looking, and plump'.

When James Lowe visited Guernsey in August 1863, he had presented the branch society with some fifty or sixty larvae of the 'Ailanthus Silkworm *Bombyx Cynthia*', which was reputedly much more hardy and tolerant of stormy weather than the species that feeds exclusively on the leaf of the mulberry, and did not require artificial feeding. These larvae were placed under netting on some *Ailanthus* bushes where, in spite of some seasonally inclement weather, by late September several had spun cocoons. 'In this cultivation', Lowe suggested, 'the ladies of the island may . . . grow their own silk dresses in their own gardens!' As an alternative to covering the *Ailanthus* bushes with netting, Lowe suggested placing over them ladies' crinolines, adding that he would 'never see that article more judiciously or tactfully employed than in such a place!'

The material produced by these silkworms had been examined by experts, who had pronounced that 'the strength of the silk is immense', to which they attributed 'the great durability of the Indian *foulards*, which are composed exclusively of this silk'. L'Abbé Incarville had stated that 'it lasts double the time of the mulberry silk, does not spot so easily, and washes like linen.' M. de Jongh found that 'the gloss of the Ailanthus silk, far surpasses any of the other known kinds of *Bourre de Soie.*' The weavers of Alsace reported that 'the cocoons are very easy to card and spin, they are easily cleaned, and take a good dye. This culture, made on a large scale, will furnish in abundance a stronger and finer floss than the Mulberry Silkworm, and will prove of immense utility in France and England.'

One of the many disadvantages of rearing mulberry silkworms was the necessity of providing expensive machinery and skilled labour for winding the silk from the cocoon: in the case of the *Ailanthus* species this was unnecessary since M. André Marchand of Paris was willing to purchase the raw cocoons and, moreover, supplied 'all that is necessary for the culture of the *Ailanthus* and its silkworm'. The provision of an adequate food supply was not a problem, since the food-plant could be acquired quite cheaply and grew well in Guernsey, while the parent Society in England had undertaken to supply such new eggs or larvae as might be required.

The increased and still increasing demand for oysters ('these delicate and nutritious Molluscs'), their growing scarcity due to the exhaustion and illegal destruction of the natural beds, and the ease with which they could be transported, had combined greatly to increase their value. The wholesale price of native British oysters had recently risen, within the space of a few months, from forty-two to upwards of seventy shillings a bushel (eight gallons), an increase of 60 per cent, while in London restaurants the price had risen correspondingly from sixpence to ninepence a dozen. In Guernsey market, where until recently large oysters, which were not in great demand in England, had sold for between eighteen pence and two shillings a hundred, they were now fetching as much as four shillings. Oyster shell, which had previously been regarded as worthless, was now sold as a base for vine-beds for four shillings per cartload.

These facts, coupled with the profit derived from the artificial propagation of oysters in France, had induced the Guernsey branch of the Society in July 1863 to lower experimental fascines in suitable localities; it was, however, considered doubtful whether these faggots were likely to retain the oyster-spat (spawn) as readily as ridge-tiles or fragments of rock. Some of the latter, together with oysters adhering to them, had been brought to Guernsey in the preceding autumn by James Lowe and Mr Henry Tupper from the artificial oyster parks of La Forêt near Concarneau, on the south coast of Brittany. It had been established that these man-made oyster parks formed by the French government could become profitable propositions, and there seemed no reason why they should not also become so in the Channel Islands, which in many ways appeared more suitable for the purpose than L'Isle de Ré in Brittany. An application for an Order in Council to authorise the formation and protection of oyster parks along the Guernsey coast was in course of preparation. Unlike the parent Society on the mainland which favoured the introduction of American and Scandinavian species, on Guernsey it was proposed to import Colchester oysters 'and other varieties which are more esteemed by connoisseurs, and fetch higher prices than the larger kinds of oyster'.

The artificial rearing of blue lobsters had also been discussed; some forty thousand a day were shipped to London alone, and it was confidently believed that 'double the number would find a ready sale at a highly remunerative price'. The branch society undertook to try to obtain further information on the propagation of lobsters from France.

Mr Dobree of St George had successfully cultivated a few pods of the lima bean, the seeds from which had been planted and had yielded such superior pods that it was planned to repeat the experiment. The honorary secretary, Dr Hoskins, had succeeded in raising a plant of the Jamaican hook-podded pea which had produced a small number of seeds; these had been planted in a greenhouse and the resulting plants were then placed in pots in a well-protected place out of doors. 'The scanty results of these careful trials go to prove that no great expectation can be entertained of cultivating this kind of West Indian Pulse in this climate, except as mere objects of curiosity.'

Mr H. O. Carré reported on his cultivation of the Chinese yam, which yielded about one pound in weight per three and a half square feet of ground. 'We, in our household, value the Chinese Yam highly for the table, where it is especially useful at the season when the best-keeping potatoes begin to deteriorate in quality.'

In concluding his report for 1863–4, Dr Hoskins said that in August 1863 James Lowe had distributed among members of the Guernsey branch some seeds of 'a beautiful variety of reed called the elephant grass, growing at Mysore, at a level of 3,000 feet above the sea', the stem of which was used in India for the making of furniture. Lowe also distributed some seeds of the American cotton plant, and of the nardoo from Australia. A life member of the parent Society, Mr John Colebrooke, had recently sent to Guernsey some seeds of the '*Paniflora Edulis* or Grenadilla', with the offer to procure other seeds from India and China. He added that the grenadilla had been picked in the 'Neilgherry Hills, that its fruit when sliced and put into tarts is excellent; and that when the ripe pulp is mixed with sherry wine and sugar, it is equally agreeable to the taste.'

8. The Society in 1864–1865

MR Waterhouse Hawkins, having succeeded Frank Buckland (who was now, as we have seen in the previous chapter, designated the 'Naturalist Manager') and James Lowe as secretary of the Society, presented to members the council's annual report for the year ending 5 May 1865.

Hawkins began by saying that the council wished to pay tribute to the efforts made on the Society's behalf by their president, the late Duke of Newcastle, who had died during the previous year, and to announce that His Royal Highness The Prince of Wales had consented to replace him as president of the Society.

In the fourth annual report for 1863–4 it had been stated that in the past year the total membership had approximately doubled, largely, it was believed, as a result of the piscicultural and fish-hatching operations then about to be started by the Society's manager, Mr Francis Francis, at Twickenham. It was thus especially unfortunate that the council and Francis should have fallen out over precisely how this operation should be managed. In particular, the council complained that it had not been permitted to read and approve, prior to publication, Francis's rather querulous report presented to members at last year's meeting; that Francis had declined to recognise the right of council to ask for explanations about his conduct of the operation; that he had considerably exceeded the sum voted by the council for expenditure on the venture, and that without authorisation by the council he had incurred further debts for more fish-hatching apparatus on the Society's behalf.

At a council meeting on 6 December 1864 a proposal was made to Francis that he should accept a reduced budget for the work he claimed still needed to be carried out; this, council reported, he 'peremptorily declined, whilst at the same time he distinctly refused to undertake any other connection with the piscicultural operations of the Society than mere superintendence.' What Francis's version of the story is we do not know, but it may well be that the onerous nature of his duties, which were clearly more than he had anticipated, coupled with a feeling that what he clearly regarded as a parsimonious council was constantly looking over his shoulder, had combined to make him heartily tired of his thankless task, and glad to be relieved of his position. At any rate, it had formerly been resolved

> That, returning the thanks of the Council to the manager for his exertions in Pisciculture, it is the opinion of the Council that, considering

all circumstances, the uncertain expense and tenure of the premises, it is advisable that the operations at Twickenham be discontinued, and that arrangements be made to carry them on elsewhere.

Thus ended, rather sadly, the Society's piscicultural and fish-hatching experiments at Twickenham. Francis seems to have been of a somewhat vindictive nature, since the council reported that 'as it was not then convenient to the manager to comply with the Council's request for the removal of their costly apparatus from his premises', it had been impossible for them to restart their piscicultural experiments elsewhere during the current season. Negotiations were, however, currently under way with the Royal Horticultural Society for permission to erect the fish-hatching apparatus for the coming season at South Kensington.

In concluding his report, the secretary announced that the council wished to place on record their thanks for their services to the Society during the past year to Miss Burdett Coutts, for offering to pay for the die for the medal mentioned in the previous report; to Mr Higford Burr, for pheasants, and for volunteering to care for the wels (or European catfish) on behalf of the Society; to the honorary treasurer, John Bush, for prairie chickens; to Sir Stephen Lakeman for providing the wels; to the Revd W. Smith for dwarf bamboo seed; to Lord Walsingham for 'Romagna Cattle'; to the Hudson's Bay Company for wild rice 'and promise of assistance', and to the Imperial Russian Acclimatisation Society of Moscow and the Zoological Society of London.

In presenting his report to members on the various animals being held by or on behalf of the Society, the naturalist manager, Frank Buckland, opened by saying that in October 1864 Lord Walsingham had presented to the Society two bulls and a cow of the Romagna breed of cattle. Soon after their arrival the cow had given birth to a calf, which had since unfortunately died. The lightness of the hindquarters of these animals, Buckland claimed, showed that they were not far removed from wild stock, and it was proposed to cross them with domestic cattle, though with what objective in mind is not stated.

For some years a pair of sambar had been at large in Windsor Great Park. Presumably because of the risk of hybridisation with other deer in the park, Queen Victoria had given instructions for their capture and removal. Captain Dawson Damer, MP, a life member of the Society, had arranged, through the Ranger of Windsor Park, General Seymour, that this pair of deer should be presented to the Society, on whose behalf they were being held by the Duke of Marlborough in the park at Blenheim Palace in Oxfordshire.

In Ireland, Lord Powerscourt reported that his herd of wapiti, which had not yet bred, and Japanese sika which had bred, were all in good health in his park in Co. Wicklow.

The Society's last pure-bred Chinese sheep had died during the past winter. Buckland considered that for their survival they required greater warmth and less damp conditions than had been provided for them, but that in the right climate the silky, hair-like wool yielded a fleece almost equal to that of the alpaca—probable descendant of the wild guanaco—and vicugna, but that their conformation was unpopular with butchers. Several members had successfully crossed Chinese sheep with Oxford Southdowns and other English breeds.

On 2 April 1865 the Society had received a pair of Kalmuck sheep and four Romanoff sheep—one ram and three ewes. These animals had been presented by the Imperial Russian Acclimatisation Society of Moscow to the Victoria Acclimatisation Society in Melbourne, on whose behalf they were being held in England before undergoing the lengthy voyage to Australia. Mr J. W. Buckland had obtained from Catalonia a pair of Spanish donkeys, for presentation to the Acclimatisation Society of Queensland. These were at present being temporarily cared for by the London zoo before being shipped out to Australia.

A friend of Buckland had recently given the Society three red-necked or Bennett's wallabies from Australia.[1] One had since died, but had been replaced while in the care of John Bush by a young joey. It was proposed in due course to send the female to join the Duke of Marlborough's four wallabies in the park at Blenheim. Kangaroos, Buckland said,

> will breed freely in England, as has been proved not only in the case of our own animals, but by numerous young ones born at the Zoological Gardens. . . . Australians tell us that the Kangaroos are very good to eat, and should their acclimatisation be continued, it may be hoped that they may be found useful as food, or at least as a new kind of game.

In April 1865 the Society possessed a flock of ten Australian wonga pigeons. One member, Dr Henry Bull of Hereford, considered that 'there can be no doubt now that these Wonga Wonga pigeons will bear our climate well. The past winter has not only been very long and severe, but the changes of temperature have been remarkably sudden . . . whether they will breed in confinement . . . yet remains to be seen.' Of the seventeen bronzewing pigeons owned by the Society, several pairs in the care of the honorary treasurer had nested and reared young successfully, and the council expressed the hope 'that one of these days Bronze-winged Pigeons may become common throughout the country, as they are quick in flight, and therefore would be valuable game birds.'

The three guans in the Society's collection had resolutely refused to breed; 'even in their native country (South America)', the council reported, 'they will not breed in poultry yards under the most favourable circumstances.' One wonders, therefore, why they were ever introduced to Britain, when there was clearly little if any prospect of breeding from them successfully.

The 'Native Companions' (brolgas) referred to in previous reports continued to thrive. 'They are exceedingly tame and highly ornamental, and fully bear out their name of Companions. They are about 4 feet 6 in. high, and allow themselves to be handled, and are apparently very proud of being noticed; they often perform the most amusing antics.' Their favourite food appeared to be grubs which they found in the roots of crowfoot.

Since the previous annual report, two of the Society's brush turkeys had unfortunately died from enlargement of the liver. Of a further pair, shipped from Brisbane, Queensland, on board the *Flying Cloud*, one died on the voyage from Australia, but was replaced on arrival in England by another purchased from a passenger. Later, a further four were despatched from Brisbane on the *Wansfell*; one was lost overboard during the voyage, but the remaining three arrived safely. None of these birds had so far bred.

The honorary treasurer had received on the *Peruvian* from Montreal a consignment of seven prairie chickens—four cocks and three hens. One pair had been presented by the Society to Queen Victoria, and another to Earl Pomfret.

The Society's flock of eight ocellated turkeys were distributed among various members. These birds were originally believed to be hybrids between the ocellated and common turkey, but had since been found, to the council's satisfaction, to be pure *ocellata*.

The four emus owned by the Society were said to be 'exceedingly tame, and form a very pretty group on the lawn or paddock. They run like race-horses, with a very peculiar and amusing action.' These birds had not yet bred. Other emus were in the possession of the Duke of Marlborough and Mr Samuel Gurney at Carshalton in Surrey. Of the Duke's six birds, a pair had laid a clutch of nine eggs, which it was hoped would hatch successfully. Mr Gurney had a cock and two hen emus, as well as a male ostrich. Gurney reported that

> The male Emu is excessively hardy. . . . After snowy nights he was frequently found enveloped in snow, with his head and neck alone protruding, so that he looked like a great snow heap. The Ostrich also . . . has held out during the whole of last winter; he, like the Emu, does not seem to care for the frost and cold.

A pair of demoiselle cranes owned by the Society had been accepted as a gift by Queen Victoria. Unfortunately, before they could be despatched to Osborne on the Isle of Wight, one of these 'highly ornamental and graceful birds' had been accidentally killed by a labourer, and the Society was currently endeavouring to obtain a replacement.

During the year under review the Society's Sub-Committee for the Introduction of Foreign Game Birds had acquired specimens of various pheasants; these comprised silver pheasants[2] and golden pheasants[3] from China; a cock 'Rufus-tailed or Firebacked Pheasant' which had been placed with common pheasant hens in the Society's aviary at Clapham, in the hope of obtaining a hybrid; one cock and three hen hybrids between the ring-necked pheasant and the Japanese pheasant; and a nearly pure-bred cock Reeves's pheasant,[4] which had been placed with three hen common pheasants.

In exchange for the brush turkeys sent by the Acclimatisation Society of Brisbane, the council had despatched to Australia in the past year on the *Wansfell* ten common pheasants, sixteen song thrushes, half-a-dozen blackbirds, and eighteen skylarks.[5] Mr J. W. Buckland had also sent to Brisbane on the *Sirocco* eight hen and four cock common pheasants, presented by Mr R. S. Holford, MP, and four partridges of unspecified species.

Although the Society had perforce abandoned its piscicultural experiments for the current season, Frank Buckland had continued operations on a considerable scale on his own account. At his personal expense he had constructed, in the kitchen of his home at 34 Albany Street, Regent's Park, a fish-hatching apparatus, in which he had placed upwards of 30,000 ova of the Salmonidae. He had also established a hatchery in the Royal Horticultural Society's gardens, on behalf of the South Kensington Museum, in which large numbers of Atlantic salmon and brown trout had been successfully reared, and from which ova and fry had been distributed to the Zoological Society of London, the Crystal Palace, and elsewhere. Buckland had further been commissioned by the Ranger of Windsor Great Park to establish a fish hatchery in the park, from which the lakes and ponds within the park might be stocked.

Other members of the Society who had been experimenting with fish hatching on their own account included Mr Higford Burr in Berkshire, Mr Henry Early in Oxfordshire, and Mr J. L. Broughton in Shropshire.

On 15 September 1864 the Society succeeded in its ambition of introducing the wels or European catfish to Britain. Thirteen (according to the Society) or fourteen (according to *The Field* magazine)—the survivors of an original shipment of thirty-six—arrived safely from Bucharest. Under the heading 'The Arrival of the Silurus Glanis in England', *The Field* published a lengthy account of the event by James Lowe in its issue of 17 September 1864:

> That much desired fish, the Silurus, has at last been brought alive to this country, after various failures. The success is entirely due to the intelligent enterprise and perseverance of Sir Stephen B. Lakeman, who himself accompanied the fish all the way from Bucharest, a distance of 1800 miles; and on Thursday night I had the pleasure of assisting Mr

Francis Francis in placing fourteen lively little baby-siluri in a pond not far from the fish-hatching apparatus belonging to the Acclimatisation Society on Mr Francis's grounds at Twickenham.

When I state that Sir S. Lakeman had to change railway carriages more than thirty times during the journey, not to mention other vehicles, such as horse-carriages and steamers; that he started on the 23rd of August, and arrived in London with the fish on the evening of the 15th of September; and that during all that long journey he had to wage perpetual battle with the indifference and stupidity of officials, from station-masters down to porters (most of whom seemed to regard the fact of his travelling with a strange fish as rather a misdemeanour than otherwise), the reader will have some notion of the difficulties which have been overcome.

The fourteen little siluri (or siluruses) which have arrived are what remain of thirty-six of the same species, which started from Kopacheni, where Sir S. Lakeman's estate is situated. This place is on the banks of the Argisch, a tributary of the Danube, and is about ten miles [16 km] from Bucharest. The Argisch abounds in silurus, and in all the other curious and almost unknown fish which swarm in the Danube, some of which (thanks to Sir S. Lakeman) we hope, at no very distant day, to reintroduce to their old friends, the siluri, in Mr Francis's pond.

By way of preparation for the journey, the Siluri were placed in a water-cask, covered with a net, and placed in a large pond or lake of about 30 acres [12 hectares], belonging to Sir S. Lakeman; which pond abounds with fish, and yields silurus weighing up to 30 lb and 40 lb [13–18 kg], which may be caught with the line. . . . Of the thirty-six fish which started from Kopacheni, some were comparatively large (weighing up to 4 lb [nearly 2 kg], and one of about 6 lb [nearly 3 kg]), and some were mere fry. . . .

Sir S. Lakeman started (as I have stated) from Kopacheni on Aug. 23. He brought the fish, by Bucharest, to Giurgevo, a distance of fifty miles [80 km]; thence by steamer to Basias (in Transylvania), and so on by railway to Pesth, Vienna, Nuremburg, Cologne, Brussels, and Boulogne. The larger fish died first, all but the six-pounder, which endured to Vienna; and he only died there, it is supposed, because the servant in charge put his barrel into a stable, and it is likely that the ammoniacal atmosphere of the place disagreed with him. . . .

On arriving at Folkestone, there were fourteen survivors of the thirty-six which started from Kopacheni, and I am happy to say that every one of these reached Mr Francis in the most lively and promising state. . . .

Immediately on his arrival in London, Sir Stephen Lakeman, with most praiseworthy public spirit, thought more of the fish than of himself; for without even driving to an hotel, he made his way to *The Field* office; and I need not describe with what delight he and his charge were welcomed. In a very short time we were on our way to Twickenham. . . .

So we got them safely down to Mr Francis's, and on the brink of the pond turned them into a trough—fourteen little siluri, all alive and kicking, and as spry and frisky as possible. Their size varied from an ounce and a half to two ounces [42–56 g], for they are not more than three months old; but Sir S. Lakeman (who is well acquainted with the fish) declares that in a few weeks, when they have had the benefit of fresh water and plenty of food, their increase will be rapid and astonishing. When put into the water, they dived down to the bottom at once, with an easy vigorous movement, and waving their long barbels about, quite as if they knew their way about the pond which they then saw for the first time. From their flourishing condition, there is every reason to hope that they will increase and multiply. Indeed, I have now very little doubt that (with ordinary luck) this country has now acquired the *Silurus Glanis*. . . .

This is (so far as I am aware) the first time that this valuable fish has been brought to our shores; and the gratitude not only of the Acclimatisation Society, but of the country, is due to Sir Stephen B. Lakeman for the admirable manner in which he has effected the task which he unselfishly (and let me say patriotically) imposed upon himself.

'The ownership of these fish,' the Society later sorrowfully reported, 'we regret to say, is now disputed'. Further altercation with the cantankerous Mr Francis!

In 1865 Sir Stephen Lakeman offered eleven more specimens of *glanis* to Frank Buckland, provided he could find someone who was willing to devote a water entirely to them. Higford Burr generously offered a pond on his Berkshire estate, to which on 27 January the fish (each weighing a quarter of a pound and measuring some fourteen inches in length) were conveyed by Buckland. 'Some three years afterwards', Buckland subsequently reported, 'this pond was let dry—the Silurus had entirely disappeared.'

Sir Stephen Lakeman also presented the Society with several examples 'of a curious kind of pond fish, called the Thunder Fish. It is a species of Loach.' These European thunderfish or pond loach were also placed in one of Higford Burr's ponds at Aldermaston.

A consignment of the eggs of the 'Yamma Mai Silkworm' from 'Monsr. Ramel' had been received by John Bush, who had placed them on the silkworm's favourite food plant, the oak, where they subsequently hatched out successfully. The *Ailanthus* silkworms were reported to be continuing to do well under the care of Lady Dorothy Nevill.

Some idea of the apparent lack of interest in the Society being shown by most members of the council at this time may be gained from the list of attendances for the year ended 5 May 1865. Of the fifteen members listed, only one, Mr Henry Hancock, attended ten meetings (out of a total of twelve); Sir Claude Scott, Bt, attended nine; Higford Burr was present at seven; and Mr J. Wingfield Malcolm MP went to six. No fewer than five members were absent from all meetings, and two were each present on only one occasion. Surprisingly, Francis Francis (three attendances) appears on the list of Council members, although he may have been there *ex officio*, as the sometime 'piscicultural manager'.

The Guernsey branch of the Society

The third annual meeting of the Guernsey branch of the Society was held on 28 December 1864—the report by the honorary secretary, Dr Hoskins, being included as an appendix to that of the parent organisation in the following May.

The island's Lieutenant-Bailiff, Mr H. O. Carré, reported that his curassows continued in excellent health and condition, but that they had so far failed to breed. In the preceding spring the male had, for a period of about ten weeks, become very ill-tempered. 'He seldom allowed people to pass him without immediately attacking in the rear . . . these constant assaults were rather annoying, especially to the female members of the family.'

The Seigneur of Sark, the Revd W. T. Collings, announced that there was little to report about his wonga pigeons, which continued in good health but remained very shy and retiring. In an attempt to persuade them to breed, he had planted in their aviary bushes for cover and Austrian pines for roosting, and had even introduced tame domestic pigeons to give them confidence, but all to no avail.

Hoskins was able to report that an interesting experiment in fish culture was currently under way. A pond near the Vale Church which contained brackish water, had attracted the attention of James Lowe on his visit to the island; Lowe had suggested that it might be a useful place in which to store fish for the market, when the weather was too severe for fishing-boats to put to sea. For many years this pond had been stocked naturally with grey mullet, plaice, flounder, eels, and other fish. It had recently been purchased by a new member of the Guernsey branch, Mr Edward Collings (presumably a relation of the Seigneur of Sark), who was currently restoring it from its hitherto neglected state. A large number of flat-fish and other species had recently been introduced, and it was hoped that they would shortly start breeding.

Following the application for an Order in Council to authorise the formation and protection of oyster parks along the Guernsey coast (referred to in the previous year's report), a number of oyster companies had been formed which had presented petitions to the Royal Court for grants of allotments on the foreshore of Guernsey, on which to construct experimental oyster breeding parks. With certain provisos these applications had now been approved, and the Receiver-General had granted leases, at a peppercorn rent, of various stretches of the foreshore to a dozen or so companies. Some of the lessees had at once

begun constructing enclosures on their allotments, and had deposited
in them large numbers of mature oysters, together with 'collecting tiles'
and slates (known collectively as 'cultch'), to which it was hoped that
spawn would adhere. The few 'cultch' which had so far been examined
had various zoophytes[6] and innumerable testaceae[7] clinging to them,
which it had been considered unwise to disturb at this stage. In the
following spring the lessee companies intended to make thorough
examinations of their 'cultch', after which some idea would be formed
of the results of the experiment.

The branch society's experiments in attempting to propagate the *Ailanthus*
silkworm had met with mixed results. From thirty-nine cocoons in the
care of Dr Adolphus Collings (presumably also related to the Seigneur
of Sark) not one imago had emerged successfully. A further supply of
eggs from the parent Society in England had been divided between
Dr Collings and a Mr Willis, who ran a nursery-garden on Guernsey.
Those entrusted to Dr Collings hatched in due course, but the larvae
were subsequently killed by ants. Those in the care of Mr Willis also
hatched successfully out of doors, and several of the larvae eventually
spun cocoons, from which a number of imagines subsequently meta-
morphosed. 'The essential fact is established', Hoskins reported, 'that
the *Bombyx cynthia* is capable of free propagation in the open air in this
climate.'

As a rider to this report, and as an example of political thought of
the period, it is apposite to quote from a letter to Dr Hoskins from a
resident of Salisbury in Wiltshire:

> I am convinced that [the rearing of *cynthia*] may be most profitably
> introduced into our Union workhouses. There is a large amount of
> labour wasted, simply because it has not been profitably applied. Plant,
> therefore, the Ailanthus shrub, and let the women and children attend
> to the worms. Pay them a per-centage upon the result, and divide the
> inmates into sections, so that there may be honest rivalry. . . . I see no
> reason why, in Reformatories, Penitentaries [sic], and the like, some
> effort should not be made to rear these worms. In fact, wherever
> there is unapplied child or female labour it can be advantageously
> introduced. . . . Habits of industry and method would be insensibly
> taught, and with care the present pauper might become a silk grower
> either for the capitalist or on his own account.

'The above suggestions', commented Dr Hoskins, 'appear to be well
worthy of adoption in some of our insular charitable institutions.'

Among the many alien plants acclimatised on Guernsey, the *Gunnera
scabra* of Chile was considered worthy of special mention, 'as affording
promise of ingredients capable of being utilized in certain arts and

manufactures'. In South America it yields a fine black die, and also an extract containing tannin, which was widely used in dressing and imparting flexibility to hides. *Gunnera scabra* is easy to cultivate, needs little attention, grows well in the shade and on damp and waste ground, can be easily propagated from either cuttings or seeds, and increases and spreads rapidly and naturally.

Repeated trials with the Jamaican hook-podded pea and lima bean had showed that, although they grew strongly on Guernsey, their fructification was too weak to be of commercial value. Finally, the Revd W. T. Collings reported that his seeds of the elephant grass had germinated successfully; that from his single seed of the Australian nardoo had grown a strong and healthy-looking plant, and that of his dozen or more American cotton plants one had blossomed.

9. The Society's Questionnaire

AS mentioned in chapter 7 a questionnaire from the Foreign and Colonial Office (under the auspices of the ociety's president, the Duke of Newcastle, as ecretary of tate for the Colonies) had in 1863 been circulated to ministers, governors and consuls of British colonies throughout the world. Under the heading 'Acclimatisation', the text of this document, which was included as an appendix to the report for 1864–5, reads in part as follows:

> The main purposes of *Acclimatisation* are to introduce, acclimatise, and propagate in the *United Kingdom* and its *Dependencies* such *Animals, Birds, Fishes, Insects* and *Vegetables* as are likely to be of *use* or *ornament,* whether for *domestication* or *for varying* the *common food of the people,* or for *manufacturing,* or for *any other useful purpose*; and whose constitution and habits offer a reasonable prospect of successful cultivation. It is obvious that in *India, Australia, Canada,* the *Cape,* and other important *Dependencies,* unlimited scope is afforded for almost any variety of experiment.
>
> In replying to questions 1, 2, 3, and 8, it is particularly requested that those special qualities which recommend the *Quadrupeds, Birds, Fishes and Vegetables* as fit for food or domestic utility may be described.

QUESTIONS

1 Is there any *Quadruped*, indigenous or introduced to the *Country* in which you reside, which (having regard to the above definition of the objects in view) merits attention with a view to *acclimatisation* in *Great Britain* or any of its Dependencies?
2 Is there any such *Bird*?
3 Is there any such *Fish*?
4 Is there any such *Insect*?
5 Is there any such *Timber Tree*?
6 Is there any such *Medicinal Plant*?
7 Is there any *Fibrous Plant* likely to be useful for manufacturing purposes?
8 Is there any *Vegetable suitable for the food of man,* or for forage, or for any other useful purpose?
9 Do you know any (a) *Quadruped*, (b) *Bird*, (c) *Fish*, (d) *Insect*, (e) *Tree or Plant* existing elsewhere, the introduction of which to THE COUNTRY IN WHICH YOU RESIDE would be likely to be beneficial; one of the objects of the *Acclimatisation Society* being to reciprocate the benefits it receives from other countries?

10 Does any *Organisation* exist, or could it be easily called into existence, capable of undertaking the task of introduction?

Under the heading 'Answers to the Foregoing Inquiries', the Society appended a note to the effect that in almost every case answers had been received to all the questions posed. The eighty-two replies ranged from as far afield as Archangel to Tasmania, and from Hong Kong to Brazil. The utter impracticality, however, of many of the bizarre suggestions made by Her Majesty's representatives abroad, which included such exotica as tropical and semi-tropical fish, mammals, birds, reptiles, amphibians, insects and plants, indicate that in general they seemed to know as little about acclimatisation as some of the members of the Society in Britain.

The questionnaire sent out to Victoria, Australia, was addressed to the governor of the colony, Sir Charles H. Darling, by whom it was forwarded to the Acclimatisation Society in Melbourne. The replies by the society to the various questions were compiled in the first instance by a sub-committee consisting of Dr Ferdinand von Mueller, first Director of the Melbourne Botanic Gardens, Professor Frederick McCoy, a founder member of the society, and Dr Madden. Their answers were then revised and amplified by the full council, before being returned by the secretary, Mr Edward Wilson, to the Governor, for onward transmission to the Duke of Newcastle in London.

As befitted the principal Acclimatisation Society outside Europe, the answers furnished by Victoria were by far the most detailed and comprehensive of all those received, and on that account may be regarded as the most valuable, and worth quoting at length. (The figures correspond to the numbered questions above.)

1 Various *marsupiata* . . . would be worth transferring from Victoria to countries of a similar climate. Their flesh, however, with the exception of that of the bandicoot, which is superior to rabbit, is scarcely equal to that of most other game, though their skin furnishes a good kind of leather. From their peculiarity of form, and their eccentric movements, they would constitute a very interesting feature in parks; and from their speed they might furnish a valuable addition to objects of sport.

   The porcupine anteater [short-nosed echidna] might be a desirable acquisition . . . its meat is excellent. This animal may possibly prove hardy in the southern part of Britain.

2 The emu *Dromaius novaehollandiae* [is of value for] the fair food which the flesh of the young bird affords . . . its abundant oil (used by the colonists for medicinal purposes) . . . its eggs . . . [and] its fecundity. . . . It would, with care, prove hardy in British parks.

   The native turkey . . . in size and excellence for the table is fully equal to the European bustard.

The Wonga-Wonga pigeon is large and excellent for the table.

The mallee hen could be readily naturalised in South Africa or in the South of Europe . . . laying a large number of delicate eggs of a surprisingly large size.

Our quail, of several species, are objects sought by the sportsman; they are also excellent for the table.

The so-called magpies and laughing jackass [the laughing kookaburra] merit, as vermin-destroying animals, introduction . . . and by the robust, jovial humour of their merry pleasant notes and quaint manners, would form most desirable additions to British parks.

The black swan deserves attention on account of its ornamental appearance, but also for its down and for its flesh, which, when obtained from cygnets, is excellent food.

3 The so-called Murray cod or cod-perch is the most important fish . . . it attains a weight of eighty or one hundred pounds, and the flesh is sufficiently good to take first or second place in the dinner *carte*.

5 The most important timber tree which we can offer is the blue gum tree. In rapidity of growth this tree excels perhaps all other trees of the globe; in regard to size, it must be reckoned amongst the most gigantic productions of the vegetation of the world; for durability of its timber, and its resistance against decay as well in water as underground, it is excellent, and it is eligible for most purposes where a hard and heavy wood is needed.

Several other *Eucalypti* are of nearly as much importance. . . . Thus the red gum tree grows also with remarkable celerity . . . its wood is extremely durable, very suitable for underground work, piles of wharves &c., susceptible of an excellent polish, and affords superior fuel. The Stringy Bark Tree is the most to be recommended where a tree is sought for extensive plantations on barren ridges, and where a fissile wood for fencing purposes is required; it attains also gigantic dimensions . . . the bark furnishes material for rough paper. . . . The famous Ironbark tree [is] singular for the toughness and durability of its wood.

Of all our *Acaciae*, the most valuable is the Blackwood tree on account of its beautiful furniture wood. . . .

6 The bark [of the sassafras tree] is a powerful tonic . . . it yields also a valuable oil. . . .

Several *Acaciae* yield a copious supply of gum similar to that of gum arabic.

The myrtaceous trees and shrubs are all more or less rich in ethereal oil, which in many instances greatly resembles the medicinal Cajaput oil.

7 The *Cyperus vaginatus*, a sedge . . . produces a remarkably tenacious fibre, which by the aboriginal population was once largely employed for cordage and for making their fish-nets.

Two fibrous plants introduced here . . . the New Zealand flax and the Rhea from which the Chinese grass-cloth is made, . . . ought to be naturalized in all tropical and temperate latitudes.

8 Of culinary vegetables indigenous to Victoria, we have three kinds of spinach.

Of forage plants we have some excellent grasses, well deserving of introduction abroad.

If the number and variety of indigenous species which the Acclimatisation Society of Victoria considered suitable for introducing overseas was great, those that they would have liked to see imported into the colony were legion.

9(a) The foreign mammals that Victorians had already attempted to acclimatise included the hog deer, axis deer, the rusa deer, and brown hare.

Among others considered suitable for the purpose were the snowshoe hare of North America; the chinchilla of South America, which 'would be desirable for its fur'; the spring hare of eastern and southern Africa 'for sandy and stony desert tracts in the northern districts, in the hope of adding to the very scanty food to be found by the explorer or pioneer in such localities'; the Rocky Mountain bighorn sheep; the wapiti; the roe deer; the rock hyrax of mainly sub-Saharan Africa; the dorcas gazelle of North Africa, 'to turn loose in the country beyond the Murray, where they would . . . afford both excellent food and sport'; the oribi of sub-Saharan Africa; the gemsbok or beisa oryx of eastern and south-western Africa which is 'of good size and most excellent flesh'; the Arabian oryx; and the kudu of eastern and southern Africa. Finally, the eland, also of eastern and southern Africa, 'is particularly desired, from its great size [and] excellent flesh . . . is expected to be a boon of inestimable value.'

(b) Victorian farmers and gardeners suffer very much from the depredations of insects, and therefore any of the soft-billed birds of Europe, or other temperate countries, are desired in unlimited numbers, particularly those which, like the robin and hedgesparrow [the dunnock], love the neighbourhood of man. The Acclimatisation Society of Victoria has introduced and liberated large numbers of the common sparrow [the house sparrow] from England, and the tree sparrow from China, to keep down the caterpillar, while feeding their young; and the mino [the common mynah] from India, to diminish the myriads of destructive grasshoppers and small locusts; also the song-thrush, to clear away the slugs. Although in all parts of the colony a great variety of ants are very troublesome, none of the ant-thrushes of India or America have . . . been procured. . . .

Our forest trees, too, are invested [sic] with very numerous larvae in the timber, while in the whole country there is no representative of the woodpeckers appointed in other parts of the world to remedy this evil.

Other birds suggested for acclimatisation in Victoria included the 'serpent-eater [the secretary bird] for the diminution of our snakes';

the crowned pigeon from Java or Papua New Guinea which 'has only been very sparingly introduced'; the Chinese ring-necked pheasant; the Chinese monal pheasant 'and all the other Himalayan pheasants are particularly desired, to be turned loose in the alpine parts of Gipps Land. . . . A few of them only have been imported by the Society, including the horned and satyr tragopans, the monal and the kaligee'; guans (*Penelope* spp.) and curassows of South America; two of the latter, the black curassow and the blue-bellied curassow, were already doing well in Victoria, and 'are desired, as large and excellent game birds for the table'; sandgrouse from India and Africa; grouse; various species of quail; adjutant storks from India 'as a scavenger'; the ostrich; and the black-necked swan from southern South America.

To these were added a large number of birds already introduced and partially acclimatised in Victoria, such as common, golden, and silver pheasants, grey and red-legged partridges, peafowl, black and grey francolins, the pintail, the blackbird, the song thrush, the skylark, the starling, mynahs and various other species.

(c) Fish suggested for acclimatisation in Victoria included the common carp, and gudgeon, from Britain, the gouramie, from China or Mauritius (to which it had been introduced from Jamaica), 'and other palatable pond-fish'; the salmon, brown trout, char, grayling, 'and other principal river fish of Europe'; also 'lobsters and crabs, and the better kinds of fish of European seas', including the grey mullet and edible crab which had already been imported into the colony.

(d)   The *Bombyx cynthia* and *B. arrindi*, to establish a supply of coarse silk, not requiring labour to feed the worms. The *Coccus cacti*; the cochineal insect.

(e) The hardier varieties of cotton were already producing valuable crops in suitable localities of Victoria, and the continued importation of seeds of the Peruvian tree-cotton and other hardy varieties should be maintained. Also recommended for experiments in acclimatisation were the senna plant; the tropical American cassava; various species of *Cinchona*, including the valuable *calisaya* (previously successfully introduced to India); tussock grass from the Falkland Islands for the prevention of coastal erosion; and buffalo grass from North America for forage.

Since the colony possessed no indigenous pine trees of any size, the introduction from Canada, British Columbia,[1] Nepal, and Britain of 'ornamental and highly useful pines' (from Britain the Norway spruce, the larch and silver fir) was to be recommended.

Useful British plants suggested for introduction into Australian husbandry included the black mustard and several of a medicinal nature, such as the monkswood, common valerian, great yellow gentian, meadow saffron and the autumn crocus. Among fruiting plants were the brambles and, for higher mountains, the bilberry. The osier was recommended for planting in extensive riverine beds for the production of long, pliant shoots for basket-weaving.

With the cooperation of acclimatisation societies in North America and elsewhere, species such as the Wellingtonia from California; walnuts; oaks of North and Central America and of the Mediterranean, including the cork and valonea, might be introduced with advantage.

From the Mediterranean could be imported the various *Astralagus* sp., which yield the gum tragacanth, the argan tree '(which is . . . particularly valuable as affording in its fruit a most nutritive cattle-food and a vegetable tallow)', and some of the larger olives and lemons.

From Hong Kong 'a copious introduction' of tea seeds would be useful, since tea had already been successfully cultivated in the more sheltered and fertile parts of Victoria. The various acacia trees of North Africa and south-western Asia, which yield the valuable gum arabic, could also usefully be introduced to the colony.

Finally, it was suggested that 'importations of plants or seeds of any of the more eminently useful kinds will be always acceptable in a new country like this, where forest culture is not even commenced, and where, in many districts, husbandry is as yet imperfectly developed.'

10   The Acclimatisation Society of Victoria is in vigorous action, and has means for transacting any such business efficiently.

10. The Acclimatisation Society of Great Britain and The Ornithological Society of London in 1865–1866

IN presenting their sixth annual report to members, the council of the Society, which in the past year had moved its offices to Exhibition Road, South Kensington (next to the gardens of the Royal Horticultural Society) announced that a merger had recently been agreed with the Ornithological Society of London, which had its offices in St James's Park. This resulted in a change of name to the Acclimatisation Society of Great Britain and Ornithological Society of London. Viscount Powerscourt, a vice-president of the Acclimatisation Society, voiced his opinion that 'The combination of Societies will tend to the benefit of each Society, in bringing them all in a convenient way under the notice of the public.'

The prospectus of the Ornithological Society, which was founded in 1837, stated that:

> Many thousands of persons have been gratified by admiring and feeding the water fowl in St. James's Park, but few are aware of the source to which the Public are indebted for this pleasure—few are aware that they may become themselves members of a Society which exists for the purpose of forming collections of water fowl in the various parks, and propagating the most useful and interesting species—first, to supply the royal parks, and secondly, to distribute duplicates among such members of the Society as may be desirous of acquiring a collection of aquatic birds.
>
> It has endeavoured to form and maintain a complete collection of water fowl—swimmers, divers and waders. The birds are kept, as nearly as possible, in a natural state in the waters in Hyde Park, Kensington Gardens, and Victoria Park, and on the island in St James's Park they may be considered in a natural cage, open to the view of all classes.

James I (1566–1625) is credited with having formed the first collection of birds in St James's Park (mainly composed of such 'outlandish fowl' as 'Cassawaries [sic] and Cormorants') as part of his menagerie of exotic animals. The duty of 'keeping and preserving the wild beasts and fowl' at that time was entrusted to the office of the Keeper of the Palace of Westminster.

Under James's son, Charles I (1600–49), the park was maintained and the waterfowl continued to be preserved. After the death of Cromwell in 1658, the park was considerably improved by Charles II

(1630–85), who appointed a 'Keeper of the King's House for Pheasants and other Fowl', a 'Nurseryman and Pond Keeper', a 'Clerk of the Aviary', a 'Volary[1] Keeper', 'Keepers of the Hawks and Cormorants', and the 'Governor of Duck Island', a sinecure held by one Charles de St Dennis.

In his diary for 9 February 1664, John Evelyn refers to the animals he saw on a visit to St James's Park, including 'several sorts of ordinary and extraordinary wild fowl breeding'. Francis Willughby and John Ray, in their *Ornithologia* (1676–8), describe in detail some of the birds that they saw in the same park.

After Charles II's death the birds were increasingly neglected until, in the early nineteenth century, they had almost completely disappeared.

For George IV (1762–1830) the park was completely redesigned by the royal architect John Nash, who in about 1826 constructed a new lake on the site of the old canal. A subsequent reconstruction in 1855–6, to combat the effects of pollution, brought the lake into the form in which it is today.

The Ornithological Society of London, formed a decade after the reformation of the park by Nash, supplied various birds for the lake. Later, in 1841, under the patronage of the Prince Consort, the society constructed The Cottage on the peninsula at the eastern end of the lake for its offices and residence of the official 'Bird Keeper'; half the cost of the upkeep of The Cottage and of the Keeper's wages was borne by the government, the other half being contributed by the society.

From the Ornithological Society's constitution it can be seen that the aims and objectives of the two societies were very similar, but that whereas the Ornithological Society had confined itself solely to the introduction of 'that large class of birds requiring water as part of their natural element' (or, less verbosely, 'waterfowl'!), the Acclimatisation Society had been unable to include waterfowl in their introductions, 'owing to their not possessing control over any locality supplied with water'. Now, however, the combined collection of ducks, geese and swans in the various Royal Parks owned by the merged societies included mallard, 'Pin Tail', gadwall, teal, wigeon, shoveller, pochard, 'Tufted Divers' (*A. fuligula*), Carolina ducks, goldeneye, black swans, 'White Swans' (*C. olor*), barnacle geese, brent geese, Canada geese, Chinese geese (descendants of the Siberian swan-goose), white-fronted geese, bean geese, and 'Hybrids (numerous)'.

The honorary secretary of the Society, Mr Waterhouse Hawkins, presented to members a review of the Acclimatisation and Ornithological Society's activities during the past year.

The honorary treasurer, John Bush, had continued to maintain a small flock of cross-bred Chinese sheep × Oxford Downs, which were said to be three-quarters Chinese. 'Their prolific character continues—always twins at least, and sometimes three at a birth.' The flesh of one recently slaughtered sheep had been pronounced excellent, being both flavoursome and tender.

The pair of sambar deer from Windsor Park, presented to the Society by Queen Victoria and transferred to Blenheim Palace, had both unfortunately died. Some Bennett's wallabies in the Society's 'depôt' at Clapham had also been sent to Blenheim.

Lord Powerscourt reported from Ireland that his herd of three-year-old wapiti continued to thrive, but had still not yet bred, whereas his Japanese sika had again successfully reared young. His sambar, like those of the Duke of Marlborough at Blenheim, had all died.

During the year under review the Society had continued its attempts to introduce and breed such game birds as 'experienced sportsmen considered desirable to add to the established favourites of our preserves'. Of seven prairie chickens imported from North America, a pair presented to the Queen had settled down well and become quite tame, 'most satisfactorily proving', so the Society rather rashly asserted, 'that so far as climate is concerned there would be no difficulty in acclimatising these birds.' Before this somewhat extravagant claim could be put to the test, however, Her Majesty's birds, 'together with a large number of pheasants', were killed by foxes. A second pair was placed in the care of Earl Pomfret, while the three hens retained by the Society were accidentally killed.

The Japanese pheasants had successfully mated with common pheasants and had laid sufficient eggs for a considerable number to be distributed among various members of the Society. A cross between the Indian bantam and the grey jungle fowl had done likewise. The kalij pheasants were viewed with some optimism, the hen having been 'sitting on a nest of eggs for several days with an assiduity almost equal to that of the hen of our common poultry'. The arrival of a consignment of Chinese pheasants (including Reeves's pheasants) was expected shortly.

The California quails had also laid enough eggs for a distribution to be made to those members who had applied for them. The 'Plumifer Quails, from the Rocky Mountains' (mountain quails) had been accidentally killed.

'Monsieur Carré', the Lieutenant-Bailiff of Guernsey (where the former members of the branch society were now referred to as 'Honorary Members', suggesting an earlier demise of the Channel Island connection), reported that the pair of curassows which he had been looking after for some two-and-a-half years had at last nested, but that the two eggs which the hen had laid had unfortunately turned out to be addled. The birds' lack of success was attributed to the fact that the female was very old and the male was 'particularly vicious, subject to periodical mad fits, when he is really dangerous, rendering it absolutely necessary for the poor creature to be shut up in solitary confinement for many weeks together'. The guans owned by the parent Society continued to be very tame, but unfortunately 'passed their healthy but unprofitable life without breeding.'

The three brush turkeys from Australia in the possession of the Society occupied themselves by constructing nest mounds without any evidence as to their gender. The emus were considered, somewhat precipitately, to be 'thoroughly acclimatised, so as to render them capable of being kept in any park in England or Scotland, dry cold, snow and frost appearing to have no effect upon them.'

A pair of wonga pigeons at Clapham had laid one egg without the usual preliminary of building a nest; a Scottish member reported that his wongas seemed quite hardy and impervious to the climate. All the bronzewing pigeons at Clapham had nested, but only a single squab had been reared; the pair in the care of Dr Henry Bull at Hereford, however, had succeeded in bringing off two healthy fledglings.

In the previous year's annual report the council had stated that it had instructed the honorary secretary to enter into negotiations with the Royal Horticultural Society, with a view to erecting the Society's fish-hatching apparatus and establishing an office and council room at South Kensington. The council was now pleased to be able to report that the negotiations had been successfully concluded, and that the Acclimatisation and Ornithological Society and its fish hatchery were now ensconced 'on easy and liberal terms' in their new home. It was not merely the improved locality of the Society's premises that was considered advantageous, but the proximity of the horticulturists, many of whom were also vice-presidents and members of the merged Society.

Immediately after the annual meeting of 1865, the council had appointed a sub-committee to resurrect, under the direction of the indefatigable Frank Buckland, the Society's fish-hatching operations. In spite of various climatic problems, a limited additional supply of brown trout and char ova had been obtained, and Buckland had donated from his own personal hatchery fifteen hundred Atlantic salmon parr and a thousand fingerling trout, which he had hatched from ova received from the *Société Zoologique d'Acclimatation* in France.

Contrary to its former declared intention not to attempt to introduce the zander or pike-perch from Europe, because of the danger this voracious alien predator might pose to native species, the council now declared its intention of carrying out 'their former arrangements to secure the introduction of . . . this valuable fish'. Of the eleven young wels or European catfish released by Buckland in one of Mr Higford Burr's ponds in Berkshire in January 1865, no report could be made since, on the water level of the pond being deliberately lowered, none of them could be seen, doubtless 'from their habit of burying themselves in the mud'. (Three years later, as mentioned in chapter 8, Buckland reported that when the pond was entirely drained, no trace of the wels could be found.)

The council announced that it had received a request from the Society's principal benefactress, Miss Burdett Coutts, 'concerning the possibility and best method of curing pilchards [sardines] by the poor fishermen on the south coast of Ireland'. The honorary secretary was pleased to report that he had managed to obtain the required information 'to the entire satisfaction' of the benevolent lady.

Last year the Society had received a small quantity of 'Bombyx Yama-Maï' silkworm eggs from their *confrères* in France. Some of these had been distributed among various members of the Society, while the balance had been consigned to the care of the honorary treasurer, Mr John Bush, at Clapham, where although many hatched successfully they invariably died after their second moult. The number was thus reduced to around forty; these, having fed readily on the common oak, reached a length of some 2½ inches (7 cm), when they were all attacked by some unknown disease, and also died. Rather more successful was the Revd W. T. Collings, the Seigneur of Sark in the Channel Islands, who managed to rear, after some cannibalism, a number on the common and the Turkey oak. The surviving seventeen silkworms proceeded to spin cocoons, from all of which moths subsequently hatched, but failed to deposit any eggs.

During the past winter the Society had received many thousand bombyx yama-maï eggs from the *Société Zoologique*. In April, Mr Edward Wilson, a vice-president of the Society, had also acquired from France many thousands of eggs of this silkworm, for presentation to the Acclimatisation Society of Victoria, of which he was the founder and president. Unfortunately, these had arrived in England too late to be loaded onto the vessel stocked with ice for conveying them to Melbourne, and they had been given by Wilson to the Society, one of whose members, Mr H. J. B. Hancock, had obtained a hundred oak seedlings in full leaf, on which the eggs had been placed. It was too early to be able to state with confidence the outcome of this latest experiment. The Society had also obtained many thousand Japanese mulberry silkworms, large numbers of which had hatched out successfully.

When the Society had been granted space at South Kensington

by the Royal Horticultural Society, it had undertaken to exhibit in their gardens any animals that the RHS might request; among those currently on show were the 'Bombyx cynthia' silkworm; the bombyx yama-maï; the Japanese mulberry silkworm; swarms of the Ligurian, Egyptian or Syrian bee; and a selection of bee-keeping equipment, including glass-sided, large Swiss and Portuguese cork hives, as well as hives designed to preserve the lives of bees while their honey was being removed, 'with a view to popularise this useful pursuit for cottagers, gardeners and others'. A particular concern of the Society was the abandonment of the 'unnecessary cruel practice' and 'barbarous system' of killing 'the industrious contributors' when taking their honey. Many thousand people, the council claimed, had visited their exhibitions at South Kensington, some at least of which, it was hoped, would in time become 'bee masters'. The council intended to seek permission to place a number of beehives near some of the lodges in the Royal Parks, 'showing simple modes of bee keeping and of taking the honey without destroying the bees'.

During the past year the council had received, and had distributed by ballot among members, seeds of a dwarf bamboo, the 'Tallow Tree' from Shanghai, roots of the 'Arundo Donax', seeds of evergreen and cork oaks, and two cypresses from Portugal, and had also exhibited tubers, plants and products of London-grown arrowroot at the International Horticultural Exhibition. It had been found that excellent arrowroot, equal in quality, so the council claimed, to the best from Brazil, could be produced from home-grown tubers, 'which could not fail to be of great benefit to the poorer classes in the event of cholera[2], or similar epidemics, again visiting this country.'

In concluding its annual report for 1865–6, the council took pleasure in announcing that the medal, kindly promised as a gift to the Society by Miss Burdett Coutts, was in the hands of Mr G. G. Adams, the artist whom she had commissioned and whose design had been formally approved, and that the thanks of the Society had been presented to the generous donor.

The seeming lack of interest in the Society's activities by council members, referred to in the previous chapter, continued. The list of attendances for the year ending in May 1866 showed that only the secretary, Mr Waterhouse Hawkins, attended all fifteen meetings, while the honorary treasurer, Mr John Bush, missed only one; at the other end of the scale, Sir Claude Scott, Bt. and Mr John Stone attended only three meetings, while Lord Tredegar was present on but two occasions; Mr Jackson Gillbanks and the Right Revd the Lord Bishop of Oxford, the worthy prelate perhaps having more weighty matters to concern him, were conspicuous by their absence from all meetings.

The financial affairs of the Society were also in decline; from cash in hand of £626.4s.8d. shown on the balance sheet for the year ending 4 April 1865, the amalgamated Society's funds had slumped by the following year to only £175.2s.8d.

11. The Acclimatisation and Ornithological Society of London in 1866–1867

IN May 1867 the council presented its seventh annual report to members of the merged and newly titled Society, which in the past year had moved its offices from Exhibition Road in South Kensington to those of the Ornithological Society in The Cottage in St James's Park. The council announced that, 'notwithstanding many serious obstacles', they were 'now in a most favourable position to carry out the objects of the Society', which were declared to be basically those of the original Society.

The council regretted that the 'most serious obstacle' had been the unforeseen and unfortunate involvement of the Society in a chancery suit against a late member of the council.

In their sixth annual report, the council had stated that 'the kind promises of Mr W. Medhurst [the British consul at Hankow in China, and a corresponding member of the Society] justify the council's hopes that they will speedily receive their first consignment of Reeves's and other Chinese pheasants.'

When no such consignment was forthcoming, the Society's secretary, Waterhouse Hawkins, wrote a plaintive letter to Mr Medhurst reminding him of his promise. The latter replied rather huffily:

I am surprised to observe . . . that you seem to be under the impression that I have done nothing towards redeeming the pledge which I gave to the Society . . . that I would assist them to the best of my ability in procuring living specimens of the Reeves's and other rare Pheasants. The moment that I arrived (now fully a twelvemonth ago) I set on foot arrangements for getting down birds from the interior, and soon after I had the satisfaction of receiving my first lot of birds. . . . I at once made preparations for forwarding the birds to Mr J. J. Stone, who had placed himself more directly in communication with me on the subject just before I left home. Some of these birds died before I could get them away; but the remainder I despatched, per overland mail; and since then I have continued to procure and to despatch birds. In every case of despatch, I have communicated with Mr Stone, and I have his letters in reply . . . acknowledging mine, and thanking me for my endeavours. The two first lots all died either here or on their way home; of the third lot I hear from Mr Stone that but one has reached home safely . . . and that it has been placed in his aviary. . . .

My agents are still out searching for birds, and by the next cold weather, I confidently look forward to receiving a further supply. . . .

Meanwhile, allow me to request that you will place this letter before the Council, so that they may satisfy themselves that I have, at any rate, done something towards fulfilling my promise of assistance.

On receipt of this letter inquiries were at once instituted, when it became apparent that Mr Stone had considered the birds consigned to him personally, had appropriated them to his own use, and had deposited some of them, in his name, with the Zoological Society in Regent's Park. Mr Waterhouse Hawkins had accordingly written on 27 September 1866 to the Zoological Society, saying that

> I beg to inform you that the Chinese birds you have received from Mr J. J. Stone . . . some of which you now possess on his account, viz: seven living specimens—three males and four females—of the bar-tailed or Reeves's Pheasants, also specimens of the Tragopan Pheasant, are not Mr Stone's property; those birds were sent to him on account of the Acclimatisation Society, and consequently are the property of that Society. I therefore beg to caution you on behalf of the Council not to deliver the above named birds to Mr Stone, or his order, as so doing might involve you in inconvenient circumstances in the event of its becoming necessary to take legal proceedings for the recovery of the said birds by the Acclimatisation Society.

A fortnight later, on 11 October, a clearly incensed Mr Stone wrote to Waterhouse Hawkins saying that:

> I received from the Zoological Society copy of a letter from you . . . stating that certain Pheasants deposited by me at the Zoological Gardens are not my property, but belong to the Acclimatisation Society, and threatening legal proceedings for the moving of the said birds. In reply to this communication, I beg briefly to state that it is untrue that these birds belong to your Society, or that the Society ever paid a farthing of the cost of them or any other birds imported by me, and in regard to your threat of legal proceedings, I am prepared to meet the same, and . . . I must express my conviction that your impertinent letter . . . has been written without the sanction of the Council, for I am confident there is not a member of that body known to me, so wanting in courtesy as to authorise such a communication without any previous application to me.
>
> I request that you will bring this letter before the Council . . . and I claim from them some explanation of the course you have adopted, and to be allowed to see the letter from China, which has justified it.

At a special meeting of the council of the Society, convened on the following day, 12 October, it was resolved that

> Mr Stone be informed that the Secretary's letter to the Zoological Society's Manager was not intended as threatening Mr Stone with legal proceedings, but as furnishing the Officers of the Zoological Society with legal grounds for declining to part with the Pheasants without the sanction of the Council of the Acclimatisation Society, and that the

Council does not doubt that Mr Stone, when made acquainted with the contents of Mr Medhurst's letter, will see that Mr Medhurst, probably not being aware that Mr Stone had retired from the Council of this Society, was under the impression that sending the birds to that gentleman was sending, in fact, to this Society.

Mr Stone be requested to furnish an account of any expenses which he has incurred in receiving the birds and depositing them at the Zoological Gardens.

The generally placatory tone of the council's resolution, and their failure to deny the accusation, implies that the secretary had indeed, as Mr Stone suggested, acted *ultra vires* in writing his letter of 27 September.

Three days later, on 15 October, the Society received notification of the arrival of a further shipment of birds from Mr Medhurst. On being sent a copy of Mr Medhurst's letter, the master of the vessel which had transported the birds from China, Captain John Steele, informed the Society that three of the seven pheasants shipped had been delivered, 'in sound and healthy condition', to Mr Stone—the others having perished on the voyage. 'I was given to understand', Steele continued, 'that the birds *were for the Acclimatisation Society*, and thought Mr Stone *represented that Society when he applied for the Pheasants*, and as Mr Medhurst . . . is aware *that I would not have taken charge of the birds for any private individual*, I am willing to assist you in recovering the birds from Mr Stone.'

This letter would seem to provide fairly conclusive evidence that the birds under contention had been misappropriated by Stone. Since repeated communications from the Society's solicitor went unanswered, it was resolved at a further special meeting of the council held on 16 November that their solicitor be instructed 'to take requisite proceedings for the recovery of the birds, the property of the Society, detained by Mr Stone'. Unsatisfactory letters from Stone having been received on the two preceding days by the Society's solicitor, a Bill of Equity was filed on behalf of the Society on 24 November, to which Stone had filed his answer. The council were now awaiting the arrival of a sworn affidavit from Mr Medhurst, 'which must, as appears from the foregoing correspondence, bring this most unfortunate matter to a satisfactory issue as regards the Society.'

Tantalisingly, the outcome of this disputation is not recorded.

On a happier note, the council were pleased to report the generous cooperation they had received from Lieutenant C. H. J. Marshall, Assistant Commissioner in Lahore, to whom they had written for help in obtaining some game birds from India. Marshall had replied that he would be 'proud and happy' to furnish the Society not only with Indian species, but also with those of the Straits, Java, Japan, China and Australia—adding that he had recently received a government grant to form an acclimatisation society in Lahore. Among the species he proposed to send to England were sandgrouse, 'Chikore' (chukar) Partridges, black partridges or francolins, painted partridges, common quail, painted bush quail, button quail, houbara bustards, (known locally as 'O'Barah') Great Indian bustards, ducks, geese, waders, greater and lesser flamingoes, cranes, 'Coolans' (? sp.), Himalayan monal pheasants, great argus pheasants, 'Kaleege' (kalij) pheasants, 'Chear' (cheer) pheasants, silver pheasants, 'Snow Pheasants' (Himalayan snowcocks), Rothschild's or Malay peacock-pheasants, fireback pheasants, golden pheasants, red jungle fowl, common or green peafowl, 'Goggle-Eyed Plovers', bar-headed geese, 'pigeons, parrots, and others'. So impressed were the council by this list that they had elected Lieutenant Marshall an honorary and corresponding member of the Society.

The Hon. Grantley F. Berkeley, apparently reconciled to the Society although no longer a member, had presented it with two pairs of teal and a drake eider—'so seldom seen in this country'[1]—all of which were now established on the lake in St James's Park.

From the Acclimatisation Society of Natal, South Africa, had come a pair of lemurs (Lemuridae) from Madagascar and two Cape partridges or francolins—the survivors of six; the lemurs (the only mammals mentioned in the merged Society's final annual report) had been presented to the Zoological Society, while the surviving partridges had unfortunately died, 'being unable to stand the exceptional severity of the climate'. Also from South Africa, Mr J. W. Malcolm, MP, had sent a pair of wattled cranes.

The Acclimatisation Society of Queensland, Australia, had announced the despatch, on the *Queen of the Colonies,* of a black cockatoo, a kangaroo, and some zebra doves. Mr J. Costeker had offered to obtain from the Philippine Islands some rare endemic pigeons.

Since the previous annual general meeting, the Society had purchased two pairs of cereopsis geese, one pair of whistling duck, one pair of mandarin ducks[2], one pair of curassows, one pair of prairie chickens, five pairs of 'European' sandgrouse (pintailed or black-bellied sandgrouse), two pairs of garganey, one pair of shovellers, and two pairs of tufted ducks. In exchange, the Society had received a single Magellan goose, a pair of summer ducks, a pair of Bahama pintail, four jungle fowl, a single peafowl, three pheasants, and a pair of crested pigeons. The Society had sold to members five black swans, three Egyptian geese[3], five pairs of 'European' sandgrouse, two hybrid geese, and two 'Buenos Ayres Ducks'.

Mr J. K. Lord had offered to obtain on behalf of the Society the eggs of some North American birds for hatching abroad, so that the young could become accustomed to the presence of humans and thus, it was hoped, travel more successfully; these included prairie chickens, spruce grouse, ruffed grouse, and bobwhite quail.

Finally, the council were anxious to secure the cooperation of any of their members who might be visiting Norway, 'in their endeavours to procure and import the Hjerper or Gelinotte [the hazel grouse] which has hitherto baffled their utmost endeavours to introduce it, notwithstanding they have offered rewards and used every means in their power.'

The council announced that it had been in touch with HM Chief Commissioner of works, offering, if the government would be prepared to construct aviaries in the London parks, to keep them stocked with exotic birds. This artful attempt by the Society to obtain aviaries at public expense came to nothing, since 'the estimates for the current year having gone in, the department was not disposed to go to the expense of erecting the Aviaries.'

Turning to other animals, members were informed that some Japanese mulberry silkworms were now available for distribution, while the eggs and fry—many from the French government's hatchery at Huningue—of some 30,000 Great Lake trout, Atlantic salmon, and brown trout and sea trout had been distributed to Queen Victoria and various members, fishery associations and angling clubs. The possible introduction from Canada of the black or largemouth bass had also been discussed.

As an indication that, notwithstanding their previous claim that they were 'now in a most favourable position to carry out the objects of the Society', it was in fact now in a somewhat parlous condition, the council announced that it had become apparent that the management of the Society's affairs required some amendments. A sub-committee had accordingly been formed on 8 February 1867, 'to inquire into the working and financial prospects of the Society'; having met on a number of occasions, the sub-committee had now made the following recommendations.

I. That Mr WATERHOUSE HAWKINS having taken into consideration the circumstances of the Society, and expressed to this Committee his willingness and intention of placing his resignation in the hands of the Council, such resignation be accepted.

II. That it is unadvisable to continue to pay the sum of £150, as the salary of the paid officer; such an amount being neither required nor justified by the circumstances of the Society.

III. That it is inexpedient that the paid officer of the Society should have a seat in the Council.

IV. That a Sub-committee be appointed to select a paid officer to attend three days in the week, and to discharge the entire duties of Secretary, under the direction of the Council, at a salary of one guinea per week.

V. That it is expedient that the office at the Horticultural Gardens be given up as soon as possible, and that the offices be concentrated at the cottage in St. James's Park.

VI. That a Sub-committee be formed to carry out this concentration, which your Committee believe will be more economical and convenient than the present arrangement.

VII. That as there appears to be a number of birds which might be advantageously disposed of, your Committee recommend that the said birds be at once offered for sale to members, and if not required by them to be disposed of in the public markets.

VIII. That communications be made from time to time by the Secretary to the *Land and Water* paper, [a rival journal started in 1865 by Frank Buckland after he left *The Field* magazine] on such subjects as the Council shall direct.

Item I suggests that the council considered that the Society's secretary had exceeded his powers and had committed a serious indiscretion in his correspondence with Mr Stone. Items II, V, VI and VII give the appearance of an organisation in serious financial difficulties, and indeed the balance sheet for the year ending 30 April 1867 (which incidentally contained no provision for the suit against Mr Stone) showed a paltry bank balance of £175.2s.8d. plus £54.2s.3d. cash in hand. Nor had the monthly council meetings been any better attended than in the recent past; the Revd Cyril Page, Mr R. E. Arden and Mr Harry Cheater had each been present on eight occasions, and Mr W. V. Morgan had attended seven meetings; at the other end of the scale Colonel Hudson and Mr R. B. Sheridan had been conspicuous by their absence from all twelve meetings, while Mr Charles Hambro, Mr J. Kaye and Lord Tredegar had managed to attend only a single meeting each.

Exactly when the Acclimatisation and Ornithological Society of London became defunct is unknown. The last reference to the Society that the author has been able to trace is in the 28 March 1868 issue of *Land and Water*,[4] where a report draws attention to the Society's activities and to the fact that it was the owner of all the birds then in St James's Park,

and that almost daily additions are being made to the collection. No pains are spared on the part of the Council to obtain living specimens of every kind of water-fowl, and their attention is equally directed to animals, vegetables, etc., which it is considered have a chance of being successfully established or cultivated in this country. The same energy is displayed in the endeavour to send out consignments to other countries.

We are anxiously looking for the publication of the Annual Report . . .

and if we are not mistaken, it will be found to be a far more favourable one than has appeared for many years.

Sadly, this optimism was unfounded, and shortly thereafter the Society appears to have become insolvent, going into voluntary liquidation—its collection of birds and other animals, plants and equipment being acquired by the government. Frank Buckland, the Society's progenitor, was appointed Inspector of Fisheries in February 1867 (over a year before the Society's demise), and was instrumental in the introduction of salmon and trout to Australia and New Zealand.

Since the demise of the Society, the birds—both natives and exotics—have been a permanent feature of St James's Park. In 1895 a rock for cormorants was introduced, and another for white pelicans four years later. In 1915, during the First World War, the lake, with the exception of the duck pond, was drained, on the grounds that it acted as a marker for enemy aircraft, and in the following year the bed of the lake was used to site various temporary structures required for military purposes. These were removed in 1922, and the restoration of the concrete bottom and refilling of the lake were completed a year later. During the Second World War, the lake was used as a source of water by the London Fire Service.

12. What Did the Society Achieve?

OSBORNE (1987) cites three principal reasons for the ephemeral life of the Society: its lack of success in attracting a sufficient membership (barely fifty in the year of its foundation and only 370 odd in 1865—less than half the number of the French society's regional branch in Grenoble), and the generally unscientific nature of those people who did become members; its failure to obtain adequate funding—from the public because of its low number of members, and from the government because it failed to establish its own acclimatisation garden for exotic species; and a lack of facilities, especially in the form of the last-named—most exotic animals (with the exception of fish) and plants, it will be recalled, were consigned to the care of those land-owning members willing and able to accommodate them. These factors together jeopardised the Society's ability to differentiate itself adequately from its competitors as doing something new, worthwhile, and unique.

The introduction and cultivation of alien plants in Britain had been conducted by various organisations for many years. In the late eighteenth and early nineteenth centuries, Sir Joseph Banks (1744–1820), Cook's naturalist on the *Endeavour* on his first circumnavigation of the world in 1768–71 and president of The Royal Society from 1778 until his death, encouraged plant collectors abroad to bring back with them to Britain samples of their discoveries. The Royal Botanic Gardens at Kew on the outskirts of London, which were derived from the private garden of exotics formed by Baron Capel of Tewkesbury (died 1696) in the late seventeenth century and which in 1840 became England's national botanic garden, were the repository for most of these early discoveries. Under the directorship, first from 1841 until his death, of Sir William Hooker FRS (1785–1865), and then from 1865 of his son Sir Joseph Hooker OM (1817–1911), Kew became the primary centre of economic botany in the world.

The Zoological Society of London, which predated the foundation of the Society by some thirty-four years and whose prospectus had anticipated many of its aims and objectives, similarly competed with the Society in the field of alien animals. Whereas the Society drew its relatively small membership mainly from the ranks of the nobility, aristocracy and landed gentry (all of whom presumably had an interest in the theory and practice of acclimatisation, but few of whom had any scientific background or even general knowledge of natural history),

94

that of the Zoological Society was composed principally of scientists and zoologists which lent it, in professional circles, an undoubted *cachet*. Similarly, the *Société Zoologique d'Acclimatation* attracted as members many celebrated biologists such as Isidore Geoffroy Saint-Hilaire, Jean Louis Armand de Quatrefages de Breau (1810–92), Antoine César Becquerel (1788–1878), and his son Alexander Edmond (1820–91) and grandson Antoine Henri (1852–1908), while men of comparable stature in England, including the Hookers, Owen and Darwin, abstained from joining the Society.

Furthermore, although the Society obtained the patronage of the Royal Family, members of the nobility and influential politicians (the Duke of Newcastle, Secretary of State for the Colonies, was president from 1862 until his death in 1864, and was succeeded by HRH The Prince of Wales), unlike the French *Société* which had managed to attract state subventions and obtain for itself a semi-official status, the Society was unsuccessful in acquiring either government subsidies or a grant of public land.

Nor was the Society's progress furthered by the apathy on the subject of acclimatisation of one of the most prestigious scientific organisations of the day, the British Association for the Advancement of Science. As Osborne (1987) points out, only four people who read papers before the association in the nineteenth century chose as their topic the subject of acclimatisation—all of them during the 1860s. Frank Buckland (1861) spoke on the theme of 'the acclimatisation of animals'; James Hunt (1862) read a paper on 'ethno-climatology, or the acclimatisation of man'; John Gray (1864b) discussed the subject of 'museums, their use and improvement, and the acclimatisation of animals'; and W. Lauder Lindsay (1867) spoke on 'plant acclimatisation in Scotland, with special reference to Tussac Grass'. The last three were united in their desire to discredit the limited variability of type theory, and challenged the proposition that animals (or humans) translocated to new environments could survive through physiological and/or morphological adaptation.

Lindsay was convinced that in general organisms are unable to adapt to new conditions, and that all attempts at acclimatisation were bound to fail unless the transplanted organism's 'natural conditions of growth' could be faithfully simulated. Gray, the Keeper of Zoology at the British Museum, went so far, according to Osborne (1987), as to link Darwinism with spiritualism, and was similarly scathing about other forms of transformism. With P. L. Sclater, Gray served in 1862 on the shortlived British Association's Committee on the Acclimatisation of Domestic Animals. Although Gray denied that he and other scientists were opposed to the general theory and practice of acclimatisation, which he noted in 1864[1] 'has become a favourite one with the more thoughtful student, [and] appears all at once to have become popular', he considered that little of advantage was to be gained from the 'schemes of the would-be acclimatizers'. Gray believed that giraffes, elands, llamas and alpacas were of interest solely as 'objects of curiosity and luxury, and as incapable of being turned out, in this country at least, to any useful domestic purpose', and did not agree with Owen that introduced African ruminants would eventually become success-fully acclimatised in Britain. Nor did Gray consider that yaks from Tibet or zebu cattle from India could survive in the British climate; in those few cases where the acclimatisation of alien species might succeed, Gray claimed that an environment that mirrored 'as much as possible their natural proclivities' was essential. These generally negative views did nothing to encourage the practice of acclimatisation or the recruitment of potential members of the Society.

In 1866 and 1867 (the last two years of the Society's existence after its amalgamation with the Ornithological Society of London), only four Fellows of learned societies in London, as Osborne (1987) points out, were members of the Society's council, and these four had little influence in scientific circles: Frank Buckland and B. Waterhouse Hawkins were Fellows of the Zoological Society and Linnean Society respectively, Lord Tredegar was a Fellow of the Royal Society, and George Scoville a Fellow of the Royal Geographical Society. Richard Owen and Albert Günther were sometime patrons of the Society, but each allowed his membership to lapse. Sir Roderick Murchison, FRS, director-general of the Geological Survey in 1855, was another distinguished but inactive member. Osborne considered that the mem-bership of but lack of participation in the Society's activities of such men as Owen, Günther and Murchison, is 'a revealing indicator of the trio's social contacts'. Owen and Murchison had been personal friends of Frank Buckland's father, and even after the latter's death in 1856 continued their personal friendship with his son. Their membership of the Society may therefore have been simply a courtesy to Frank Buckland, and in spite of their lack of interest in, or even disapproval of, the Society's activities. If members of the scientific standing or people such as Owen and Murchison had been prepared to play a more energetic rôle in the activities of the Society (which is really to say if the work of the Society had held a greater appeal for them), then even without government support the Society might have become a potent and long-lasting organisation.

Instead, the annual reports of the Society show it to have been an institution which, though not perhaps actually 'dominated by field-sport enthusiasts' as claimed by Osborne, certainly leaned in that direction. In comparison with the French *Société*, which examined the commercial and economic benefits for the entire community to be derived from the acclimatisation of exotic animals, the activities of the

Society, despite its declaration to have as one of its objectives the provision of additional sources of food for all social classes, inclined instead towards the importation of game species or those most suitable for keeping in private parks. Thus, in contrast to those animals defined by the *Société* as having potential aesthetic, agricultural, commercial or economic value, the Society based its idea of 'useful species' on very similar criteria to those of the Zoological Society of the mid-1820s.

As Ritvo (1987) rightly says, the Society's activities exhibited a 'lack of system and restraint'—a claim which is amply confirmed in the foregoing chapters. Although in view of their many and continuing failures, the persistence of members of the Society in their attempts to acclimatise totally unsuitable animals shows great tenacity of purpose, it comes as something of a surprise to modern scientists. It soon became apparent that animals already established were far better adapted than new exotic ones to fulfil the requirements of domesticated or acclimatised species in Britain, and a contemporary writer in the respected scientific journal *Nature* pointed out that 'no addition of any practical importance has been made to our stock of truly domestic animals since the commencement of the historic period of man's life upon the earth.'[2]

Another reason why one of the Society's principal declared objectives, the provision of additional supplies of food, was bound, in any event to have foundered, was the innate conservatism of the British palate. Until comparatively recently, deer-farmers have met with marked sales resistance when trying to market venison, which is still by no means either universally popular or even sometimes acceptable; neither are frogs' legs, snails, octopus, squid and edible dormice to everyone's taste. The British abroad are notoriously unenterprising in experimenting with exotic foods. How much more difficult it would undoubtedly have been, more than a century ago, to sell at home such delicacies as wombat, kangaroo or eland. (The editor of the *Gardener's Chronicle*, one of the Society's most scathing contemporary critics, scornfully reported that a wombat had been acclimatised in England before being fattened and cooked, 'but when it was introduced to the table the whole company turned pale and rushed out of the room, never to return.') As an anonymous writer put it in *All the Year Round*,[3] a magazine 'conducted' by Charles Dickens:

> The president of the French Acclimatization Society is . . . an intrepid horse-eater who would accord a fair tasting to donkey-flesh, and who appreciates even rats when properly fed; but both he and the English Acclimatization Society have one obstacle before them—popular prejudice. . . . That universal favourite, the potato, was but slowly and reluctantly accepted by the masses. . . . The Christian pities the Jew and the

Mussulman, because they hold pork in abhorrence, and yet the Christian repulses the notion of touching horse-flesh. The Hindoo has an equal horror of beef. Mutton is by no means a cosmopolitan dish. Calves' feet, the livers of fowls, and goose giblets, were formerly thrown away as unfit for human food. The Russians still abstain from pigeon . . . the Italians hold the rabbit in aversion. The French eat on a small scale frogs, and on a large scale snails, dog-fish and sorrel-soup; all of which would be rejected by the English labourer, even if starving; while rhubarb, sea-kale, and parsnips, are scarcely yet appreciated on the great majority of Gallic tables.

In the course of his address to the Botany and Zoology Section of the British Association for the Advancement of Science at Bath in 1864 (referred to above), the president, Dr J. E. Gray, said that

> Some of the schemes of the would-be acclimatizers are incapable of being carried out, and would never have been suggested if their promoters had been better acquainted with the habits and manners of the animals on which the experiments are proposed to be made.

In the same vein, an editorial in *The Field*[4] (which, it will be remembered, had been the Society's sponsor in the euphoric days of 1860, and which, until Frank Buckland's departure to found the rival *Land and Water* in 1866, had been the main organ of the Society in the dissemination of news of its activities, rather as the *Bulletin* was of the French *Société*), after summarising the Society's fifth annual report for 1864–5, voiced its opinion that

> The meagre results enumerated above are all that the society has to show at the conclusion of the fifth year of its existence. During the past season its expenditure has been, as nearly as possible, £400, an amount of money that no one would think large, even if the society had made but one useful addition to our fauna. But letting the past alone, we may ask, is there any prospect of the society doing better in the time to come? Is there a single animal that can be named, whose claims to be regarded as a really useful addition to our stock of wild or domesticated species will stand the test of a critical examination?

The wide variety, and in many instances total unsuitability for purposes of acclimatisation, of many of the animals and plants imported by the Society, undoubtedly lent substance to Dr Gray's disparaging claim. Similarly, the strictures of *The Field* cannot be denied. It was probably a combination of views such as these, coupled with the facts discussed above, ridicule like that printed in the *Gardener's Chronicle* (referred to in chapter 5), a falling membership, a correspondingly depleted bank balance, the pressure of the chancery suit with Mr Stone, and not least a manifestly uninterested council, which led to the Society's decline and fall into eventual oblivion.

13. Acclimatisation Societies in Australia

'NO British colony', wrote Osborne,[1] 'boasted more collective and voluntary acclimatisation activity than Australia', where independent societies were formed in Sydney, New South Wales, in 1879 (which evolved from an earlier society founded in 1852); Melbourne, Victoria, in 1861; Adelaide, South Australia, in 1862; Brisbane, Queensland, in 1862; Hobart and Launceston, Tasmania, in 1895 and 1899 respectively; Perth, Western Australia, in 1896; and at various provincial centres. Many of these colonial Australian (and indeed New Zealand) societies outlived the one formed in the United Kingdom, of which it would be wrong to regard them as mere offshoots. Although all these organisations described themselves as 'acclimatisation societies', they were for the most part engaged in attempts at 'naturalisation'—attempts which had previously been made by private individuals for many years before the societies were founded.

As in Algeria, the activities of acclimatisation societies in Australia reached their zenith during the final years of economic protectionism, especially in colonies such as Victoria which possessed the wealthiest, largest, and by far the most important such society and which, contrary to free-trading New South Wales where there was only a society of modest size, still depended in the 1860s on protective tariffs.

Osborne (1987 and 1988) draws a close parallel between the position and status of Victoria within the British Empire and that of Algeria in its French counterpart. The economic situation of both colonies was remarkably similar, and in Victoria, as in Algeria, advantageous tariffs on imports, together with government grants of cash, land and resources, resulted in an increasing interest in acclimatisation. Algiers and Melbourne, where the colonies' acclimatisation societies were formed, were each situated in localities of rapid demographic growth. Although outside the capital mineral-impoverished Algeria attracted only a small number of European settlers in the 1860s, the city of Algiers expanded more rapidly. In Australia, the gold rushes of the 1850s drew miners to the south-east like bees to a honey-pot, where they settled towards the end of the decade when the goldfields became worked out. By 1861, when the Acclimatisation Society of Victoria was founded, Melbourne was a rapidly expanding industrial and commercial city, whose population had risen during the previous decade from 77,000 to 540,000.

In 1860 the first of a series of Land Acts was passed, with a view

to encouraging small freeholding settlers. Although the Land Acts
only partially achieved their objective, Victoria became an important
agricultural centre, exporting large quantities of dairy and other farm
produce.

The system of landholding in Victoria and Algeria, as Osborne
points out, shared common features; one of these was a scheme of
smallholdings combined with the raising of 'acclimatised' exotic
animals and crops, as also practised in Queensland and elsewhere in
Australia. One of the features of this scheme was the economical multi-
functional use of species such as the llama, which was used to provide
meat and wool and as a beast of burden.

There were other similarities, too, between Algerian and Australian
acclimatisation, the most notable of which was intercolonial mutual
cooperation in the form of an exchange of both organisms and information. The Paris society, for example, offered a prize for the successful
acclimatisation in Algeria of fast-growing eucalyptus trees (which were
believed to be able to dry up swampy areas and thus make fever-ridden
localities habitable, and also provided timber for railway sleepers and
telegraph posts) and kangaroos for their meat and skins.

Just as there was a noticeable parallel between the position and status
of Victoria and Algeria within the British and French empires, so was
there a striking similarity between the membership of acclimatisation
societies in the metropolitan and colonial cities of the two empires, in
which scientists, landowners, farmers, civil servants and politicians pre-
dominated, although there was a greater proportion of the first-named
in France and Algeria than in Britain and Australia.

In Australia, the acclimatisation movement, far from arousing popular interest and sympathy, met rather with, albeit covert, hostility, or
at best apathy, based on the not entirely misplaced belief that the
societies were acting in the interest of the privileged minority. In
their turn, members of the societies looked on Australia as a country
bereft of such attractions as melodious songbirds and animals of the
chase—omissions which they sought to remedy. This objective, actu-
ated by nostalgia and a professed sense of social responsibility for their
fellow settlers, led to their efforts to acclimatise (which to the societies
and their members was synonymous with 'naturalise') British animals
and plants in their new homeland.

What did the acclimatisation movement in Australia achieve? The
societies claimed that the introduction of insect-eating birds increased
agricultural, horticultural and pomological crop yields, while their
detractors claimed that the new arrivals caused more harm than good
by eating grain, vegetables and fruit. In many instances exotic birds
tended to displace native ones, sometimes to the detriment of the
latter's populations. Deer, while providing sport and an additional

supply of food, often caused damage to garden and farm crops and to arboriculture. The passing of the Game Acts, for the protection and preservation of both indigenous and exotic animals, was largely enacted at the behest of the societies, and helped to prevent the annihilation of many native species.

Although most Australian acclimatisation societies started out with at least some apparently sensible objectives, many degenerated into importing species purely as curiosities or for ornamental purposes. In several instances, once the craze for acclimatisation had passed, the societies, in order to survive, turned themselves into zoological gardens, the existence of which, in our more enlightened age, is increasingly being brought into question.

Few if any attempts were made by the acclimatisation societies to 'improve' the breeds of domestic stock or cultivars on which the prosperity of Australia depended. Those societies that are still active in Australia are concerned primarily with the introduction of freshwater fish, and are subject to the Wildlife Protection (Regulation of Exports and Imports) Act, which is administered by the National Parks and Wildlife Service.[2]

The New South Wales Zoological (Acclimatisation) Society

The New South Wales Zoological (Acclimatisation) Society had its origins at a meeting held on 28 June 1852 and advertised by the following notice:

ZOOLOGICAL GARDENS

A PUBLIC MEETING will be held in the Saloon of the Royal Hotel, George Street, THIS EVENING, Monday 28th June instant, at Seven o'clock precisely, to take into consideration the desirableness of establishing a ZOOLOGICAL INSTITUTION in or near the City of Sydney, for the Encouragement of Science and the Recreation of the Public. The attendance of all parties interested in supporting the above object is respectfully requested.[3]

The meeting, which attracted some two hundred people, was chaired by the chief justice of New South Wales, Sir Alfred Stephen, who considered that as the city possessed a 'Museum for dead specimens . . . they should have an institution for living specimens also'.[4] Sir Alfred's proposition was unanimously approved, and it was decided, after some discussion, to site the new 'Zoological Institution' in the Botanic Gardens adjacent to the museum. Dr George Bennett, the first president and later secretary of the new Society, expressed the hope that 'new and rare animals such as the Llama'[5] would be introduced, and suggested as suitable candidates for domestication such native species as lyrebirds and brush turkeys.

In 1864 permission was given for the construction in the Botanic Gardens of an aviary to house exotic birds, and in the same year Bennett, by then the Society's secretary, reiterated, somewhat pretentiously, the object of the organisation as 'spreading over the length and breadth of the land inestimable acquisitions to the wealth and comfort of the people'.[6]

On 24 March 1879, a meeting, under the chairmanship of the Mayor of Sydney, was held in the Commerce Exchange to consider the 'PROSPECTUS of the NEW SOUTH WALES ACCLIMATIZATION SOCIETY'.[7] Despite the title on the prospectus, it was decided instead to name the new society the New South Wales Zoological Society, but to concentrate on the introduction and acclimatisation (naturalisation) of gamebirds and songbirds. The reason for the change of name, in spite of the Society's proposed objectives, is unknown. The governor of New South Wales, Lord Carrington, was elected the Society's first patron.

The early collections of exotic animals exhibited by the Society were financed principally by donations and members' subscriptions. In 1880, however, a grant of £500 was made by the state government, on condition that it was matched by a similar amount from the Society, and an additional sum was voted for the construction in the Botanical Gardens of a monkey house. Two years later the main grant was doubled to £1000, and in the following year was further increased to £2500. In the former year (1882), 'Dr George Bennett . . . was instrumental in [the new society] receiving . . . the funds (£33.4s.6d.) which had been lying for many years to the credit of the old Acclimatization Society'.[8] In the present century, according to Jenkins (1977), financial support for the Society from the state government has fluctuated greatly, but in general has been confined to expenditure on capital projects, the Society being responsible for funding the day-to-day running costs of the gardens.

In 1881 the Society was given permission by the city council to take over a 2.8-hectare site, known as Billy Goat Swamp, at Moore Park, where new gardens were opened to the public some three years later. The gardens were soon increased to 5 hectares, and in 1906 to 6 hectares. Two years later the Society was granted a royal charter.

In 1912 the Society moved again, to a larger, 17-hectare site at Taronga[9] Park, Athol Gardens, which was first opened to the public two years later. In 1927, an aquarium was added to the amenities at Taronga.

In 1973, with the help of a A$11,400 grant from the government of New South Wales, the Western Plains 'open type' zoo was established on a 284-hectare site at Dubbo, some 275 kilometres north-west of Sydney, which was opened to the public for the first time in March 1977.

In the 1930s a number of regional acclimatisation societies were formed in New South Wales, principally for the introduction and establishment of trout. These included: the New England Trout Acclimatisation Society, formed at Inverell in 1936; the Central Acclimatisation Society at Bathurst; the Monaro Acclimatisation Society at Tumut; and the Orange Trout Acclimatisation Society at Orange.

In the early 1860s a flock of 336 alpacas from Peru, in the care of Mr Charles Ledger, who had, as Jenkins (1977) says, gone to amazing lengths of subterfuge and endurance to overcome a ban on their export from South America,[10] arrived in Sydney, where they were acquired by the New South Wales government for £15,000 (around £45 a head). After a large number had died, the rest were sold at auction—five to the Zoological Institution—at £15 each. These, too, soon died, and the venture was finally abandoned.

In the 1860s the Zoological Institution also acquired from South America a pair of agoutis, which it was planned to breed for their flesh and also for their skin which makes into high-quality leather. What became of these destructive animals is unknown, but fortunately they seem never to have been released into the wild.

In the 1870s Mr Edward Cox of Mulgoa accepted custody of a pair of brown hares on behalf of the Zoological Institution, but reported that the grass on his station was so high that nothing had been seen of them since their release. By the end of the decade, however, they had overrun much of the south of the state.

At around the same time, the Zoological Institution also acquired, from its *confrères* in Victoria, a flock of angora goats, which were placed in the charge of Mr J. Black of Muswellbrook. Unfortunately, they proved to be surprisingly delicate, and this enterprise, too, eventually foundered.

The introduction of deer to New South Wales met with rather better results than did most other mammal importations.

In July 1862 Mr Edward Cox transferred half-a-dozen fallow deer from Tasmania to Mulgoa, which by late 1864 had increased to eighteen. Two years later a pair was released on the eastern side of Lake George, north-east of Canberra, followed at a later date by others at nearby Bungendore. By the outbreak of the First World War they had increased to around 200, and had considerably extended their range. The population in the hill country around Lake George, which is believed to number over 1000, is probably the largest and most stable on the Australian mainland.

In 1885 and 1886 some red deer were released by the recently formed Zoological (Acclimatisation) Society in the moist sclerophyll forests of the Royal National Park south of Sydney; what became of them is unknown, but they have not been seen in this locality since before the First World War. The red deer in the Quidong region of south-eastern New South Wales, near the headwaters of the Snowy River, are descended from some which escaped from Mr J. R. Logan's Aston Station between Cooma and Bombala, augmented by deliberate releases of the remainder when the property was sold in 1918. A small population persists in the high country of the Monaro near Delegate, from where it is spreading slowly south into the Snowy River country and eastern Victoria.

In 1893 some timor or rusa deer from New Caledonia—to which they had been introduced from the Dutch East Indies (probably Java) in about 1870—were imported by the Society to New South Wales, and released in the Royal National Park, where today herds of 100–200 can be seen, especially around Bundeena in the east of the park.

In the 1880s or 1890s ostriches were introduced by the Society to New South Wales to stock a plume farm owned by Mr J. T. Barracluff at South Head. Some were also sent to the Hawksbury Agricultural College and the Yanco Experimental Farm, but with the collapse of the plume trade in the 1920s the venture was abandoned.

In about 1865 the Society imported secretary birds from South Africa to combat venomous snakes, and at around the same time also curassows from South America as potential game birds, but neither was ever released into the wild.

At least one pair of house sparrows was despatched from the Acclimatisation Society of Victoria in Melbourne to New South Wales in 1863, where on 9 February it was announced that eggs were being incubated. Some of the subsequent fledglings were translocated to Murrurundi early in 1865, where they nested successfully later in the same year. The present population of house sparrows in New South Wales has been augmented by dispersal northwards from Victoria.

A large shipment of songbirds—yellowhammers, skylarks, gold-finches, greenfinches and starlings—and California quail was imported from New Zealand into New South Wales by the Society in 1880, who in the same year also introduced red-whiskered bulbuls from China; only the yellowhammers and quail failed to become established.

Yellowhammers, in lots of fifteen to twenty, were released in 1880 or shortly thereafter on the Liverpool Plains and at Bathurst, Inverell and Mudgee, and in the Blue Mountains, but apparently soon disappeared.

Skylarks were first introduced to New South Wales near Sydney in 1866 and 1870–2, but with what results is unknown. Seventy of the 200 imported in 1880 were in 1883 released in the Blue Mountains, Maneroo, Ryde and elsewhere; by the late 1940s, skylarks were common along the state littoral and westward to some inland areas.

Thirty-two goldfinches from the 1880 shipment were liberated in Maneroo, Bodalla, Ryde, the Blue Mountains, and other localities, and were established in Sydney by 1886. By the outbreak of the Second World War they were well entrenched in townships along the western railway as far as Dubbo, and stragglers had penetrated further north still to Gilgandra. Today they occur through much of eastern and southern New South Wales, and from the south-west of the state to the highlands of the north-east. Goldfinches were also introduced to New South Wales in 1856 and 1863, but what became of these birds is uncertain.

Greenfinches, too, were imported to the state in 1856, but again with unknown results. Those introduced in 1880 were released in small batches of between fifteen and twenty in Maneroo and Bodalla, south of Sydney, where in 1896 they were said to be flourishing. By about 1910 they had spread south and west to Albury and to Bathurst, and by the late 1940s were fairly common in Sydney, and by the following decade had spread west as far as Orange. Today, greenfinches are established in parts of Sydney intermittently westwards to Orange and south-west to between the ACT and Albury.

Starlings from the 1880 shipment were freed in Sherwood Scrubs, and three years later were reported to be breeding at Ashfield.[11] By the mid-1920s they were established throughout settled areas of the state, where today they are abundant and virtually ubiquitous. Starlings were also released in Sydney in 1856, where they seem soon to have disappeared.

In 1880 California quail were released in lots of fifteen to twenty at Liverpool Plains, Bathurst, in the Blue Mountains, and elsewhere in New South Wales, but failed to become established.

Red-whiskered bulbuls imported from China by the Society in 1880 apparently disappeared. Others introduced about the turn of the century were more successful, and soon became established around Sydney, where by about 1920 they were said to be common in the city suburbs, and where by 1933 flocks of up to 100 were proving a nuisance in soft-fruit orchards. By 1950 they had spread up to 100 kilometres from Sydney, and a decade later were reported to be abundant within a radius of 150 kilometres north, south and west of the city. Red-whiskered bulbuls are today common in city and suburban gardens of Sydney, and have even colonised some nearby semi-rural localities. A discrete population, presumably emanating from a separate source, occurs at Coffs Harbour, 450 kilometres north of Sydney. Red-whiskered bulbuls are considered a horticultural and pomological pest, but in compensation destroy vine moth larvae and other injurious invertebrates. Although it seems unlikely that the birds will be able to spread very far north of Sydney through the sandstone gullies and *Eucalyptus* forests where there is little fruit, were they ever to reach the coastal rainforests, where wild figs and other soft fruits are plentiful, they could theoretically travel north from there at least as far as Queensland. Red-whiskered bulbuls in New South Wales have been recorded as foster parents of the native parasitic pallid cuckoo.

Most of the early attempts by the Society to introduce brown trout to New South Wales between 1852 and 1864 failed because of premature hatching of the ova as the transporting vessels entered the tropics. In 1888, however, some brown trout from England were successfully released by the Society in the Cotter, Queenbeyan, Little Naas, and Molongolo rivers, and in Ollera creek, where they became established. In 1894 rainbow trout were imported to New South Wales, where they did especially well in the Snowy Mountains, New England, and the central tablelands.

In 1863 the New South Wales Society tried unsuccessfully to introduce cochineal-producing insects[12] from England to feed on the prickly pear cacti that had been imported from Brazil. In the following year Sir George Grey (1812–98), then governor of New Zealand, shipped a further consignment of insects to the Society in Sydney, but these too failed to become established.

In 1864 Dr Bennett, then secretary of the Society, said:

> On introducing plants for naturalization, proper precautions should be taken of previously ascertaining their utility for commercial or other purposes, as many injurious plants have been imported which afterwards could not be eradicated, which we have experienced in the Scotch thistle, Bathurst burr, also the elegant variegated or milk thistle and the Scotch burr.[13]

Yet at a meeting of the Society in the previous year, Bennett had strongly advocated the introduction of blackberries as a suitable food for curassows!

The Acclimatisation Society of Victoria

It seems incongruous that one of the principal reasons for the formation of the Acclimatisation Society of Victoria[14] was the working-out, in the late 1850s, of the colony's goldfields.

The decline in the rate of gold production, which caused an ever-increasing number of miners to quit the diggings in search of work elsewhere, forced the government to seek ways in which to mitigate the problem of potential massive unemployment. One of the solutions proposed was the introduction from abroad and acclimatisation of exotic animals and plants, which would both help to develop the land and make it more productive, and would also be labour-intensive. Furthermore, the introduction of game birds and mammals would provide a source of sport and an additional supply of food, while the importation of songbirds would, it was hoped, compensate for the existence of what the poet Adam Lindsay Gordon disparagingly referred to as the native 'songless bright birds', and help to assuage the homesickness of the nostalgic antipodean settler.

Spurred on by the formation in France and England of societies for the acclimatisation of foreign species, Mr Edward Wilson, then editor of the Melbourne *Argus* newspaper—aided and abetted by Dr Thomas Embling, a medical practitioner and politician, and Dr (later Sir) Ferdinand von Mueller, director of the Melbourne Botanic Gardens, and a number of other interested private individuals—was a strong supporter of the government's proposal. Several scientific and commercial institutions also declared their interest, and both houses of parliament, the Melbourne Chamber of Commerce, the Royal Society of Victoria, and its predecessor the Philosophical Institute, all set up sub-committees to examine the pros and cons of introducing animals and plants into the colony for the purpose of acclimatisation and to improve land development. One such sub-committee of the Legislative Assembly, appointed in 1857, was of the opinion that

> the bush solitudes of Victoria should be invaded by some other of the myriads of feathered fowl which gather in clouds in other, but not fairer, lands, and that the vast nations of indigenous quadrupeds which throng over distant and less civilized scenes, should add their quota to give voice and life, activity and food, to where now . . . the almost unbroken repose of ages holds its sway.[15]

As might be expected, Wilson's *Argus* was vociferous in its advocacy of the introduction from abroad of alien species, in which it was supported by other periodicals ranging from the privately published *Facts and Figures* to the *Government Gazette*. Partly as a consequence of this intensive lobbying, on 6 October 1857 a meeting was convened in St Patrick's Hall, Melbourne, for the purpose of forming an ornithological society, principally for breeding 'the finer kinds of poultry and cage birds'. During the meeting, however, the activities were widened, at the suggestion of the chairman, Dr Thomas Black, to include the introduction and acclimatisation of exotic mammals and birds, 'under the name "Zoological Society of Victoria" '. The objects of the Society included

> The introduction and improvement of domestic birds and animals . . . the importation, care, and domestication of mammalia, fishes, birds, and reptiles of this and other countries, more particularly those of rare and uncommon species. The encouragement of singing birds, and the endeavour to propagate them in the country.[16]

The Age and *The Argus* both spoke out eloquently regarding the advantages of acclimatisation, the former hoping to see the horse-chestnut and the oak add grandeur and variety to our woods, to have the Chinese sugar-cane filling the cultivator's purse, to hear the nightingale singing in our moonlight as in that of Devonshire, to behold the salmon leaping in our streams as in those of Connemara or Athol, to have antelopes gladdening our plains as they do those of South Africa, and camels obviating for us as for the Arab the obstacle of the desert.[17]

The latter, while advocating the introduction of such trees as Spanish and horse-chestnuts, cork oaks and mulberries, also hoped that the Zoological Society would

confer a lasting boon upon the country by establishing the several sorts of deer, antelopes, and gazelles, which would swarm in the unenclosed country, unmolested by beasts of prey. Not only partridges and pheasants, but many kinds of feathered game, from the Cape, from India, and the coast of South America . . . and . . . the various kinds of fresh water fish.[18]

Doubtless influenced by the fact that the Governor, Sir Henry Barkly, was the Zoological Society's patron, the government acceded to a request for 'a grant of land and a sum of money, in order to enable them to commence proceedings without delay',[19] by providing £3000 and 'thirty acres [12 hectares] of land in Richmond Paddock opposite the Botanical Gardens'.[20] This site was subsequently found to be too barren and damp for its purpose, and the Zoological Society's growing collection of animals was, with government approval, transferred in the summer of 1858 to the care of Dr von Mueller in the Botanical Gardens.

By the turn of the decade scientific, public and government support for the Zoological Society was running high, while the Philosophical Institute, reborn as the Royal Society of Victoria, continued to provide a platform for debate on animal and vegetable introductions, while newspapers such as *The Age* and *The Argus* in Melbourne and *The Times* of London remained loyal in their support of the Zoological Society's activities. The government of Victoria continued to promote any scheme that would increase land productivity in order to lessen the colony's dependency on gold and wool and to reduce unemployment.

It was to this scenario that Edward Wilson, the most enthusiastic of acclimatisers, returned to Australia in 1860 from a visit to England for treatment for his failing eyesight. By early 1861, Wilson had persuaded most of the members of the Zoological Society, together with many other influential people, to form with him a new society—the Acclimatisation Society of Victoria. While continuing the work of the old Society, the new Society had as its principal aim not the mere exhibition of exotic animals and plants but rather their dissemination into the wild throughout the colony. The published objects of the new

Society were almost verbatim those of the United Kingdom Society (see chapter 3).

The Acclimatisation Society of Victoria was formally established at a public meeting presided over by Sir Henry Barkly on 25 February 1861. The government agreed to make a grant to the new Society of £5500 and to provide land for it in Royal Park, provided that the two societies agreed to merge. Within a year all the property owned by the Zoological Society had been transferred to the Acclimatisation Society's gardens in Royal Park, where it was intended that animals could recover after their long sea voyage to Australia before being released into the wild, but where by public demand they were also on display in what eventually became the Melbourne Zoological Gardens.

To mark the completion of the first year of the Society's activities, a lecture was given by Professor F. S. McCoy, professor of natural sciences at Melbourne University, at the annual meeting in November 1862, in which (McCoy, 1862) he referred to

> the great task which has been reserved for us—the stocking of our new country with all the more important, useful and ornamental kinds of animals . . . which are to be found in other parts of the world in similar climates, but of which the vast continent of Australia has been left by nature most singularly and exceptionally destitute.

Aided by vice-regal patronage and a distinguished council composed of doctors, lawyers, scientists, politicians, wealthy ranchers and pastoralists, the Society played an influential rôle in the 1860s both inside and outside Victoria, initiating meetings in the suburbs of Melbourne and forming branch societies in such provincial Victorian towns as Ballarat, Beechworth and Portland, and providing the inspiration for the foundation of sister societies in other Australian colonies. In order to advance the objectives of the Society, acclimatisation reserves were established in various parts of Victoria and elsewhere, including Ballarat, Beechworth, Creswick, Gembrook (1873), Kerang, Cape Liptrap, Phillip Island (1862), Portland, Quail Island (1867), Tower Hill, and Wilson's Promontory (1887).

As mentioned in chapter 9, a questionnaire on acclimatisation from the Foreign and Colonial Office in England (under the auspices of the United Kingdom Society's president, the Duke of Newcastle, as Secretary of State for the Colonies) was in 1863 circulated to ministers, governors and consuls of British colonies throughout the world. As befitted the largest and wealthiest acclimatisation society in the British Empire, the response to this document provided by the Victorian Society was by far the most detailed and comprehensive of all those received.

In defence of its work, if any such defence was required, the Society claimed 'the aggrandisement of the colony, the multiplication of its industrial resources, [and] its attraction as a place of residence'.[21] For the pastoralist it offered the camel, the alpaca, and angora and cashmere goats; for the sportsman, deer, hares, rabbits, gamebirds and wildfowl; for the angler, both game and coarse fish; for farmers and pomologists insectivorous song thrushes, blackbirds, starlings, house sparrows, and Indian mynahs; and for cottagers, the Ligurian bee.

In the conditions prevailing in mid-nineteenth century Victoria—the extraction of wealth from natural resources and the tacit acceptance of acclimatisation as a means of attaining that end, coupled with the clear need for the post-gold-rush Victorian economy to widen its base to avoid its reliance on gold and wool—the rise of acclimatisation societies and their support by the government and public was, as Gillbank (1986) says, not surprising.

By the mid-1860s, however, enthusiasm for acclimatisation had started to wane, and the fortune and membership of the Victoria Society (which between 1860 and 1864 had risen to some 500) began to decline; they did not revive until in 1872 the Society adopted a zoo-keeping rôle, and became the Zoological and Acclimatisation Society of Victoria. The Society was incorporated by Act of Parliament in 1884, and obtained a Royal Charter in 1910. In 1937, as a result of legal and financial difficulties, control of the Society passed to the government of Victoria, under whose guidance the title of Royal Melbourne Zoological Gardens was granted on 6 October 1977—120 years to the day since the formation of the Zoological Society of Victoria.

The Acclimatisation Society of Victoria introduced a large number of animal species (mainly mammals and birds) to the colony, the majority of which failed to become established.

These included camels, alpacas, llamas, agoutis, angora and cashmere goats, eland, brush-tailed possums, chaffinches, linnets, yellowhammers, ortolan buntings, siskins, Java sparrows, European robins, canaries, rooks, red jungle fowl, helmeted guineafowl, curassows, various species of quail, partridge, francolin and grouse, peafowl, sandgrouse, mute swans, Egyptian geese, ostriches, roach, tench, Atlantic salmon, Ligurian bees, silkworms of various species, including the ailanthus, glow-worms, and *Dactylopius coccus* insects which produce the dye cochineal, together with the food plant, the prickly pear cactus.[22]

The following table gives brief details of those introductions of mammals, birds, and fish which proved successful. The dates given are for the first introduction of each species by the Society; in several cases, as elsewhere in Australia, prior introductions had been made by private individuals and/or sporting organisations. (Full details on mammal and bird introductions will be found in Lever, 1985 and 1987.)

Mammals

Species	Date	Locality
Axis deer	1862	Sugarloaf Hill
Fallow deer	1862	Longerenong, Wimmera
Sambar	1861	King Parrot Creek (1863)
Hog deer	1865 or 1866	Cape Liptrap and Snake Island
Timor or rusa deer	1867	Dandenong Range (1890)
Brown hare	1861	Phillip Island (1863)

Birds

Species	Date	Locality
House sparrow	1863	Melbourne Botanic Gardens, Royal Park
Tree sparrow	1863	Melbourne Botanic Gardens, Royal Park and Pentridge Stockade
European starling	1861	Melbourne Botanic Gardens, Royal Park
Skylark	1861	Melbourne Botanic Gardens, Royal Park
Song thrush	1861	Churchill and Phillip Islands
Blackbird	1861–2	Geelong and Port Albert
Goldfinch	1863	Melbourne Botanic Gardens, Royal Park
Greenfinch	1863	Melbourne Botanic Gardens, Royal Park
Indian mynah	1862	Melbourne metropolitan area
Mallard	1866	Phillip Island
Spotted dove	1866	Near Melbourne and at Cape Liptrap (1870)
Common pheasant	1861	Phillip Island (1863)
California quail	1862	Melbourne Botanic Gardens, Royal Park

Fish

Brown trout	1866	Jackson's Creek, Sunbury

The Acclimatisation Society of South Australia

In a paper read before the Philosophical Society of Adelaide on 13 May 1862,[23] Mr G. W. Francis, director of the Botanic Gardens, perhaps prompted by a letter from Edward Wilson in the *South Australian Register* of the preceding March urging the benefits of acclimatisation, and while agreeing with the advantages of animal and plant introductions, suggested that the term 'acclimatisation' was something of a misnomer, and that 'naturalization or adaptation would be more correct'.[24]

Francis, as Jenkins points out, was not only enthusiastic about the possible introduction to South Australia of a wide variety of such animals as antelope, deer, buffalo, bison, cattle, fish, game birds, songbirds, and such insectivorous species as swallows and sparrows, but was also keen about trying out 'plants of a useful character', which would help to make South Australia 'a pleasanter and happier place to live in'. He suggested that even the great 'central deserts' could be 'cropped', and that explorers and prospectors 'might take the seeds of all kinds of melons, oranges, lemons, guavas . . . grain of many sorts—even slips of pineapple and banana might be carried three or four hundred miles—and the sugar-cane too', so that 'notwithstanding its drought' the desert would be 'teeming with animal and human food'. In an amusing aside, and as a reason for wishing to improve the standard of oxen in the state, Francis said: 'I have often grieved over the immense loss of time in employing our usual oxen, and still more in seeing boys thus acquiring a movement which may last them through life, of two miles an hour.'[25]

So persuasive was Francis that at the conclusion of his address it was unanimously decided to form an Acclimatisation Society of South Australia, with Francis himself as honorary secretary.

In spite of the early enthusiasm of its founders the infant Society soon fell into decline, and it was not for another sixteen years that the South Australian Acclimatisation Society was formally established on 23 July 1878, with the Governor, Sir William Jervois (1821–97), as patron, and Chief Justice S. J. (later Sir Samuel) Way as president.

On 17 October 1879 the new Society held its first annual general meeting in the South Australian Institute in Adelaide. In the course of his presidential address, Mr Justice Way stated that the Society would be at great pains not to introduce 'any bird that would be likely to do mischief to gardeners or farmers'. In 1881 the annual report, while disclaiming responsibility for the release of rabbits or house sparrows and claiming that 'some misapprehension . . . had been entertained by the public' since both species had arrived in the state prior to the Society's formation, mentioned the introduction of 'songsters and insect destroying birds of the mother country . . . in the hope that they may . . . impart to our somewhat unmelodious hills and woods the music and harmony of English country life'. In 1882 the disclaimer regarding rabbits was repeated, when the annual report, perhaps in the light of continuing criticism, stated categorically that 'the Society is not responsible for the presence of these pests, or for the ravages they have committed. The rabbits were turned out on our lands by private individuals.'

Soon after the society's rebirth, aviaries and pre-release holding pens were constructed in the Botanic Gardens, then under the directorship of Dr Schomburgk, and on the property of the honorary secretary, Mr R. E. Minchin. While initially concentrating on the attempted acclimatisation of exotic songbirds and insect-eating species, the Society also conducted experiments in the farming for their plumes of ostriches and on the improvement of domestic turkeys.

In 1881 plans were made for the formation of a zoological garden, and

Frank Buckland Physicking A Porpoise.
'There was only one way; so I braved the cold water and jumped into the
tank with the porpoise. I then held him up in my arms (he was very
heavy), and, when I had got him in a favourable position, I poured a
good dose of sal-volatile and water down his throat with a bottle.'
From *The Curious World of Frank Buckland* by G. H. O. Burgess.

Frank Buckland aged 2¾ years. The crocodiles were purchased in Southampton by Black Will, the coachman of the 'Defiance' coach, and sold by him to Dr Buckland in Oxford; the sketch on the wall labelled 'the last hyena' refers to Dr Buckland's work on cave deposits. (From a sketch by Philip Duncan in the Devon Record Office and Exeter Diocesan Record Office.)

Frank Buckland with oyster-breeding tile, *c.* 1875.
Courtesy Royal College of Surgeons of England, London.

Edward Wilson from the *Australasian Sketcher,*
16 February 1878. Courtesy of the La Trobe
Collection, State Library of Victoria, Australia.

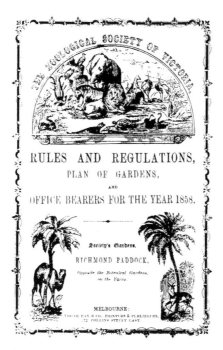

Reproduction of the cover of the Zoological Society of Victoria's
'Rules and Regulations and Office Bearers for the year 1858.'
This is probably the first printed matter published by the Society.

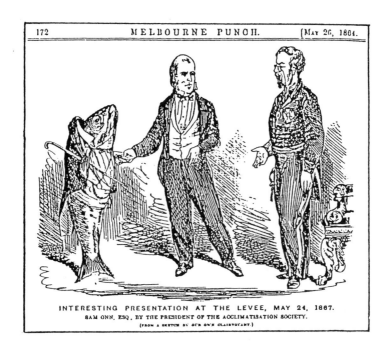

INTERESTING PRESENTATION AT THE LEVEE, MAY 24, 1867.

SAM ONN, ESQ., BY THE PRESIDENT OF THE ACCLIMATISATION SOCIETY.

(FROM A SKETCH BY OUR OWN CLAIRVOYANT.)

Cartoon from *The Melbourne Punch,* 26 May 1884.

Emu. From *Voyage de Découvertes aux Terres Australes,*
by Louis C. D. Freycinet, 1824–25.

Wallaby. Copper engraving from the 3rd edition, 1793, of Thomas Pennant's *History of Quadrupeds.* From a painting by George Stubbs.

Kangaroo. Copper engraving from the 3rd edition, 1793, of Thomas Pennant's *History of Quadrupeds.* From a painting by George Stubbs.

Secretary Bird. Hand-coloured copper
engraving from Aernout Vosmaer's
*Description d'un Receuil Exquis d'Animaux
Rares 1776–83.*

Nilgai. Copper engraving after George Stubbs, from Thomas
Pennant's *History of Quadrupeds*, 3rd edition 1793.

Gazelle. *Gazella Dorcas*. From *Illustrated Natural History*
by J. Wood, 1861.

Ostrich. Woodcut from Conrad Gessner's
Icones Animalium 1560.

Gems-Bok. *Oryx Gazella*. From *Illustrated Natural History*
by J. Wood, 1861.

Guanaco by Jacques-Laurent Agasse 1831 or 1848. *Courtesy Yale Center for British Art, Paul Mellon Collection.*

Three Vicunas by Jacques-Laurent Agasse 1831.
Courtesy Yale Center for British Art, Paul Mellon Collection.

in the following year the Society's name was formally changed to the South Australian Zoological and Acclimatisation Society, and Minchin was appointed director. In 1938, on the occasion of the Society's diamond jubilee, the prefix 'Royal' was granted by King George VI and the term 'acclimatisation' was dropped.

Although Rolls (1969) states that in the 1880s Bishop Kennion of Adelaide advocated the introduction to South Australia of the (small Indian) mongoose to control rabbits, and that the Acclimatisation Society already had a pair and that no more were brought in, the Society introduced few if any mammals into the state, red foxes, rabbits, fallow deer, and red deer becoming established as the result of releases by private individuals.

The Society's annual report for 1879–80 lists the introduction of the following species of birds: one pair of golden pheasants; one pair of 'China Geese'; one pair of 'India Ducks'; a dozen 'English' thrushes (song thrushes); 8 blackbirds; 11 goldfinches; one pair of California quail; 80 skylarks; 14 bullfinches; and 7 pairs of greenfinches. Of these, blackbirds, goldfinches, greenfinches and skylarks are currently established in South Australia.

A few months later, 147 skylarks, 78 bramblings, 110 goldfinches, 20 song thrushes, and 3 chaffinches were released, followed in 1881 by 20 'Indian' doves (spotted doves), 9 'Toulouse' geese; 45 blackbirds; 30 goldfinches; 89 starlings, and 36 skylarks.

In the following year's annual report, the president announced that 'it is the intention of the council to continue to import and set loose English blackbirds, starlings and other insectivorous birds which have been ascertained to be beneficial and in no way injurious to gardens and farms.' With evident satisfaction he added that at Torrens Park 'Mr Barr Smith has seen young blackbirds; and goldfinches now beautify the hedgerows of Unley and Burnside'. This despite a note of caution issued by Mr Curnow, an honorary sub-inspector of fisheries, who 'wished to warn the Society against introducing blackbirds, for in Cornwall they were very destructive to gooseberries and apples, and might also be to grapes here'. In his address, the president drew attention to the attraction to goldfinches of 'Scotch and variegated thistles', and the advisability of liberating the birds 'where these were most abundant'. It is, as Jenkins (1977) points out, of interest to note the success of goldfinches in South Australia, where thistles and artichokes abound, and their decline in Western Australia where such favourite foodstuffs are relatively scarce.

The present population of spotted doves in the Botanic Gardens in Adelaide is descended from some that escaped from the zoo when their aviary was destroyed by a storm in 1931. From Adelaide they dispersed northwards and southwards to Clare and Victor Harbour respectively; they were first noted on Dudley Peninsula in 1951, on Kangaroo Island in 1953, in the Mount Lofty Ranges and the Barossa Valley in 1961, and on Eyre Peninsula in 1966. By 1980 they ranged upstream on the Murray River at least as far as Loxton, and northwards to Port Augusta.

More skylarks were released in and around Adelaide by the Acclimatisation Society from 1879 until after 1889 (and by private individuals from as early as 1862) than any other single species, and by the late 1940s the birds were well established on the Adelaide Plains.

By the mid-1940s blackbirds had also become widespread and fairly abundant on the Adelaide Plains, around Mount Lofty, at Victor Harbour, at Coorong (Salt Creek), and near Mount Gambier northwards to Oodnatta. They appeared on Kangaroo Island in 1947. Their present range on the South Australian mainland extends from Adelaide and the Mount Lofty Ranges throughout the south-east of the state.

Between about 1910 and 1920 goldfinches succeeded in colonising Kangaroo Island, and by 1923 had spread to Mount Remarkable. By the late 1940s they were established on the Adelaide Plains, from the Mount Lofty Ranges to Victor Harbour, on the south Yorke Peninsula and on Kangaroo Island, around Tantanoola, north to Clare, and east to the Victorian border. Goldfinches, which in Australia are locally nomadic in autumn, are today widely distributed in south-eastern South Australia.

By the late 1940s greenfinches, too, were well established in southeastern South Australia and abundant near Adelaide, in the Mount Lofty Ranges, and south to Victor Harbour. Thirty years later they were described as common around Adelaide and in the adjoining hills, but less so elsewhere in the state.

Starlings in South Australia increased rapidly, were common in some places as early as 1894, and had spread to Eyre Peninsula by around the turn of the century and to Kangaroo Island a decade later. By the late 1940s they were abundant in both these localities, but had spread no further north from Adelaide than Port Augusta. Today, they are found north to the Oodnadatta/Birdsville Track north of Lake Eyre, and west to Ooldea on the southern fringe of the Great Victoria Desert. Reports from around Nullarbor Station on the Bight coast in the west of the state suggest the probability of a gradual expansion westwards.

At the fourth annual general meeting of the Acclimatisation Society of South Australia in November 1883, the patron, and state Governor, Sir William Jervois, announced that 'there is a Bill before Parliament to encourage ostrich-farming.' The enactment of this Bill empowered the

South Australia government to provide potential ostrich farmers with cheap land, as a result of which the Society sponsored the introduction of ostriches from South Africa with success to some of the more arid parts of the state, such as the Younghusband Peninsula of the upper Coorong south of Adelaide, Gawler, and to Port Augusta where, by 1888, the South Australia Ostrich Company had a flock of 510, some of which may have been liberated before the First World War. Before 1933, farm-reared birds were released at Point Sturt on Lake Alexandrina and on Mundoo Island at the mouth of the Murray River, where they increased to such an extent that they eventually became a pest.

After the First World War the trade in ostrich plumes dramatically collapsed; this was due partly to a change in fashion, partly through the difficulties sometimes experienced in catching the birds for plucking (an adult ostrich can easily outrun a mounted horseman), and partly because it became apparent that wool and mutton where more prof-itable than plumes. Even well-established South African farmers were ruined when the price of a breeding pair of ostriches fell from a peak of £250 in 1882 to only £14 in 1920. When farms in South Australia, where plumes were said to be superior in quality to those produced in South Africa, closed down, most of the birds escaped or were released, and feral flocks became established in the sandhills of the Coorong, Narrung and Port Augusta. Today, a few birds still survive north of Port Augusta, and hundreds or even thousands around the Flinders Range north-east of Port Augusta.

The Queensland Acclimatisation Society

Following his receipt of a letter on the subject in July 1862, from Sir Henry Barkly, Governor of Victoria, the Queensland Acclimatisation Society was formed in the following month by the state's first Gover-nor, Sir George Bowen.

The aims of the Society were

> to obtain from various parts of the world seeds, trees, plants and animals possessing intrinsic value in one form or another . . . [and] to protect and propagate the more valuable indigenous growths of the colony for the purpose of distribution in the colony and exchange with other countries.[26]

Shortly afterwards, the Society acquired Bowen Park, named after its patron, in the city of Brisbane, and it was announced that:

> the contemplated improvements are now finished. They comprise . . . the enlargement of the flower garden . . . and include the aviaries and

parrot house, the laying out of a long and wide avenue which has been well drained and trenched and is now planted with quick-growing conifers and deciduous trees.[27]

In spite of this and other references to aviaries and birds (including an advertisement for 'Native BIRDS and ANIMALS (Bears, Flying Foxes and Hawks excepted)',[28] the Society's interest, as Jenkins (1977) points out, was principally botanical, especially the introduction and propagation of exotic plants with commercial possibilities, but also emphasising the need for the preservation and cultivation of native species. Some of the suggestions regarding the latter were rather fanciful, such as that put forward by Dr Schomburgk, director of the Royal Botanic Gardens in Adelaide, South Australia, and favoured by the Society, who advised

> the extensive planting of the jarrah and red gum as growing freely in the most exposed parts of South Australia. . . . so that if beside the railways they had been planted then an ample supply of sleepers would be now growing along the lines to replace the old ones as they decay.[29]

The Society's grounds at Bowen Park prospered, and were reported to be

> a well regulated nursery for the propagation of many useful and valuable plants, some of which may form the foundation of thriving industries, while they are a very pleasant place of public resort.[30]

The various plants of economic value listed by Jenkins as having been tried out at Bowen Park in the 1870s included bananas, cotton, apples, jute, pineapples, grape vines, poppies (for the production of salad oil), wheat, chicory, coffee, mulberries (as a food for silkworms), sorghum, cocoa, tea, and, most important of all, sugar cane. This last was undoubtedly the most valuable cash crop to be introduced by the Society to Queensland, whose climate and land were ideally suited to its cultivation. Unfortunately, due to inadequate quarantine legislation, sugar cane rust soon made its appearance, first in Brisbane in 1872. Within two years it had taken a firm hold in the state and, profiting from poor husbandry, wreaked untold damage.[31] Only the development of plant pathology and the selection of strains of cane with some resistance to the blight prevented total disaster.

Potentially even more destructive than sugar cane rust to the economy of Queensland was the prickly pear cactus which, until the introduction of *Cactoblastis cactorum* moths, overran over 310,000 square kilometres of pasturage in southern Queensland and northern New South Wales. Prickly pears were originally introduced to Australia from Brazil by Captain Phillip with the First Fleet in 1788, to ensure a supply of food for the cochineal-producing insects he imported at the same time to furnish scarlet dye for his soldiers' uniforms. Later, prickly pears were brought in for hedging purposes, for its fruit, and as stock fodder and garden plants. Cochineal is obtained from the dried bodies of female *Dactylopius coccus* hemipteran insects, which feed on cacti and are native to Mexico and Peru, and are cultivated in parts of Central and South America, southern Europe, and North Africa. In spite of the problems it created, however, the prickly pear had its supporters: one such was Mr Lewis Bernays, a vice-president of the Society, who claimed that

> The succulent, mucilaginous and innocuous character of the leaves and branches obviously point to the plant as more or less fit for use as fodder for various animals in arid country and in times of drought.[32]

Another supporter wrote, somewhat ingenuously, in 1877 that 'the fault is scarcely that of the prickly pear, but rather of those that permitted it to attain unmanageable dimensions and to grow where it is not required'.[33]

In support of his claim, Bernays quoted a letter from a member of the legislative council, the Hon. J. D. Macansh of Canning Downs who, in alluding to the plant's nutritional value as fodder for pigs and cattle, was of the opinion that

> The plant is undoubtedly a terrible nuisance in many places but it is a loss to the country simply destroying it as a noxious weed when it might be made a profitable use of.[34]

Although Bernays also referred to the prickly pear's reputed medicinal and other uses, he was obliged to admit that 'the most general opinion of the plant is an unmixed evil.'

Unfortunately, the Society's zeal for introducing exotic plants, such as avocado pears, and mangoes, led to altercations between its members (who in 1870 numbered 116 and almost double that figure two years later) and the Brisbane Botanic Gardens. Several shipments intended for the Society, including an especially important one from Trinidad, were instead delivered to the curator of the gardens, a Mr Hill, who was condemned for 'appropriating so valuable a consignment without at least making some enquiries as to its exact ownership'.[35] (A situation reminiscent of the United Kingdom society's lawsuit with Mr Stone.) At the same time, it was questioned

> whether the people ought to be asked to support a private institution which concerns itself almost entirely with the introduction of new plants . . . when there is a Government establishment in existence for the very purpose of experimenting in vegetable acclimatization.[36]

In spite of these difficulties, the Society continued to further its botanical researches in various ways: it sent its plant collector, F. M. Bailey (later appointed Colonial Botanist) on a collecting visit to northern Queensland;[37] it offered prizes in the form of cash for botanical essays and plant collections by the pupils of Brisbane Grammar School;[38] it suggested a licensing scheme for timber felling;[39] and organised 'a series of Soirees . . . at the Town Hall', at which the patron (and governor) took the chair.[40]

Although Bowen Park remained the Society's headquarters, repeated requests were made to the state government for land elsewhere on which to release exotic animals and propagate imported plants. The first choice was an island in Moreton Bay north of Brisbane 'where their operations could be carried on directly under their own management',[41] but eventually, in 1871, the Society was presented with Woody Island in Wide Bay south of Maryborough, since

> The feeling of the people of Maryborough had been found to be favour-
> able and it was proposed that three gentlemen of that district should be
> nominated in conjunction with two Vice-Presidents of the Society to act
> as trustees.[42]

Completion of the deal was somewhat delayed, since 'An Aboriginal Protection Society wished to secure the island and was urging the modest request that the Association [the Acclimatisation Society] should give up their claim to it.'[43] On 28 October 1871, however, the Queensland *Government Gazette* published official notification that the Acclimatisation Society had been granted rights to establish 'Permanent Reserves on Woody Island for Acclimatization purposes'.[44] Rabbits were already established on the island, and common pheasants, which had been liberated by Mr R. B. Sheridan, were shortly to be augmented by additional importations from New Zealand. Several other small islands were from time to time used unsuccessfully by the Society as trial grounds for the release of alien animals, so-called 'Chinchilla' rabbits being freed on Booby Island north-west of the tip of the Cape York Peninsula in about 1870, and helmeted guineafowl being turned down on Albany Island off the north-east coast in the same year.

In 1882 the Society leased some seven hectares of land at Bowen Park to the National Association of Queensland, which was mainly concerned with the organisation of agricultural and horticultural shows. Six years later, after the association's offices on this site had burned down, the association sought government support to meet the costs of rebuilding their headquarters, freehold rights over the site, and amalgamation with the Society, since 'many well-known gentlemen are on the boards of both societies.'[45] It seems probable that this last suggestion met with opposition from at least some members of the Society. The dispute rumbled on for several years, but was eventually resolved in 1890 when the Society stated that it was willing to surrender the land at present occupied by the Queensland National Agricultural and Industrial Association upon receiving . . . annual payments of £750 for a period of 20 years.[46]

Until 1892 the Society depended for publicity about its activities on *The Brisbane Courier*, which gave generous coverage to the deliberations of its monthly meetings, lists of plants available for distribution, and details of past and forthcoming lectures. In December of that year, however, Mr Bernays proposed that 'fresh life and increased usefulness might be imported to the operations of the Society if their transactions were published say quarterly, in a permanent form.'[47] The first issue of the *Transactions of the Queensland Acclimatization Society*, for the quarter ending 31 December 1892, appeared in the following year.

By 1895 excessive and increasing use by the public of Bowen Park had become something of a nuisance to the Society, which had already been criticised in the press for attempting to close the park on Sundays. It was reported that on a clement Sunday

> it was no uncommon thing for two thousand people of various ages and conditions of life to use the gardens, and of these probably not half a dozen did so by right of membership.[48]

In spite of its primary interest in botanical matters, the Society was responsible for the introduction to Queensland of several species of mammals and birds.

In 1865 Mr John Bisdee, a member of the Society, introduced ten fallow deer from Tasmania to Bowen Park, which were released at Maryvale in 1870. Their descendants are today established in rugged mountainous country of the Upper Freestone Valley in the Maryvale State Forest of the Darling Downs. In 1890, fallow were released on the Pikedale station west of Stanhope, where their descendants survive in the Pikedale/Jubbinbar Mount area. Fallow introduced in the 1870s at Westbrook near Toowoomba, and six turned out at Canning Downs near Warwick by Mr F. J. C. Wildash, another member of the Society (both on the Darling Downs) in 1872, have since died out. The largest concentration of fallow in Queensland today is probably that established in tropical monsoonal woodland of the Atherton Plateau south-west of Cairns.

In 1865, 1867 and 1872 the Society unsuccessfully introduced axis deer to the Toowoomba area of the Darling Downs. In 1886 (not 1866 as stated by G. K. Whitehead in *Deer of the World*, 1972) an axis hind from Ceylon (Sri Lanka) was landed by Mr William Hann, a Society member, at the port of Townsville. A few years later she was joined by a further hind and two stags imported by Mr Hann, and from these two pairs (not a stag and two hinds as stated by Whitehead) are descended the considerable population currently established in and around the

Maryvale Creek property formerly owned by Mr Hann, from where they are apparently spreading slowly northwards.

The six red deer presented to the Queensland Acclimatisation Society by Queen Victoria in 1873 were released on Mr David McConnell's Cressbrook station at Toogoolawah in the foothills of the Darling Downs. In the following year, a further three red deer, either from the Duke of Richmond's Goodwood estate in Sussex or from Scotland, were presented to the Society via Lord Lamington, and these were also released at Cressbrook, where within a few years they were beginning to spread, and by 1896 had increased to around 300. Shortly afterwards the Society reported losses through poaching, and the Commissioner of Police was urged to enforce the prescribed fine of £15 for each animal killed.

In 1874, the Queensland Acclimatisation Society presented a 'Humble Memorial' to the Governor, outlining its achievements to date and seeking future help in establishing red deer; it requested

> that a further estimate of £150 may be proposed to Parliament as a special grant towards defraying the expenses attendant on the introduction of the red deer . . . [and that] the importation of this beautiful and useful animal may be regarded as a national undertaking: and that once released they be regarded as a 'national property'.[49]

Some two years later this petition was granted, but a request for a 6000-hectare reserve for red deer near Cressbrook was refused.

Around the turn of the century, two pairs of red deer were landed on Hinchinbrook Island north of Townsville, where they were reinforced in 1915 or 1916 by a further pair imported on behalf of the Queensland government; whether any remain on the island today is uncertain.

Seven red deer presented to the Society by Mr Thomas Chirnside are believed to have been released at Canning Downs in 1903; others were freed in the Stanley Mountains between 1905 and 1909. The main concentrations of red deer in Queensland today, in the south-east, occur in mountainous country around the head of the Brisbane and Stanley rivers.

In 1912 eight or ten Timor or rusa deer were imported by Mr R. A. C. Hockings to Thursday Island off the Cape York Peninsula, from where they were subsequently transferred to the neighbouring Friday Island and released. They rapidly increased, and before long had swum to the much larger Prince of Wales Island, where by the late 1960s the population was estimated to number around 5000. In 1914 Mr H. N. Hockings moved some of the deer from Friday to Possession Island west of Cape York (not east, as stated and shown by Whitehead, 1972), from where they are believed to have swum to the Cape York Peninsula mainland.

Early in the Society's life a rabbit warren was established in Bowen Park, and a number of releases were made on islands off the Queensland coast, including Woody Island in 1866. By the end of 1870, however, rabbits had disappeared from the park,

> as it was found that the cats in the neighbourhood had destroyed nearly all. The wild rabbits also had been nearly all eaten by cats, and what remained were sent up to Mr F. J. C. Wildash's station.[50]

The last statement, as Jenkins (1977) points out, is in marked contrast to a claim by the Society ten months later, assuring

> our fellow-colonists that the Society had been most careful to liberate rabbits only on islands along the coast and where they cannot reach the mainland.[51]

Most of Queensland, however, escaped major infestation. Large numbers in the 1870s were turned out by the Society around Helidon and on the Darling Downs, but apparently did not thrive, due in part at least to predation by marsupial cats. Until 1889 the only stations to suffer serious infestation were some on the Bulloo, Paroo and Balonne rivers; thereafter, several stations in southern Queensland owned by the Australian Pastoral Company were overrun.

Angora goats and llamas were introduced by the Society at an early stage to Bowen Park where, as elsewhere in Australia, attempts to make the animal commercially viable were unsuccessful.

In 1869 a consignment of birds from England, comprising hedge sparrows (now known as dunnocks), skylarks, blackbirds, song thrushes, house sparrows, rooks and starlings, were landed at Brisbane, from where they were transferred by the Society to Bowen Park and released in the hope that they would help in the control of injurious insects; few seem to have survived for long.

At a meeting of the Society in June 1895, Mr W. J. Palmer, pomologist for the North Island of New Zealand, while admitting that chaffinches and goldfinches were very destructive 'to small fruits . . . and the young buds of fruit trees', considered that the damage done by house sparrows was much exaggerated, and 'unhesitatingly recommended starlings as the best birds to deal with insects'.[52] In fact, starlings and house sparrows in Australia cause far more harm than good, feeding largely on cultivated fruits, vegetable crops, seeds and grain, and carrying and transmitting a variety of parasites and diseases.

The Queensland Acclimatisation Society showed an early interest in the promotion of sericulture; by 1870 some twelve hectares of land at Pine Mountain and elsewhere in West Moreton had been planted with mulberries, and consignments of up to 15,000 silkworm cocoons had been sent for appraisal to the Silk Supply Association in England. As an inducement to potential silkworm farmers, in 1871 the Society joined with the Agricultural Society of New South Wales to offer a prize of £5 should 'sericulture form a feature in the exhibition in Sydney in August next'.[53] As with angora goats and llamas, however, the Society failed to convince its members and the public of the economic viability of sericulture.

Unlike the other acclimatisation societies on the Australian mainland, but in common with that on Tasmania, the Queensland Society, perhaps because its interests tended to be botanical rather than zoological, did not sponsor any form of zoological garden; thus, as the attempted acclimatisation (or really naturalisation) of exotic plants and animals grew out of favour, and as the fortunes of the Brisbane Botanic Gardens waxed, so those of the Society waned. Eventually, the Society relinquished its property at Bowen Park, mostly to the National Association, and moved its headquarters to Launton, some 24 kilometres north of Brisbane. The soil at this new site was found to be much impoverished, and the Society later acquired a more fertile plot at Redland Bay. Increasingly strict quarantine regulations, however, made the continued importation of alien fauna and flora to Australia more and more difficult, and eventually the Society decided to go into voluntary liquidation; in 1956 it handed all its assets, including animals, land, and some £10,000 in cash, to the University of Queensland.

The Tasmanian Game Protection and Acclimatisation Society

The Tasmanian Game Protection and Acclimatisation Society was formed in Hobart in 1895, with the Governor, Viscount Aarmanston, as patron. It was followed four years later by the founding in Launceston of the Northern Tasmanian Acclimatisation Society, under the presidentship of Sir Richard Dry of Hagly.

In the first few years after its formation, the Hobart Society was responsible for the introduction and unsuccessful release in Tasmania of several English songbirds, including the chaffinch, hedge sparrow, skylark, and tree sparrow.

At the annual general meeting of the Launceston society in 1907, the chairman, Mr E. H. Panton, announced that the descendants of thirty-six skylarks imported from New Zealand in 1899 by Mr Talbot of Malahide were established in several localities, including Invermay, East and West Tamar, at Ormley near Avoca, at Cataract Cliffs, at Risdon, and at Glenorchy near Hobart. By the late 1940s, skylarks were established in many agricultural districts, especially in southern Tasmania, and on King and Flinders islands in Bass Strait.

Mr Panton also reported that after Mr W. McGowan had failed in an attempt to establish laughing kookaburras from the Australian mainland on Tasmania in 1902, successful releases had been made on Waterhouse Island off the north-east coast, from where they subsequently colonised Flinders Island, and at several points on the Tasmanian mainland. The chairman also referred to the rapid spread on Tasmania of the starling, and to the destruction of native birds by poison put down for rabbits—imported long before the Society had been formed—and by shooting; four people, Mr Panton claimed, had recently killed twelve dozen little wattle birds and yellow wattle birds within the space of two hours.[54]

Four alien species now established in Tasmania, the goldfinch, and the destructive house sparrow, starling and blackbird, all arrived on Tasmania before either of the acclimatisation societies were founded.

In about 1910 the two organisations joined forces under the name of the senior society. One of the new Society's first actions was to release common pheasants, which in 1882 had been unsuccessfully turned down on the Tasmania mainland, on King Island in Bass Strait. In the mid-1940s others were freed at Sandford, Carlton, Cambridge and elsewhere in Tasmania, in some parts of which they are now established, and in the 1960s also on Flinders Island. Chukar partridges, grouse, and mallard were liberated by the Society in Tasmania in the 1930s, but failed to become established.

More successful was the mute swan, six of which were introduced in about 1920 to the civic park by the Society on behalf of the Launceston city council, from where a few years later their progeny were transferred to Lake Leake on the Eastern Tiers; stragglers occasionally leave the lake and have been sighted on the Derwent River in the south and on the Meander River in the north. Other birds successfully introduced to Tasmania by the Society include spotted doves, which occurred in Launceston and were said to be common in Hobart in 1918; feral pigeons; and common peafowl which are found both on the mainland and on East and West Sister islands and Prime Seal Island in the Furneaux group in Bass Strait.

In 1908 the Tasmania Field Naturalists' Club proposed the introduction from the Australian mainland of superb lyrebirds which, the club wrote: 'owing to the destruction . . . by foxes on the mainland . . . are threatened with extermination . . . it is proposed to import some into Tasmania where the deep mountain gullies with fern glens would make ideal resorts for these unique birds.'[55] Twenty years later the advisability of such a move was still being debated by the Royal Australasian Ornithologists' Union,[56] which had proposed releasing birds in southern Tasmania. Finally, between 1934 (when some were freed in the south-west) and 1949, eleven pairs were imported from Victoria: by 1943–4 the birds were apparently well established, and in the early 1960s were said to be spreading slightly.

In 1864 a consignment of brown trout ova from England arrived in Hobart, where some hatched successfully; two years later thirty-eight fish were released in the River Plenty, where they became established. In 1894 some rainbow trout were also imported to Tasmania, where in the early 1900s Lake Leake was described as 'the greatest rainbow fishery in the world'.

The Western Australia Acclimatisation Society

The Western Australia Acclimatisation Society held its inaugural meeting in Perth on 16 July 1896, under the presidentship of the Hon. J. W. (later Sir Winthrop) Hackett.

One of the newly formed Society's first steps was to seek from its *confrères* in New South Wales a supply of mute swans, California quail, laughing kookaburras, brown hares and deer for acclimatisation in Western Australia. Shortly afterwards, the Society reported that

> Four hares were brought to the colony, but a protest against their liberation having been received from the Bureau of Agriculture, the Committee decided not to proceed at present with any further efforts in this direction, at any rate not until the receipt of a paper from the Director of the Zoological Gardens on the matter.[57]

The introduction of a further twenty brown hares by the Society was approved in 1902, and although none seems to have been released on the Western Australia mainland, some were reported to have been unsuccessfully liberated on Rottnest Island.

In February 1897, only seven months after its formation, the Society considered the question of establishing a zoological garden in Perth, which was opened to the public some eighteen months later. The committee of management for the zoo was known as the Acclimatisation Committee until 1969, when the name was formally changed to the Zoological Gardens Board.

During its early years, and indeed until the late 1920s when the practice met with increasing opposition, a wide range of mammals, birds and fish were released by the Society in Western Australia. Thereafter the Society's interest in acclimatisation decreased, and it concentrated instead on running the zoo.

The Bureau of Agriculture's objections to some of the Society's proposals, such as the release of starlings to combat an outbreak of cattle tick in the Kimberley area (from where it was claimed they would be unlikely to spread south to fruit-growing localities), were not well received. In his presidential address for 1897, Hackett said:

The Committee also devoted their attention to the acclimatisation of birds, and have successfully introduced the giant kingfisher or laughing jackass [kookaburra] into the Swan and Southern Districts. Next season an endeavour will be made to introduce the Californian Quail, the Redlegged Partridge of India [the chukar], the Forktailed Jungle Fowl [? the red jungle fowl], and the [common] Pheasant. The Committee hopes that many portions of the country will be found very suitable for these species of bird.

In connection with this subject, and as a result of much inquiry, the Committee are of the opinion that some of the recommendations of the Bureau of Agriculture, in regard to the exclusion of certain kinds of birds, have been acted upon hastily and without full consideration, and they earnestly hope that these suggestions in future will be submitted to the Committee for an expression of their views before being carried out.[58]

Time, as Jenkins (1977) rightly says, was to show the wisdom of the Bureau's opposition, and the folly and lack of understanding which, as with other acclimatisation societies around the world, characterised much of the committee's proposals.

The first deer, four red and four fallow, were presented to the Society by Queen Victoria in 1899. During the next few years more were released, and in 1904 the Society reported that:

the deer are doing well in the various districts in which they have been placed, notably at the Leeuwin and at Pinjarra.[59] At the Leeuwin the Red and Fallow Deer have separated, and now form two herds. A private herd is being started by Mr Edgar, at Gingin, and another by Mr Grant at Newmarracarra, while Mr A. E. Morgans has the nucleus of a herd at his property on the Porongorup Range, so that it would seem that in a few years these beautiful animals will be fairly acclimatized in the less populated parts of the State, and later on afford good sport. The deer already introduced by the Committee include Red, Fallow, Rusine [rusa] and Hog Deer.[60]

Although it does not appear that any of these deer became established except the red, at Pinjarra, the latter increased considerably; as early as 1905 the Society rejected a claim for compensation by a Mr Maxwell, who had complained to the Department of Lands about alleged damage to his potato crop. Seven years later, red deer stags were being culled on the McClarty and Paterson ranches at Pinjarra, and more were shot in the same region in 1916.

In 1912 a pair of Indian blackbuck was released by the Society at Dinninup, and a further three pairs were liberated at Nuwmarracarra near Geraldton by Mr Mackenzie Grant. In the following year, further consignments were despatched to Nuwmarracarra, Roelands near Bunbury, and Wiluna. Two years later, in spite of poaching, the herd at Wiluna was reported to be flourishing, and by 1920 blackbuck were said to have been well established also in the Murchison area. In 1929, when the acting director of the zoo, Dr Leslie Le Souef, claimed that the blackbuck 'were increasing with great rapidity' and that 'it would be extremely difficult to get rid of them', some released 500 km north of Perth had increased to pest proportions, and required culling. A free-ranging herd of 100–150 was still in existence at Numarracarra in 1946. During the 1960s, blackbuck were maintained and protected in fenced enclosures at Numarracarra and Coolya stations, where many are said to have died as a result of eating poisoned oats put out for rabbits. A remnant population of about thirty at Kojarena in the early 1970s may still survive.

A pair of eland was released by the Society on Mr Bruce Leake's ranch in the wheat belt near Kellerberrin, where they were both found dead three days later, 'possibly because they had eaten poison weed'—probably box poison or cluster poison.

In about 1898 Lieutenant-Colonel E. A. Le Souef released some northern palm squirrels from India in the grounds of the Perth zoo, of which he was at the time director, where they settled down well, multiplied, and were soon firmly established. For some years they have also occurred—though in lesser numbers—outside the zoo grounds, especially in residential districts of south Perth and Como, where they have, however, spread only slowly.[61]

The part played by the Acclimatisation Society in the establishment in Western Australia of domestic goats, wild boar, and domestic pigs is uncertain. In 1904[62] the Society reported that:

> during the year twelve Angora Goats were obtained for acclimatization purposes, the trial being made under conditions especially favourable for judging their value from a practical point of view. The experiment has proved most successful, and it has been reported that on country capable of carrying 2,000 sheep, namely, second-class, rough scrubby land, it will be possible to run 2,000 goats, in addition to the sheep, as the goats, being browsers, only eat the scrub, and do not interfere with the feed eaten by the sheep.[63]

In 1915, the Society despatched some wild boars for release on Mr McCallum Smith's ranch at Cookernup, where what became of them is unrecorded.

Although, so far as is known, the Society never released rabbits on the Western Australia mainland, in 1912 it did plant some 'as food for shipwrecked mariners' on Eclipse Island off the southernmost tip of the state, where they still survive.[64]

Between 1897 and 1912, several hundred laughing kookaburras (natives of eastern, north-eastern and south-eastern Australia) were obtained from Victoria by the then director of the Perth zoo and by the Acclimatisation Society, by whom they were released in several places in south Perth and throughout the south-west of the state. They were well established in various localities before 1912, and by the 1920s were becoming fairly common between the Darling Range and the coast. By the mid-1960s, they had spread into forested districts in the south-west from Albany and Bald Island northwards to Jurien Bay. Kookaburras are said to have been introduced to Western Australia to kill tiger snakes, but are also alleged to destroy native birds and domestic poultry chicks.

In 1898–9, laughing doves and spotted doves were released from the Perth zoo by the Acclimatisation Society at Northam, Yatheroo, and Dardanup. Both species became established before 1912, and until at least 1920 were being recaptured for translocation elsewhere in the state, where they seem to have thrived wherever pine trees were available for nesting, but spread little beyond the Perth metropolitan area. Since the 1930s both species have been slowly but steadily expanding their range—the former more rapidly and further than the latter. On Rottnest Island off Perth, for example, laughing doves were first seen in about 1930, some seven years in advance of their congeners.

At around the same time—certainly before 1912—some 200 goldfinches were released by the Acclimatisation Society in Perth, where they slowly spread from the metropolitan area into several suburban districts. Since the late 1960s the population has declined, probably through a combination of disease, shortage of food as a result of land development, predation, trapping for the cagebird trade, and direct attacks from the aggressive native singing honeyeater.

In 1897, three pairs of mute swans, presented by the Worshipful Company of Vintners in London, were landed at Perth; in 1901–2 (and/or possibly in 1912) their progeny were 'turned out for acclimatization' by the zoo and the Society, and the present small breeding population at Northam on the Avon River east of Perth is believed to be derived from this source. Mute swans in Western Australia are said to be competing, to the latter's disadvantage, with native black swans.

Common pheasants were unsuccessfully liberated on the Western Australian mainland by the Acclimatisation Committee between 1897 and 1912, and in 1905 and/or 1912 on Rottnest Island, where they are said to be 'moderately common'.

Young peafowl reared in Perth zoo were turned out by the Acclimatisation Society in various parts of the state before 1912, and in that year and also probably again in 1915 or 1917 on Rottnest Island. A small number are believed to survive both on the mainland and on Rottnest.

Prior to 1912, mallard released by the Acclimatisation Society were breeding on and spreading from several ornamental waters around Perth, and by 1920 were established in various parks in the metropolitan area, where they remain but show little signs of spreading further or increasing. Mallards in Australia hybridise freely with the native black duck, the dominant genes of the former obliterating the latter's characteristics.

Birds unsuccessfully released in Western Australia by the Acclimatisation Society include California quail, skylarks, 'Peking nightingales' (probably the Pekin robin or red-billed leiothrix), Mongolian pheasants, helmeted guinea fowl, Canada geese, spurwinged geese, and ostriches: the last named were unsuccessfully released before 1912 at Gingin and Mount Morgan east of Leonora.

Although the Society's efforts to acclimatise fish were largely unsuccessful, the following extract[65] from the annual report for 1897 shows its enthusiasm for matters piscicultural:

> The first matter to receive their attention was the selection of a site suitable for the purpose of hatching trout and other ova. This work was entrusted to Mr W. C. Doncaster, who had had previous experience of a similar kind at Ballarat, Victoria. Mr Doncaster after inspecting various streams in the South Districts, came to the conclusion that the Brook at Whitby Falls, in the neighbourhood of Jarrahdale, presented most of the natural advantages required for a first-class hatchery. The building of the hatchery was at once proceeded with, and Mr Doncaster was despatched to Victoria to procure a supply of the necessary ova. Owing to the late period of the year the Committee was unable to obtain as large a supply as had been anticipated, but were successful in obtaining 20,000 trout ova, part from the Acclimatization Society of Ballarat and the rest from Messers. Wilson Bros. estate at Ercildoune. These were received in good condition, and at once placed in the hatching boxes provided for their reception. The process of hatching was most successful, but, owing to the want of artificial ponds, the Committee were obliged to liberate the young fry at a much earlier stage than would otherwise have been deemed advisable.

Two years later, in 1898, the hatchery was transferred from Whitby Falls to the Canning River.

Apart from brown trout, attempts were made by the Acclimatisation Society between 1896 and 1907, mostly unsuccessfully, to acclimatise various species of freshwater fish in Western Australia: these included eels, tench, Atlantic salmon, perch, and common carp.

Also on the Society's list for acclimatisation in Western Australia were oysters. In 1896,

> Taking advantage of the presence in the Colony of Mr Learoyd, who had had previous experience in the cultivation of the oyster, the Committee decided that two oyster beds should be laid down in Oyster Harbour in Albany. This work has been successfully carried out, and a good stock of oyster from New South Wales and Shark Bay planted. From the report of the caretaker in charge of the beds, the cultivation of these oysters is proceeding most satisfactorily, a large number of young fish being plainly visible in both beds.

Mr Learoyd also inspected and reported on the oysters planted by Mr Saville Kent in Princess Royal Harbour and on the North Mole of the Fremantle Harbour.[66]

Other plantings were carried out in the following March, when some 14,000 oysters, comprising 8000 Sydney rock oysters, 4000 Sharks Bay oysters, and 2000 north west oysters, plus spat[67] from a Perth shop, were placed in the King River at Albany.

Although, as previously mentioned, after the late 1920s and early 1930s the Society became more involved in running the Perth zoo than with acclimatisation, there were two attempts at least to revive the latter interest. In the mid-1930s the newly formed Fish and Game Society suggested the introduction of California quail and of more brown trout. The importation of the quail met with considerable opposition, on the not unreasonable grounds that adequate sporting birds already existed in Western Australia; the suggested rearing of more trout, on the other hand, found almost universal favour, and resulted in the establishment of the hatcheries at Pemberton.

In 1960 the Western Australian Avicultural Society sought agreement from the Rottnest Island Board for establishing 'dozens of rare and colourful birds . . . as the first step in converting the island into a naturalists' paradise'.[68] With the Board's approval, aviaries on Rottnest were stocked with rare finches and parrots, and it was suggested that the birds, and some koalas which were to be imported from the mainland, would become a tourist attraction. Initially the proposal received some support, and a few birds (though no koalas) were actually released. Following strong opposition on conservation grounds, the project was fortunately abandoned.

14. Acclimatisation Societies in New Zealand[1]

IN his classic *The Naturalisation of Animals and Plants in New Zealand*, G. M. Thomson wrote:[2]

> The early settlers of New Zealand found themselves in a land which, as far as regards climate and natural conditions, seemed to them to reproduce many of the best features of the homeland from which they came.[3] . . . Here, in a land of plenty, with few wild animals, few flowers apparently, . . . with streams almost destitute of fish, with shy song birds and few game birds, and certainly no [indigenous] quadrupeds but lizards, it seemed to them that it only wanted the best of the plants and the animals [of their homeland] to make it a terrestrial paradise. So with zeal unfettered by scientific knowledge they proceeded to endeavour to reproduce—as far as possible—the best-remembered and most cherished features of the country from which they came. . . . They recked not of new conditions, they knew nothing of the possibilities of development possessed by species of plants and animals which, in the severe struggle for existence of their northern home had reached a more or less stable position. . . . No biological considerations ever disturbed their dreams, nor indeed did they ever enter into their calculations.

'From the day when the first emigrant of ships left the English shores to the present time', wrote the editor of *The Press* in 1861, 'Canterbury has carried on an endeavour, desultory indeed, and unsuccessful, but never wholly relinquished, to naturalise[4] in our new home many of the birds and other animals of England: rabbits, hares, pheasants, partridges . . . and, with the one exception of rabbits, we believe without result.'[5] In 1852, for example, the *William Hyde* brought out from England some muscovy ducks, a few geese, a hen pheasant and a goat. Later in the same year, the *Samarang* arrived in Lyttelton near Christchurch with a consignment of rabbits, and two years later on the *Akhbar* from Calcutta came a donkey, eight 'Tibetan goats', twenty rabbits, one hare, a pair of 'Chinese pigs', an Arab horse, and nine peafowl.

Among those who deplored these haphazard attempts at acclimatisation were the geologist and explorer Dr (later Sir) Julius von Haast and Mr (later Sir) Frederick Weld, prime minister of New Zealand from 1864–6. Under the guidance of von Haast, Weld, and like-minded people, the acclimatisation societies which were formed from the 1860s had two main objectives—the introduction to the colony of game animals for sport and of insectivorous animals (mainly songbirds) to control pests. More broadly, their declared aims were almost verbatim the same as those of the Acclimatisation Society of Victoria, Australia, which were themselves based on those of the United Kingdom Society (see chapter 3).

The first piece of legislation to deal specifically with acclimatisation was an act passed in 1861, first by the provincial council in Nelson and later by the colonial parliament, 'to encourage the importation of those animals and birds, not native to New Zealand, which would contribute to the pleasure and profit of the inhabitants, when they become acclimatised and were spread over the country in sufficient numbers.' The act went on to specify the game birds that were being introduced, which 'would contribute to the pleasure of the settlers of New Zealand and help keep up these associations with the Old Country which it was desirable should be maintained.'[6] In *New Zealand, the Britain of the South* (1875), an early settler, Charles Hursthouse, believed that 'New Zealand should swarm with game. . . . Deer, once introduced into feeding grounds and noble coverts like Mount Egmont's ranges and the "Black Forest" (Nelson) territory, would never be exterminated. . . . No man can better deserve, no man can better afford a day's pastime than a New Zealand colonist.'[7]

Before long, the colonial government began to take an interest in acclimatisation. On 1 February 1901, Thomas Edward Donne, a senior official in charge of the tourism branch of the country's railways, established the Department of Tourist and Health Resorts, of which he became the director; later he was also appointed under-secretary of the Department of Industries and Commerce. These offices gave him the opportunity to travel abroad, and enabled him to arrange for the introduction to New Zealand of exotic animals, for whose hunters he established a series of tourist resorts and health spas.

The annual report of the Wellington Acclimatisation Society for 1903 stated that:

> One of the most important events during the past year has been the for-
> mation of an Acclimatisation Societies Association for the whole Colony
> on 23 January. It is a governing body for the Colony to which the various
> Societies can become affiliated on application—the main purpose is to
> secure the uniformity of action on acclimatisation matters.[8]

The object of forming this new body was to improve the management of acclimatisation administration and techniques and, since the government was now actively involved in acclimatisation on its own behalf, to present to the legislative body a united front on all matters to do with acclimatisation. The Association continued to meet, though not annually, until its replacement by two administrative councils for the North and South Islands in 1936.

The Tourist and Health Resorts' annual report for 1907, presented to parliament on behalf of Donne by the minister, Sir Joseph Ward, stated that:

> The Department has since its establishment been in very close touch with sport and the acclimatisation of game and fish; but a somewhat new departure has been made during the year in placing Rotorua [in the Hot Lakes District] under immediate control of the Department. This step was taken in direct response to the petitions of the residents of the Rotorua district, who were dissatisfied with the control of the administration of the fishing and the assistance given them by the Auckland Society. The trout fishing in the Rotorua district has become a matter of colonial importance, and it is considered advisable that it be controlled directly by the Government. . . . Since the taking-over of the Rotorua district by the Department of Tourist and Health Resorts the Government has received a petition from the Wairoa Acclimatisation Society asking that its registration be revoked and their district attached to the Rotorua district and placed under the control of the same Department. . . . The sport in the Rotorua district has in the past year been well up to the previous year's standard, and an enormous number of fish have been taken.[9]

Shortly after the presentation of this report, the government took over a fish hatchery constructed by the marine department, and in 1913, with the cooperation and agreement of the Acclimatisation Societies' Association, assumed the management of the fishing in the Hot Lakes District. It thus seems clear that, as with the United Kingdom Society, some of the New Zealand societies, which had been founded on a wave of enthusiasm for acclimatisation, eventually failed due to lack of support and falling incomes, coupled with increasing criticism of some of their introductions. As early as 1897, for instance, a speaker at the Otago Institute had claimed that:

> It is a matter for regret that the zeal of the earlier acclimatisers was greater than their knowledge, and that mistakes were made by them fraught with evil results of a far-reaching and permanent nature. Due care and consideration would have prevented the introduction of several undesirable immigrants, which now, like the poor, are always with us.[10]

As another speaker said, at the New Zealand Science Congress of 1929, 'It is time drastic steps were taken to cope with the evil being done to our fauna and flora by foreign importations.' A familiar story.

One of the main problems with New Zealand's acclimatisation societies was their generally unprofessional conduct; founded, as so often elsewhere, and run largely by enthusiastic amateurs, they failed to keep proper records of their work, believing that trout in the rivers, deer on the mountains, and the presence of insect-eating songbirds were evidence enough of their benefaction. The public, however, looked at hillsides over-grazed and forests over-browsed and ringbarked by deer rather than at their sporting potential, and at damage to crops rather than any reduction of insect pests. Had the societies recorded the revenue derived from visiting sportsmen and tourists and the agricultural, horticultural, silvicultural, and pomological benefits created, they would have been better able to defend themselves against the criticisms of later years.

At the annual conference of the Acclimatisation Societies' Association in 1936, the Minister of Internal Affairs proposed its replacement by two councils to control the administration of acclimatisation societies on the two main islands. The North and South Islands were each divided into six geographical districts, each of which had an individual delegate, and the two councils acted in liaison with the government department.

The annual report of the Department of Internal Affairs for 1945 stated that:

> At the request of the Lakes District Acclimatisation Society the Government decided to assume control of the district controlled by the Society. The boundaries of the Southland, Otago and Westland Acclimatisation Districts were altered to permit of certain portions contiguous to the Lakes District being added thereto, the new district thus formed, called the 'Southern Lakes Acclimatisation District', being administered by this Department as from 1st September 1945.[11]

Thereafter, control by the government of the societies increased, and their operations were mainly confined to conservation, through the preservation of protected wildlife; the promotion of sport, through the issuing of shooting and fishing licenses and the management of fisheries; administration, in particular ensuring that the provisions of the Wildlife Act 1953 were being observed; and, in a complete rôle reversal, making sure that there were no unauthorised introductions to New Zealand of non-native species.

The only outside income of acclimatisation societies in New Zealand today is derived from the sale of fishing and gamebird shooting licences. A portion of this income is used to purchase wetland habitats, pay staff salaries, and fund research projects; it has also been utilised to educate the public about the potential damage to estuaries resulting from the construction of industrial projects, and the harm to river systems from the creation of dams for hydro-electric schemes. The balance of the income is retained by the societies to fund their own conservation programmes and to cover the costs of administration.

New Zealand was geographically divided into twenty-four acclimatisation districts, twenty-two of which (twelve in the North Island and ten in the South Island) were governed by Island councils and two—the Rotorua/Taupo region, or Central North Island Wildlife Conservancy, and the Wanaka/Wakatipu/Te Anau region, or Southern Lakes Conservancy—were administered by the Department of Internal Affairs. Each society elected its own council, from whom were chosen members to represent it on the appropriate Island council. A national executive based in Wellington provided a focus for issues of national concern to acclimatisation societies by making, when appropriate, representations on their behalf to the national government.

In 1983 steps were taken to reconstitute the societies' association with the formation of a national council, and both it and the North and South Island councils met annually. Following the establishment in 1987 of the Department of Conservation, there has been a major reappraisal of the administrative structure and functions of the acclimatisation societies and various wildlife conservancies. The government has announced the formation of a substantially reconstituted organisation to oversee recreational angling and gamebird shooting, which will largely reflect the acclimatisation societies' present rôle and administration. In place of the existing divided responsibilities of the societies and government conservancies there will be a single administrative body, the current North and South Island councils of acclimatisation societies being replaced by a unified national council, similar to that formed in 1983. The number of regional councils will be reduced from the existing twenty-two to ten or twelve, and the administrative districts will be larger and more uniform in extent.[12]

In the early 1900s there were at least thirty acclimatisation societies established in New Zealand. The following accounts are histories of the formation and activities of a representative selection only of some of these societies. In general, only those species successfully introduced by the societies are discussed. Other societies, with the date of their formation (where known) in parentheses, included those at Ashburton (1886), Bay of Islands (1895), Feilding (absorbed into Wellington), Coromandel (joined with Auckland), Hawera (1879), Hobson (1901), Mangonui-Whangaroa (1900), Marlborough (1880), Opotiki, South Canterbury (1895), Stratford (1894), Waitaki Valley (an amalgamation in 1967 of the Waitaki (1877) and Waimate (1888) societies), Wanganui (1868), West Coast (an amalgamation in 1951 of the Grey and Buller societies), Westland (1888), and Whangarei (1896). At one time societies also existed at, among other places, Waimarino (1903), Wairarapa, and Wairoa.[13]

The acclimatisation movement in New Zealand has seldom been static, and the status and indeed boundaries of the societies have frequently changed. Thus the Auckland Society acquired the Rotorua district from Tauranga in 1896, but lost the Rotorua-Taupo area to the government in 1906, when it came under the control of the Tourist Department. In 1930, the districts became the Central Conservancy of the Department of Internal Affairs. Sixteen years later the department assumed responsibility for the Southern Lakes district. Since then, the

Central Conservancy has gradually taken over further acclimatisation society districts surrounding its boundaries, i.e. all those in the Bay of Plenty/East Cape/Poverty Bay areas, as well as the Waimarino district in the upper Wanganui River catchment. Shortly before the Wildlife Service of the Department of Internal Affairs was absorbed into the new Department of Conservation in 1987, it had tried to take over the Hawera, Stratford, and Wanganui societies. In this way, as McDowall (1989) says, the Central Conservancy has expanded at the expense of the acclimatisation societies.

Nevertheless, as McDowall points out, the societies still retain strong legal powers, and are a powerful force in New Zealand's legal and administrative system.

The Nelson Acclimatisation Society[14]

On 23 April 1863 a notice was published in *The Nelson Examiner and New Zealand Chronicle* announcing that:

> Persons desirous of aiding the formation of an Acclimatisation Society for this Province, are requested to meet at the Trafalgar Hotel on Wednesday next the 29th Instant at three o'clock in the afternoon.[15]

Following that meeting, *The Examiner* reported that its owner/editor, Mr Charles Elliott, had taken the chair and

> After giving a brief outline of the meeting's purpose, and explaining what he as the Convenor of the meeting felt should be achieved by the formation of such a body, Mr Elliott put the following motion, which was resolved unanimously. 'That a Society be now formed for the purpose of introducing into Nelson from other countries, birds, fish and animals, and that such Society be named the Nelson Acclimatisation Society.[16]

At a further meeting held on 6 May 1863, the rules and objects of the Society were presented and adopted; Elliott was appointed honorary secretary, and Mr (later Sir) Edward Stafford, subsequently prime minister of New Zealand, was elected chairman of the committee.

On 1 November 1863 the *Prince Alfred* from Sydney, Australia, berthed in Nelson with a small shipment of insectivorous songbirds from England, comprising skylarks, linnets, chaffinches, canaries, and a solitary goldfinch; these birds were released in the following month, and were thus the first animals to be turned into the wild by an acclimatisation society in New Zealand. They were followed later in the same year by consignments of house sparrows, blackbirds, song thrushes, starlings, European robins, rooks, jackdaws, goldfinches, greenfinches, bullfinches, redpolls, yellowhammers, and black swans, the majority of which are now established in the wild in New Zealand.

Skylarks are now widespread and common throughout the country; as long ago as the 1920s, Thomson (1922) said that 'next to the [house] sparrow the skylark is considered by farmers to be the most destructive of the small birds which have been introduced into New Zealand. They are particularly destructive in spring, when they pull wheat and other grains out of the ground just as they are springing. They also uproot seedling cabbage, turnip and other farm plants.'[17]

The chaffinch has been suggested as New Zealand's most abundant and widespread bird, being found wherever there are trees and shrubs, up to an altitude of 1400 metres; it also frequents gardens, parks and agricultural land, and has proved an energetic colonist of nearby offshore and distant subantarctic islands. Although chaffinches in New Zealand cause some damage to grain and fruit crops, their most serious ecological impact may be to inhibit the natural regeneration of some exotic pines through their consumption of seeds.

House sparrows were introduced to New Zealand, where they are widespread and common, mainly for nostalgic reasons, but also to combat caterpillars and insects in grainfields and orchards. As elsewhere, they have long been regarded as a serious pest, and as early as 1882 the Small Birds Nuisance Act was passed in an attempt to control them. They attack such grain crops as barley, oats, wheat and linseed at all stages of their cultivation, and destroy the blossom and buds of a wide range of fruits.

Blackbirds are today one of New Zealand's most abundant and widely distributed birds, occurring on the mainland from sea level to around 1400 metres and on many offshore islands. Their favourite habitats are gardens, parks and farmland, but they also frequent large stands of dense native forest and bush which are shunned by song thrushes. They are a serious pest of soft fruit crops.

Song thrushes, too, are one of the commonest and most widespread birds in New Zealand, being found in gardens, parks and farmland and in some open forested areas on the two main islands and on several offlying groups. They seem to be rather less successful than the more aggressive blackbird in colonising distant offshore islands, but like their congener are a serious pest of soft fruits.

Starlings in New Zealand are a familiar sight in all habitats except dense bush over 1200 metres on the two main islands and most offshore groups. In urban areas their communal roosts create unwelcome noise and deface and damage buildings; in rural localities they compete successfully with native species for food and nesting sites, and cause extensive damage to a variety of grain and fruit crops. They also kill considerable numbers of beneficial bumble bees and hive or honey bees, and disseminate, through their droppings, the seeds of several noxious plants. In compensation, they eat various injurious invertebrates. On balance, the starling is regarded as beneficial to gardeners and farmers except in forested areas; its colonisation of New Zealand has been helped by the provision of nesting boxes, since it is widely believed that it assists in the control of grassland insect pests.

Rooks have not proved adventurous colonists in New Zealand, where they are only well established in a limited number of localities. They have been accused of eating walnuts, sprouting oats and wheat and even (presumably sickly) adult sheep, as well as on occasion other cereal crops (especially maize), pumpkins, potatoes and peas. By way of compensation, they eat many injurious insects including the grass grub *Costelytra zealandica*.

Greenfinches are widely but unevenly distributed in New Zealand, where in some places they are abundant to around 600 metres. They have colonised Chatham Island naturally, but occur only as vagrants on other subantarctic islands. They favour mainly open country, farmland, scrub and exotic—especially pine—forests. In winter they feed mainly on the pine seeds they extract from fir-cones; they also eat the seeds of several noxious alien weeds. Large flocks gather in late autumn, winter and early spring, particularly in coastal urban areas. Although greenfinches are destructive to cereal, vegetable, fruit and flower crops, they also destroy injurious insects and grubs.

Goldfinches are abundant over much of New Zealand's two main islands to around 1000 metres, and are natural colonists of the Kermadec Islands, but occur only as vagrants on most subantarctic islands. In winter, large flocks up to 2000 strong often frequent coastal saltings, where they feed on succulent annual glassworts. At other seasons they inhabit open country and farmland, where they help to spread the seeds of tree lupins, thistles, and other weeds. In some districts, they are a local minor pest of grain, rape, and some soft fruits, but also eat various injurious insects. Goldfinches are now said to be more abundant in New Zealand than in the British Isles.

As an introduced species, redpolls occur in the wild only in New Zealand, where they are well distributed and abundant in a wide variety of habitats, especially in South Island from near sea level to around 1600 metres, and have colonised naturally most of the country's subantarctic islands; they are possibly the commonest passerine on Campbell Island. In some fruit-growing districts, redpolls can be a significant nuisance to orchardists.

The yellowhammer, similarly, is found as an introduced exotic solely in New Zealand, where it is widespread on the two main islands in all kinds of open country from sea level to 1600 metres. It breeds regularly on the Chatham Islands, but occurs only as a vagrant on other off-lying groups. Large flocks sometimes assemble in winter. Although at one time regarded as a serious pest of grain and seed crops, their consumption of injurious invertebrates and weed seeds is generally considered to outweigh any damage they may cause.

Gamebirds introduced by the Nelson Acclimatisation Society included common and ring-necked pheasants, California quail, red-legged and grey partridges, Australian brown quail, Australian stubble quail, mountain quail, bobwhite quail, black swans, Canada geese, Egyptian geese, and mallard.

Ring-necked pheasants were first introduced by the Society to Nelson in 1879–80; today, *colchicus, torquatus* and, most commonly, hybrids, are widely but irregularly distributed in New Zealand, where they are most abundant in North Island. Minor localised damage to maize crops and in market gardens is occasionally reported.

The Nelson Society first released California quail in 1867; they are now widely distributed, being found throughout most of North Island and in South Island north and east of the Southern Alps, on some settled off-lying islands, and on the Chatham group.

Australian black swans, which were introduced by the Nelson Society before 1864, occur in the wild as introduced aliens nowhere but in New Zealand, where they are resident on many of the larger lakes, lagoons and estuaries on both main islands; they are regarded as a commercially important natural resource, providing both food and sport.

It was not until 1953 that mallard were introduced by the Society to Nelson where they are now well established. Elsewhere in New Zealand they are widespread and abundant on both main islands and on Stewart Island, occur in small numbers on Chatham Island, and are occasional vagrants on the Antipodes, Auckland, Campbell and Macquarie groups. Except in the undeveloped back country, where the native grey duck predominates, mallard are the commonest New Zealand duck.

Red deer have been the most frequently introduced and are the most widely distributed large mammal in New Zealand. Although as early as 1851 the first pair, presented by Lord Petre from his herd at Thorndon Hall in Essex, were released by his brother, the Hon. W. E. Petre, in the Maitai Valley, it was not until 1910 that the first importation, from Warnham Park in Sussex, was made by the Nelson Society. Today, red deer are widely established in all suitable habitats, ranging from montane forests, scrub and grasslands to higher lowland pastures. Although they may live almost entirely in woodlands, their preferred habitat remains the high country of beech forests and tussock grass in South Island. The economic damage they cause—for example by over-browsing and trampling in forestland, by accelerating erosion through excessive grazing of sub-alpine meadows, by competing for grazing with domestic livestock, and by feeding on growing crops—is only exceeded by the havoc wrought by rabbits. On the other hand, red deer are a valuable sport animal, attracting tourists and foreign currency from many parts of the world.

Fallow deer were first successfully introduced to New Zealand by the Nelson Acclimatisation Society in 1864, when a buck and two does from Richmond Park in Surrey were released in Aniseed Valley. During the 1920s, fallow spread through the Bryant Range and merged with those established since 1906 in the Teal Valley at the north-western end of the range. Between Brunner and the Buller River on the west coast of Nelson a population is established in the Paparoa Range. In the rest of South Island, fallow are found in widely scattered localities, and they are also well established in parts of North Island. Relatively little damage—apart from fraying[18]—is reported in exotic wood-lands; elsewhere, agricultural crops, especially turnips, sometimes suffer.

White-tailed or Virginia deer were introduced by the Nelson Society for hunting in 1901, when five bucks and two does were released at Wainui Bay, in Golden Bay. Four years later others were turned out in Fiordland and on Stewart Island. The Nelson planting eventually died out, and that in Fiordland was only moderately successful. The deer flourished, however, on Stewart Island, where they have caused considerable ecological damage by over-grazing and over-browsing.

In November 1891 six pairs of Australian brush-tailed possums from Southland were released by the Society, as potentially valuable fur bearers, at Hillwood, Suburban North, in Nelson. Elsewhere in New Zealand, many more were turned down between about 1840 and 1920. They soon became widespread and abundant countrywide, and proved a serious pest to orchardists, farmers, foresters, pastoralists, and market gardeners alike, as well as causing considerable damage to the native bush. Although as long ago as 1963 over 1 million possum skins were being harvested annually, the damage the animals cause far outweighs the revenue derived from their pelts. They are also known to provide a reservoir which is hampering the eradication in New Zealand of bovine tuberculosis.

In August 1868 a pair of European brown hares from Victoria, Australia, was turned out by the Society on the Suburban North Hills, Wakapuaka, where in January 1870 a family of leverets was reported. Others were released in Nelson in 1869, 1872 and 1873. Today, brown hares are established in all suitable habitats on both main islands from sea-level to the snow-line at around 2000 metres. Introduced to New Zealand for coursing and shooting, they cause a certain amount of damage to various agricultural and horticultural crops.

In 1865 some rabbits (of the silver-grey domesticated variety) were presented to the Nelson Society, which in the following year placed them on some small offshore islands, including Rabbit, Rough, Fellow's or (as it is known today) Bell's, Hardy's, and Best's, where they became established. By the 1940s, as a result of numerous releases elsewhere, wild rabbits had colonised all suitable habitats on both main islands—only dense forest, heavy secondary growth and exposed montane regions being uninfested. The damage caused by rabbits is too well known to require further documentation. The success achieved in reducing their numbers in New Zealand has resulted in them being under at least some degree of control throughout the country.

On 29 August 1868 a consignment of 750 brown trout ova from Tasmania arrived in Nelson, where they hatched in the following month. The fry were introduced by the Society to the Maitai River in the summer of 1869, and by the end of the following decade all the rivers under the jurisdiction of the Nelson Society had been stocked with brown trout reared from ova either acquired from other societies or stripped from local fish. Brown trout are now a popular game fish in many parts of New Zealand.

In 1898, 2500 rainbow trout fry purchased from Wellington were released by the Society in the Maitai and Roding Rivers. In succeeding years many more were planted in these and other rivers in Nelson and elsewhere in New Zealand where, like the brown trout, the rainbow is now a popular game fish.

In November 1877 some 50,000 ova of American Chinook salmon—known in the antipodes as quinnat salmon—arrived from Auckland in Nelson, where in the following year 25,000 of the resulting fry were introduced to the Wairoa and Motueka Rivers. Although the Chinook failed to become established in Nelson, it is a sought-after game fish in several east and west coast lakes and rivers in South Island.

In and after 1886 attempts were made to establish the migratory Atlantic salmon in Nelson, but as elsewhere in New Zealand they were unsuccessful.

The (North) Canterbury Acclimatisation Society[19]

Dr Julius von Haast, in his address at the inaugural meeting of the Philosophical Institute of Canterbury in 1862, was the first to suggest the formation of an acclimatisation society in Canterbury.

We should like to see the hare and the partridge in our fields, the stately deer, the roe, and the pheasant occupying our hills and our forests, whilst our Alpine rivers are well calculated for the propagation of the salmon and trout. The most rugged of our mountain summits might become the venue of the chamois, and offer not only to us, but to future generations, the exciting pleasure and manly exercise of the chase.[20]

On 26 January 1864 *The Lyttelton Times* reported: 'We are glad to announce that acclimatisation at last stands a chance of being vigorously prosecuted in this province.'[21] Less than a month later, on 18 February, the same newspaper printed a letter from Mr Mark Stoddart urging the formation of a society for acclimatisation, and stating that: 'We want flights of insectivorous birds to correct the multiplication of destructive insects, caterpillars, blight, etc. . . . Many of our mountain ranges would form a home for the deer . . . and our sons may hunt venison introduced by their fathers.'[22]

Two months later, von Haast, Stoddart, and a group of like-minded men organised a meeting in Christchurch town hall, at which it was proposed: 'That a Society be formed called the Canterbury Horticultural and Acclimatisation Society'. The motion having been carried unanimously, the Society was formally constituted on 25 April 1864. In the following month the provincial government granted the new society the use of 1.6 hectares of the Domain, between the River Avon and the public hospital, where a cottage was constructed for the curator and enclosures built for the animals. Two years later, the designation 'Horticultural' was dropped from the Society's title.

The Society soon became actively involved in the introduction of animals and plants from abroad, and its gardens at the Domain became a popular destination for family outings from Christchurch. In 1917 it changed its name again to the North Canterbury Acclimatisation Society, presumably to distinguish itself from the South Canterbury society which had been founded in 1895.

In 1930 the Society moved from the Domain to a larger four-hectare site at Greenpark. Today it is mainly concerned with fish management, the conservation of wetlands and water resources, the management of wildfowl populations (especially at Lake Ellesmere), and the rearing of Hungarian or grey partridges.

Insectivorous songbirds from England were among the first animals imported by the Society, which, in common with others, advertised in England with details of payments it would make for various species that settlers or seafarers might bring out with them to New Zealand. Those successfully established include skylarks, first introduced in 1867; hedge sparrows or dunnocks in 1867–8; blackbirds in 1865; song thrushes before 1866; yellowhammers in 1867 and 1871; chaffinches in

1865–6; greenfinches in 1863 or 1866; goldfinches in 1865; redpolls in 1867 or 1868; and house sparrows in 1864. Other birds successfully introduced by the Society include black-backed magpies from Australia in 1864 and rooks from England from about 1862. Common pheasants first appeared in 1867; chukar partridges from India in 1932; California quail before 1865–6; mallard in 1897 and 1908; Canada geese from England in 1920; black swans from Australia in 1864; and mute swans from England in 1866.

In 1922 Thomson wrote of the dunnock (then known as the hedge sparrow) that it was 'the one bird against which no word of complaint has ever been raised'.[23] Today, dunnocks are well established in all kinds of cover (including coastal mangrove swamps, saltmarshes, parkland, gardens, exotic forests and subalpine scrub) between sea level and 1600 metres on both main islands, and on most offshore and subantarctic islands.

Black-backed magpies have proved aggressive and successful colonists in New Zealand, favouring open grasslands, agricultural land and shelterbelts, as well as urban and suburban parks and wooded gardens. Although they sometimes prey on the eggs and young of small birds and on lizards and bees, they also destroy injurious insects and mice. They are widely distributed on both North and South Islands, apart from most of Northland and Southland and the west side of the Southern Alps.

There is a breeding population of between fifty and seventy mute swans on Lake Ellesmere in Canterbury, with smaller groups on Lake Poukawa, Wanstead Lagoon, and other lakes in central and southern Hawke's Bay.

Canada geese in New Zealand are most abundant in Canterbury and northern Otago, where they breed mainly in the grass-covered montane valleys and around high altitude lakes. Small numbers nest in other parts of South Island east of the divide, and a few in North Island. They have become something of a problem, since they feed almost exclusively on private farmland which domestic animals are then reluctant to graze. The present population may be in the region of about 20,000.

Chukar partridges are today widely distributed in high country (up to 1800 metres) from Nelson to Otago in South Island, mainly east of the Southern Alps, where they favour dry rocky areas with an annual rainfall or less than 65 cm—a habitat and climate very similar to those of their natural range in India. They do not occur in North Island.

As early as 1913 California quail had become an agricultural pest in some parts of New Zealand, eating newly sown and germinating seeds, and spreading, through their droppings, the seeds of blackberry. More recently, grape and strawberry crops have been damaged, although by way of compensation the birds also eat harmful insects and the seeds of noxious weeds. They are widely distributed as the result of natural dispersal and repeated translocations and introductions, occurring in suitable habitats throughout most of North Island and in South Island north and east of the Southern Alps, on some settled offshore islands, and on the Chatham group. They are scarce or absent in areas of high rainfall.

Among mammals, the brush-tailed possum was first introduced from Australia to Canterbury by the Society in 1865; the red-necked or Bennett's wallaby from Tasmania in 1867; European hedgehogs in 1892 or 1894; ferrets in 1867 and stoats and weasels in 1885; fallow deer to the Culverden estate in 1871; red deer from Stoke Park near Windsor Castle to the Rakaia Gorge, where their descendants survive today, in 1897; brown hares in 1865; and rabbits of the silver-grey domesticated variety in 1865; the last were presented to the Society by Sir George Grey (governor of New Zealand 1845–53 and 1861–7, and prime minister 1877–9), and, according to the Society's annual report for 1866, 'have thriven well and increased to a great extent, and have been distributed to members far and near.'

The European hedgehog is widely distributed and common in suitable habitats—primarily settled suburban districts with gardens, orchards and farmland, followed by scrub, bush, and secondary growth forest up to around 2000 metres—on both main islands; on occasion, even coastal sand dunes and open tussock-country have been occupied. Imported to control injurious insects, hedgehogs also damage young seedlings and orchard and vegetable crops, and eat the eggs and fledglings of various ground-nesting birds.

The red-necked or Bennett's wallaby is the only wallaby to occur on South Island and does not occur on North Island. In the former, where they are established only in parts of the southern half of the island, they cause a considerable amount of damage to agricultural crops and by browsing on shrubs and young plantations of exotic trees.

Mustelids were introduced to New Zealand to try to combat the ever-increasing rabbit menace. This they only succeeded in doing to a limited extent, preferring instead to prey on many species of native birds, whose populations in some cases they have seriously affected. Today, stoats are widely distributed in considerable numbers throughout New Zealand, especially in native forests. Weasels have declined in numbers considerably, and are now of little economic or ecological importance. Ferrets occur mainly on pastoral farmland,but are also locally abundant and potential pests elsewhere.

Bumble bees were first successfully introduced by the Society in 1880 and 1884; today, in Nelson and Canterbury the most abundant species are *Bombus ruderatus* and *B. terrestris*, of which the former is an efficient pollinator of the alien red clover.

In August 1867 the Society imported from Tasmania 400 brown trout ova from fish shipped out from England three years previously. Rainbow trout fry were introduced to Lake Lyndon in about 1907, where they did so well that in 1911 75,000 more were placed in Lake Coleridge, 10,000 in Lake Georgina, and 60,000 in a tributary of the latter. Chinook or quinnat salmon were first released, in the Rakaia River, in 1876; all three species are now popular game fish in Canterbury.

In 1906 the New Zealand government imported 50,000 ova of the lake trout from North America, which the Society hatched out in the Domain. 4000 fry were placed in Lake Pearson, where the species survives in limited numbers.

In 1867 the Society received a small consignment of Australian green tree frogs from Hobart, Tasmania. It was some time before the species became established in South Island, but it is now widespread and abundant in streams, ponds, and marshes on both main islands.

Many species of plants and trees were introduced to Canterbury before the Society's formation in 1864. In 1868, the Society began planting mulberry trees, first imported in 1853, as a food for silkworms. In the same year it also introduced the seeds of sugar beet to encourage the production of sugar, and at a later date such trees as the Douglas fir, Norfolk Island pine, and *Pinus insignis*.

The Otago Acclimatisation Society

The Otago Acclimatisation Society was founded at Dunedin in 1864. It was one of the most active of the New Zealand societies, importing a large number of species—mainly mammals and birds. The following table gives brief details of these introductions. (The first date given is for the original introduction of each species by the Society; in several cases, as elsewhere in New Zealand, prior introductions had been made by private individuals and/or sporting organisations. Full details will be found in Lever, 1985 and 1987).

Birds

Species	Date	Locality	Status
Mute swan	1868–9	?	Established
Black swan	1866–70	?	Established
Canada goose	1905	?	Established
Mallard	1867, 1869, 1870, 1876, 1881, 1896	Kakanui and Riverton	Established
California quail	1868; 1871	Inch Clutha; Waikouaiti, and Popotunoa (Clinton)	Established

Species	Date	Locality	Status
Bobwhite quail	1898–9; 1947	?	Failed
Chukar partridge	1920, 1926–8	Hunter Valley, Lake Hawea, Green Bush, Floor and Northburn Creeks	Established
Brown quail	1868, 1870	?	Failed
Common pheasant	1865–70; 1874, 1877	?	Established
Ring-necked pheasant	1864	?	Failed
Common peafowl	1867	?	Failed
Spotted dove	1907	Dunedin	Failed
Crimson and eastern rosellas	1910	Otago Heads	Established
Little owl	1906–08, 1910	Ashley Downs, Waiwera, Alexandra	Established
Barn owl	1899	West Taieri	Failed
Laughing kookaburra	1866, 1869	Silverstream	Failed
Skylark	1867–9	?	Established
Dunnock	1868, 1871	?	Established
Blackbird	1865, 1867–9, 1871	Dunedin	Established
Song thrush	1865, 1867–9, 1871	?	Established
Yellowhammer	1868, 1871	?	Established
Cirl bunting	1871	?	Established
Chaffinch	1868–9, 1871	?	Established
Greenfinch	1868	?	Established
Goldfinch	1867–9, 1871	?	Established
Redpoll	1868, 1871	?	Established
House sparrow	1868–9	?	Established
European starling	1867–9	?	Established
Common mynah	Early 1870s	Dunedin	Failed
Black-backed magpie	1865–9	Inch Clutha, Dunedin	Established

Crimson and eastern rosellas (and hybrids) are today established in hill country near Dunedin, where their destruction of fruit is more than compensated for by their consumption of golden-haired blowflies. The former also occurs in the north-western suburbs of Wellington, and the latter near Auckland.

Little owls were released in New Zealand to prey on the various species of alien birds that had been introduced to control insect pests but which were, instead, themselves proving a nuisance in crop-growing districts of Otago. Although according to Thomson (1922),[24] 'several fruit growers in Central Otago reported them as having proved already a great boon to their orchards', the relief seems to have been short-lived because, despite the continued presence of little owls, small birds are still troublesome in both Otago and Canterbury. Although it has been suggested that little owls may have been implicated in the decline of several native birds in New Zealand, insects, as in Britain, comprise by far the greater part of the little owl's diet, of which only about 8 per cent in New Zealand consist of avian prey. It has nevertheless been argued that the little owl's contribution to destroying insects in New Zealand is as doubtful as its alleged usefulness in combating the problem caused by small birds. Today, little owls are established in South Island east of the Southern Alps from Southland to Marlborough, and have also colonised much of Westland where they are increasing; in North Island their status is uncertain.

Mammals

Species	Date	Locality	Status
Brush-tailed possum	1891, 1894–5	West Coast Sounds, Catlins	Established
Hedgehog	1885	Dunedin	Established
Weasels, stoats and (ferrets)	1885 (1867)	?	Established
Fallow deer	1867, 1869–70, 1899	Morven; near Tapanui, Blue Mountains; Cairn Bush	Established
Red deer	1871, 1898, 1902, 1914, 1919–20, 1924	Morven Hills, Lake Hawea, and Bushey Park, Palmerston South; Pomahaka Valley; Dunedin	Established
Sika deer	1885	Otekaiki near Oamaru	Failed
Brown hare	1863, 1867, 1869, 1875	Lake Waihola	Established
Rabbit	1866–8	?	Established

The sika deer (a stag and two hinds) were presented to the Society by Mr John Bathgate of Dunedin, and were turned out on the coast south of the Waitaki River where, although by 1890 they were said to be increasing, they eventually died out.[25]

In September 1868 Mr G. P. Clifford or Mr A. M. Johnson (accounts differ) imported 800 brown trout ova from Tasmania to Dunedin, the fry from which were released in various streams in the provincial district. In the following year Mr Clifford (or Mr Johnson) brought over a further shipment of ova from Tasmania, from which a thousand fry were hatched, most of which were released. In 1870 another consignment of ova was imported, which yielded 1084 fry. From these three shipments, plus two smaller ones to the Southland and Canterbury societies, are believed to be descended most of the brown trout stocks in New Zealand today.

In 1895 the Society obtained 5000 rainbow trout ova from their *confrères* in Wellington, 1500 of the resulting fry being liberated in the Waipahi and 400 being retained for breeding. By about 1920 the Society had released a total of over half a million rainbows in various waters in its district—especially in Lake Hawea.

In 1885 the Society received 400 American brook trout or brook charr fry from the Canterbury Society, which were placed in stew ponds at Opoho where, although many of the young fish died, the remainder spawned successfully. In 1886 and 1887 1400 and 18,000 fry respectively were turned out, and by 1915 around 800,000 had been distributed throughout Otago.

Atlantic salmon were first introduced to Otago jointly by the provincial Government and the Society in 1868, when according to Thomson (1922)[26] 100,000 ova from the Tay in Scotland and Severn in England were imported on the *Celestial Queen*. Despite this and subsequent other large introductions to Otago the species failed to become established.

50,000 Chinook or quinnat salmon ova were imported from North America to Otago in 1877; 13,000 of the resulting fry were placed in the Kakanui River and 18,000 in the Waipahi. Quinnat salmon are now established in seven or more east-coast rivers of South Island.

Again according to Thomson (1922), in 1901–02 some 160,000 sockeye salmon ova out of a shipment of 500,000 Canadian sea-run fish arrived in good condition in Otago, where they were reared by the Society in a hatchery on the Hakataramea River. Some of the fry were placed in waters in the Waitaki River system, the remainder being retained in the hatchery for subsequent release elsewhere. A few stunted but apparently sea-run fish were later recorded by Thomson, but thereafter, according to McDowall (1978), their presence seems to have been largely forgotten until, in the 1960s, landlocked sockeye were 'rediscovered' in Lake Ohau and in parts of the Waitaki River system. This is the only known introduction of sockeye salmon to New Zealand.

In 1888 the Society obtained around sixty Australian green tree frogs from Napier, which were released in a marsh near Dunedin where they all soon disappeared, eaten, it was conjectured, by ducks. Later others were introduced to Otago and to Southland where, as elsewhere in New Zealand, they are now widespread in suitable marshes, ponds, and streams.

The Auckland Acclimatisation Society[27]

Although according to Auckland's *Daily Southern Cross* of 3 July 1862, 'It is to our credit to have established the first Acclimatisation Society in New Zealand' (ante-dating the Nelson Society by over nine months), nothing more seems to have been heard of the Auckland Society, due largely to the Maori wars of 1861–71, until the formation of its first council over four and a half years later on 2 February 1867.

Basing its operations on a 1.6-hectare site in the Auckland Domain, in its first year the Society imported from England more than thirty species of mammals, birds, and fish; its expenditure, covered by contributions, subscriptions, game licences, sale of stock, entry fees to its property, and fines, exceeded £1000.

As a result of a declining income and increased expenditure in running the Domain, in 1882 the Society handed over the control of its property there to the Domain Board. A decade later, in 1892, the Society's financial position had improved sufficiently to enable it to purchase, for £20, its own first property, an 8-hectare site on the banks of the Waimakiriri stream some 6 kilometres from Oxford.

Among the insect-eating song-birds introduced by the Society in the first year of its existence were starlings, yellowhammers, skylarks, hedge sparrows or dunnocks, linnets, goldfinches, greenfinches, house sparrows, chaffinches, blackbirds, song thrushes, and magpies from England, as well as emus and black-backed magpies from Australia, Java sparrows, 'Rockhampton sparrows', pigeons, doves, and, surprisingly, gulls. A few of these birds were placed for exhibition in an aviary in the Domain and some were sold to defray expenses, the balance being released into the wild. The house sparrows, especially, soon became established, and bred successfully within a couple of months of being liberated at Freeman's Bay. All the English insect-eaters apart from magpies are now established in the wild in the Auckland district.

In its second year the Society imported whitethroats, 'Cape cardinals', European robins, 'Solomon Island cassowaries' (double-wattled cassowaries), bronze-winged pigeons, chestnut sparrows, New Caledonia pigeons, canaries, bantams, wekas, geese, and more of the species brought in in the previous year.

Within a year of their introduction most of these species were established and breeding in the Domain, from where some were beginning to spread; the starlings, for example, which multiplied more rapidly than any other introduced species, had extended their range as far as Tauranga.

In 1869, in response to requests from other districts on both main islands which had heard of the benefits to be derived from exotic insectivorous birds, the Society distributed starlings to Mangere and Hokianga, chaffinches to Mangere, house sparrows to Remuera and Hokianga, and pigeons to Howick, Napier, Northern Wairoa, Wellington, Canterbury, Dunedin, and Bathurst.

In 1870, sixty-four rooks, which it was believed would greatly benefit farmers and orchardists, were imported from England and released in the Domain to join a pair freed there in the previous year. The Society's annual report for 1872 states that 'eight nests were built in the Gardens, but unhappily a night review of the volunteers took place just as incubation commenced, when the firing caused the majority of the rooks to forsake the nests, so that only three small broods were hatched. In January a severe epidemic broke out amongst them which destroyed several.'[28] A year later a few pairs nested, but the Society's report for 1874 concluded that 'they are not doing so well. The young have died', perhaps because the climate was too hot for them.

Several species were acquired by the Society as gifts; these included fire-tail finches, red-browed waxbills, nutmeg mannikins, chestnut-breasted mannikins, redpolls, 'Californian or red-winged starlings', parrots, and various Australian and Solomon Island pigeons. At their own expense the Society imported lapwings, tree sparrows, and more robins, yellow-hammers and goldfinches. Although the lapwings, robins and sparrows all disappeared, and the goldfinches only became locally established, the yellowhammers were soon widely distributed.

By 1872, when it imported woodlarks, blackcaps, and more redpolls, lapwings, dunnocks and robins, the council noted in its annual report that 'Starlings, thrushes, blackbirds, goldfinches, yellow hammers, skylarks, chaffinches, and several other introduced birds are now becoming common around Auckland, and are rapidly spreading from simple increase of numbers.'

In an attempt to find other species to combat the insect plague, the Society orderd long-tailed tits, pied, yellow, and grey wagtails, European nuthatches, golden plover, and woodpeckers from England. None of these species, however, survived the long sea voyage.

In 1876, in an effort to fulfill the requests for insect-eating birds from provincial Auckland and other parts of the country, the Society employed a full-time bird-trapper through whose endeavours starlings and skylarks were sent to the Waikato, Taranaki, Napier, Tauranga, Poverty Bay, Kawau, and the Kaipara. Chaffinches were despatched to the Bay of Islands, and goldfinches and blackbirds to Thames, Tauranga, Kawau, and Hamilton.

After 1878, when a single 'Native Companion' or brolga, a couple of pairs of 'diamond sparrows', redpolls, bronze-winged pigeons and firetail finches were presented to it, the Society appears to have concentrated almost exclusively on the introduction of gamebirds.

As with insectivorous species, gamebirds were first introduced to Auckland in 1867, when common pheasants, grey partridges, California quail, and brown quail, were imported. Within a year the California quail were reported to be established and breeding. Shortly after-wards Barbary partridges, stubble quail, and brush turkeys were also introduced. The partridges were released at Howick, and the stubble quail were distributed locally and sent to the Waikato, Nelson, and

Poverty Bay. The brush turkeys were freed in the Kaipara, where they apparently disappeared.

Peafowl were imported in 1869 and red grouse in the following year, both unsuccessfully. In 1871, 500 brown quail were distributed from the Waikato north to the Bay of Islands, and were soon said to be breeding around Whangarei, Mangawai, Kaipara, and northern Waikato. Brown quail are today widespread throughout the lowlands of North Island (apart from the south where they are scarce), favouring swamps and the perimeter of tidal marshes. Their presence on offshore islands is probably the result of natural dispersal from the mainland.

In 1876 sharp-tailed grouse from Utah and some mountain quail were unsuccessfully liberated at Piako and Matamata respectively. Five years later, twenty prairie chickens were imported from North America, but were apparently never released. In 1893, chukar partridges from India were freed near the Kaipara Heads, where they became temporarily established. Six years later, bobwhite quail were turned down near Waimakariri, Waingaro, Hinuera, the Whangarei, and Churchill in central Waikato; they are currently confined to the Wairoa/Waikaremoana district of Hawke's Bay.

'It is now generally recognized', the Society conceded in its annual report for 1903, 'that the establishment of game birds in any part of the colony is by no means the easy matter that it was when acclimatisation societies were first founded. Old members will recollect the comparative ease with which the pheasant and Californian quail were established, and the rapidity with which they spread through the country. Now, matters are altogether different. Despite repeated attempts . . . no game birds of any kind have been successfully established during the last twenty years.'

In confirmation of this admission, after 1911 numerous attempts were made by the Society to establish red-legged or French partridges, grey partridges, black-breasted quail from India, chukar partridges, bobwhite quail, and Indian sandgrouse in Auckland, but all ended in failure.

Pheasants were already established in Auckland when the Society became active in 1867. Nevertheless, nine common pheasants were acquired by the Society and released in 1867-8, and in 1869 a member, a Mr Wentworth, turned down some more on the Hokonuis. The only Chinese ring-necked pheasants introduced to Auckland in the nineteenth century were imported by Mr Thomas Henderson in 1851 and 1856, a decade or more before the Society was founded. These birds, released at Waitakere, slowly increased, and as early as 1865 large numbers were being shot. They were first noted in the Waikato in 1864-5, and by 1869 were abundant from Auckland through the Waikato and Thames nearly to Taupo. In the same year they arrived at

Whangarei, but were reported only infrequently further north. It seems probable that hybridisation with common pheasants began shortly after their introduction.

'It is said by the settlers of some districts', claimed the Society's annual report for 1869, 'that if it were not for the aid of the pheasant they could scarcely hold their own against the depredations of crickets and other insects. Although there may be murmurings at the small tribute occasionally exacted by pheasant and other introduced birds from grain and fruit, it is a trivial matter when compared with the vast benefit derived by the province.' Five years later, the Society stated in its annual report for 1874 that 'the Chinese pheasant is the common bird of this Province.'

Other members of the pheasant family introduced to Auckland include golden and silver pheasants, and Temminck's tragopans from Asia, all of which failed to become established.

Black swans from Australia were the first wildfowl to be introduced by the Society to Auckland, when four were released in 1864. Five years later, the Society's annual report for 1869 said that 'Black swans have become established on the lakes about Ahipara (near Kaitaia) where six or seven have been seen together on several occasions. An intelligent native reports seeing on the wider parts of the Awanui River . . . as many as 28 together.'

Mallard were first introduced to Auckland by the Society in 1870, when a pair was imported from England, followed by a further four in 1886; these birds were kept in the Domain for breeding, but initially appear to have met with only limited success.

Other wildfowl unsuccessfully introduced to Auckland include mute swans, North American wood duck, wigeon, and grey geese.

Among mammals, fallow deer were first introduced to Auckland by the Society in 1877, when twenty-eight (the survivors of an original shipment of thirty or thirty-three) from Carshalton and Richmond Parks in Surrey, presented by Mr Falconer Larkworthy, were divided between the Society and its confrères in Wellington. These deer were liberated in the Maungakawa Ranges near Ngaruawahia and at Matamata, where some remain today. In the same year, the Society unsuccessfully released eleven mule or black-tailed deer from California near Mercer on the Waikato River, and in the Piako and Upper Thames regions, where they were all killed by settlers and Maoris.

In the previous year, Mr Larkworthy also presented the Society with a pair of sambar, of which the hind died shortly thereafter; the stag turned vicious, and once attacked a man with a wheelbarrow who, with commendable presence of mind, turned it upside down and took refuge inside it until help arrived. Larkworthy obtained a replacement mate for this stag from Colombo (Sri Lanka), and the pair was released between

Cambridge and Morrinsville, Waikato, where they thrived and multi-plied until the late 1940s, when their progeny had all been shot out.

Strangely, although in 1916 the Society recommended the intro-duction to Auckland of red deer, claiming that the wild, bush-covered Coromandel Peninsula was 'capable of carrying many thousands', this suggestion was never implemented. The reason may be that by 1926 reference was being made to 'the society's red deer country', to which animals from the south had presumably spread naturally.

In 1868 or 1869 a pair of brown hares was received by the Society from the Victoria Acclimatisation Society in Australia, and released in 1870 in the Tamaki/Howick district; a year later a further nine brown hares from Australia were liberated in the same area.

Brush-tailed possums were first introduced to Auckland in 1869, and to Kawau Island by its owner, Sir George Grey, in the following year. Kawau Island was also stocked from Australia by Grey at around the same time with tammar wallabies, parma wallabies, and brush-tailed rock wallabies, all of which are currently established there.

Fish were first introduced by the Society to Auckland in 1867, when it imported 114 'Russian carp', which were released in Lake Pupuke, where they are today abundant, and to St John's Lake at Remuera, Mangawai, and to Raglan. A year later Australian green tree frogs were imported from Sydney and released in waters at One Tree Hill and Mount St John, from where they soon spread to many of the marshy areas around Auckland.

Until 1872, when the Society made enquiries about the introduction of Atlantic salmon and silver and black bass from North America, the only other fish imported apart from brown trout were more carp, which were released in the Whau Creek, Onehunga Springs, St John's Lake, Whangape Lake, and at Kawau, Takapuna, Whangarei, Coromandel, Shortland, Hamilton, Ngaruawahia, Cambridge, Otahuhu, Maraetai, Mangawai, New Plymouth, Wanganui, and Napier.

The first attempt, in 1873, to introduce Atlantic salmon ova from England via the Country Club of San Francisco failed when all the eggs died on the voyage. Until November 1875, when it unexpectedly received a consignment of 20,000 Chinook or quinnat salmon ova originally intended for the Hawke's Bay Society, the Auckland Society imported few fish apart from brown trout. Half the quinnat salmon ova were placed in the upper waters of the Thames and Waikato Rivers, the balance being retained in the hatchery in the Domain.

In 1876–7, the Auckland, Canterbury, and Wanganui Societies together imported 250,000 quinnat ova from the McLeod River in California via the Country Club of San Francisco: Auckland's share was divided between the Rapurapu—a tributary of the Upper Thames—and the Oratia which flows into Waitemata Harbour, and the Domain hatchery. Some 10,000 fry from the hatchery were placed in the Waikato River, 3000 in the Tuakau Stream, 2000 in the Mahurangi River, and 600 in the Southern Wairoa River.

In 1877 the Society received 100,000 quinnat ova as its share of a government importation of half a million; these were divided among the Mangakahia and Puniu Rivers and the hatchery in the Domain.

A year later two shipments of channel catfish were released in St John's Lake, from where by 1885 they were being translocated to other parts of the province and to acclimatisation societies elsewhere in New Zealand. Also in 1878 the Society received a further consignment of 200,000 quinnat eggs from the United States, which were placed in tributaries of the Upper Thames.

A few years later the Society acquired half a million whitefish ova; 50,000 were retained in the hatchery, where they died because of polluted and too warm water, the balance being planted in Lakes Taupo, Tarawera, Okataina, Tikitapu, and the Awahou Basin debouching into Lake Rotorua.

In 1885 and again in 1886, due to the failure of previous attempts to establish the fish in Auckland waters, the Society declined offers to join with other New Zealand acclimatisation societies and with the government in the importation from the United States of further shipments of quinnat salmon ova.

In 1890 five edible crabs from Fiji were planted in Rangitoto, but were never seen again.

In spite of a warning from one of its founder members against the introduction of perch, the Society sanctioned the release of these fish by the Waikato Anglers' Club in 1907. A previous attempt by the Hamilton Domain Board to naturalise this species in 1885 had apparently failed. More perch were freed in 1912–13 by the Huntly Gun Club in Lake Hakanoa, and in 1914 the Society placed a further 625 in Lake Waikare. In its annual report for 1915, the Society reported that large numbers of perch had been caught in Hamilton Lake, where they had been introduced in 1907.

After the Auckland Exhibition of 1914, over 1500 quinnat salmon were released at Huntly, Ngaruawahia, and Hunua, but like their predecessors they all disappeared.

Because of the considerable expense involved, the Society sensibly never again attempted the establishment in Auckland of Atlantic salmon. In 1926 the government offered to stock the Waikato River with this species, but whether it ever actually did so is unrecorded.

Later in the same year, the Society received from the government of Samoa a gift of one hundred freshwater prawns, sixty-six of which were unsuccessfully released at Rotowaro.

In 1956–60 the Society pioneered the air-dropping of smelt, a small species of salmonid, in Parkinson's Lake at Waiuku, where within a year the fish were established and breeding. A few years later a proposal to import black bass was placed in abeyance until the possible consequences to introduced trout had been examined.

In 1869 the Society constructed its first fish hatchery in the Domain, and a year later received from Tasmania its initial consignment of 1000 brown trout ova. Unfortunately, the ice in which the eggs were packed melted during the voyage, and only sixty, which were placed in Edgecombe's Creek, arrived alive.

In 1871–2 three further batches of brown trout were received by the Society—two of fry from their fellow acclimatisers in Canterbury and one of ova from Tasmania. Half the fry from South Island were retained in the hatchery in the Domain, the other half being released in the Waitoa stream at Matamata. The Tasmanian ova were hatched in the Domain, the resulting fry being sold for release at Shortland, Tauranga, Alexandra, Papakura, Ohinemuri, and in Western Springs. In 1873–4 more brown trout ova were acquired from Otago and Tasmania, and after hatching in the Domain the fry were despatched to Hokianga, Riverhead, Mahurangi, Coromandel, the Whau Creek, Papakura River, and the upper reaches of the Thames, Waipa, and Waikato rivers.

In 1876 the Society reconstructed its hatchery in the Domain, and in the following year purchased 5000 American brook trout or charr ova from the Country Club of San Francisco and a year later 30,000 lake trout ova. The former arrived in New Zealand in poor condition, and only 400 hatched successfully; these fry were freed in a feeder of the Waikato near Cambridge, Lake Pupuke, and the Kaikapakapa Stream. From the latter barely 1000 fry were hatched, which were placed in Lakes Waikare and Omapere and the Onehunga Springs, where they were never seen again.

In 1881 the Society built a new hatchery beside Henderson's Creek, and by early 1883 had succeeded in encouraging two of its members to erect their own private hatcheries near Paeroa on the Waikato River, and at Raglan, to both of which were despatched ova received from the Otago Society. Two years later, thirteen more privately owned hatcheries were set up between Opotiki and the Bay of Islands.

Also in 1883 there arrived in Auckland from Sonoma Creek via the Country Club of San Francisco in California the first shipment of 32,000 rainbow trout ova, believed at first to be brook trout. From these eggs only 5000 viable fry were hatched, a hundred of which were retained in the Domain, the balance being freed in Hay's and Symond's Creeks in the Hunuas, the Waikato at Tuakau, the Patetere and Puniu, and in Asylum Creek near Western Springs.

In 1893 the Society bought a ten-hectare site beside the Waimakariri near Oxford, on which a further hatchery, dam, hatching-house, and four stew-ponds were constructed. In 1935 work was begun on an additional hatchery at Puketurua, with an annual output of over one million fry.

Thereafter, large numbers of English brown trout and American rainbows and brook trout continued to be stocked annually by the Society in numerous Auckland waters.

As with other wildlife organisations in New Zealand, the Auckland Society regarded any animals which preyed on species under their care as 'vermin', to be slaughtered whenever possible. Mammals and birds which at one time or another fell into this category included introduced domestic cats, stoats, weasels, hedgehogs, black rats, brown rats, and native spotted shags, moreporks or boobook owls, kingfishers and hawks. Today, fortunately, wiser counsels prevail.

Although over the years well over 200 species of flora have been introduced to Auckland by the Society, this aspect of acclimatisation has, until recently, tended to play second fiddle to the Society's interest in the importation of exotic animals. Plants with which the greatest efforts towards acclimatisation were made were those considered suitable as foods for imported wildfowl and gamebirds. Thus in 1916 the Society began cultivating wild peas as a food for pheasants, and in the following year wild rice for ducks, which was first sown, with some success, in Lake Waikare: later, wild rice was also successfully cultivated in Ohinewai, Rotorua, Matamata, Tuakau, and Rangiriri.

Since the late 1960s, the Auckland Society has disposed of its trout hatchery and reduced its pheasant release programme, concentrating instead, as have other New Zealand acclimatisation societies, on habitat conservation. Since 1981, however, it has persisted with attempts to establish French or red-legged partridges in its area, so far without success. It opposes the reclamation of wetlands (of which it holds some 1700 hectares), the pollution of waterways, and habitat degradation in general. It is presently attempting, through the creation of a series of weirs, to rehabilitate around 2000 hectares of the Whangamarino wetlands—a site recently registered under the Ramsar Convention—and in preventing the Auckland Regional Council from using an adjacent mine as a landfill. Every year between 10,000 and 12,000 trees are planted by the Society to provide an additional source of food for introduced and native waterfowl and upland gamebirds.

In spite of losing the Hot Lakes District to the government in 1905, the Auckland Acclimatisation Society is today territorially the largest such organisation in New Zealand, extending from West Taupo in the south northwards to Rodney.

The Southland Acclimatisation Society[29]

The Southland Acclimatisation Society was founded at a public meeting held in Invercargill on 14 March 1867; this followed a preliminary meeting at the Mechanics' Institute on 7 September 1863, at which a provisional committee was formed and requested to obtain all information necessary for the foundation of such a society. The provisional committee was instructed to report on its findings early in 1864; whether it did so or not is unrecorded, as are the reasons for the three-and-a-half years' delay until the Society's actual formation.

The first animals to be received by the Society were some geese presented by Mr C. W. Jackson of Waikaia Plains, which were released on the banks of the Mataura in April 1867; what species these birds were is not known, but they are unlikely to have been Canada geese, which were first acquired by the Society from the Tourist Department in 1905, and liberated four years later on Lake Manapouri. These unnamed geese were followed in 1869 by some black swans from the Victoria Society in Australia, which were liberated in the same year at the New River Ferry. Their fate is unknown.

The only passerines recorded to have been acquired by the Society were eleven European starlings from the Dunedin Society in September 1872, which in the same year were freed at Wallacetown. What became of them is unrecorded.

Gamebirds were turned down by the Southland Society as follows: ring-necked pheasants first in 1869; California quail in 1870; brown quail from Australia in 1872; mallard in 1896; and grey or Hungarian partridges from England and red-legged or French partridges in 1900.

From about 1875 to 1925 large numbers of pheasants, California quail and grey and French partridges were reared and released by the Society in a variety of localities, including on Stewart Island, but predation by introduced stoats and weasels and the consumption of poisoned grain caused most of these plantings to be unsuccessful.

Between 1910 and 1923 a total of 1381 mallard were released at various sites in the Society's district, including Lake Te Anau, Mossburn and on Stewart Island, where despite predation by mustelids they, and to a much lesser extent, Canada geese, succeeded in becoming established.

Five species of deer were introduced by the Southland Society. Four red deer from lake Hawea and Nelson were released at Birchwood in 1898–9, followed by a further ten, descended from those introduced to Nelson by the Hon. W. E. Petre in 1851, which were turned out on Davis Flat at the head of the Lillburn Valley in 1900. In the following year a further nineteen, presented by Sir Rupert Clarke of Victoria,

Australia, were released at The Monument, Lake Manapouri, near Waiau, and The Hump, Hauroko. In the same year, six hinds from the Wairarapa herd, descended from those in Windsor Park in England, were released on the banks of the Freshwater River, at the head of Paterson's Inlet, Stewart Island. In 1903, seven or eight calves from Miss Audrey Chirnside of Werribee, Victoria, were introduced to Mount Tuhua. Finally, in 1909 three red deer from Warnham Park in Sussex were liberated at Dusky Sound in the Fiordland National Park.

In 1908 or 1909 five or six Axis Deer were released at Dusky Sound, where although Stock (1915) says that 'from reports received from time to time they are becoming well established', nothing has been heard of them since 1920–30.

Ten moose from Saskatchewan, Canada, were turned out at Supper Cove in Dusky Sound on 24 February 1910. This locality was selected because of its swampy nature and the absence of precipitous hills, and because its remoteness ensured that it was seldom visited by man. Although two years later some miners reported evidence of both adults and calves, little seems to have been recorded of the animals' early history. According to Thomson (1922),[30] 'these deer were in considerable numbers round the Sound.' The precipitous slopes of the valleys away from their point of release, coupled with their very slow breeding rate, are believed to have been responsible for their limited distribution, which forty years ago was confined to a few valleys surrounding Supper Cove. The higher mean temperature and precipitation of Dusky Sound compared to Saskatchewan, and the mooses' inability to scale the steep slopes from the dense rainforest to the mountain tops in warm weather, together with interspecific competition from red deer, probably accounts for their dwindling range and numbers. In the late 1940s the population had fallen from a previous high of sixty-to-seventy to only thirty or forty, and recent evidence suggests a continuing decline which may well end in extinction, if indeed this has not already occurred.

On 5 April 1905 eighteen white-tailed or Virginia deer were imported to New Zealand, nine of which were released in the Rees Valley at the western end of Lake Wakatipu in Fiordland, and the other nine at Port Pegasus on Stewart Island. The first of these plantings proved only moderately successful, but on Stewart Island the deer fared much better, and by the early 1960s were found over most of the island, where they mainly frequent bush below 300 metres and gently sloping coastal valleys, seldom penetrating the subalpine belt of dense scrub to the mountain tops. They are, perhaps, more common in the south than in the north of the island, and have caused considerable ecological deterioration by over-browsing.

On 3 March 1905 ten wapiti from the National Zoological Park in Washington, DC, were released at the head of George Sound in Fiordland. Today, the species is established in about one sixth of the Fiordland National Park from Bradshaw Sound and Coronation Peak in the south to between Sutherland and Milford sounds south of the Castle Mountain/Mount Mackenzie massif in the north (a distance of some 80 kilometres), and 50 kilometres inland to the western shore of the northern half of Lake Te Anau. The species' further expansion is inhibited in the south by the firmly established red deer population, and in the north by the precipitous slopes of Milford Sound and human settlement in the Cleddau Valley.

Brush-tailed possums were first introduced to Southland long before the formation of the Society—to Riverton by Captain John Howell between 1837 and 1840 and by Mr Christopher Basstian in 1858. In 1890 the Society imported eighty-three possums from Australia, which were turned out on Stewart Island, at Lake Te Anau and on the west coast sounds, and an unrecorded number were freed in the same year on the Auckland islands.

Brown hares were liberated by the Southland Society as follows: in 1869, some from the Victoria Acclimatisation Society in Australia; in 1871, a pair at Half Way Bush; in 1874, another pair at Half Way Bush; and forty in 1887. Coursing in Southland commenced in 1878, and was finally declared illegal throughout New Zealand in 1960.

From its early days, the Southland Acclimatisation Society was an ardent importer of various species of game fish: brown trout were first placed in the Upper Waiau and Otamita in 1869; sea trout—a migratory form of brown trout—were first introduced from Tasmania in 1870; Atlantic salmon first in 1868; Chinook or quinnat salmon in 1876; American brook trout or charr in 1887; rainbow trout in 1900; and lake trout from Canada in 1905. Brown and rainbow trout are now established in, among other waters, Lake Te Anau and the Waiau River, while the Te Anau and Manapouri lakes system is the only place in New Zealand where the Atlantic salmon has been successful. Where this latter population originated is uncertain, as importations were made of both migratory British Atlantic salmon and eastern North American landlocked fish. The Te Anau and Manapouri population has access to the sea, but as McDowall (1978) points out, is voluntarily confined to the lakes. This, as McDowall says, does not necessarily imply that the fish are derived from landlocked stock, and indeed there is some evidence to the contrary. In the 1960s the Southland Society introduced more Atlantic salmon from Scotland, and from Sweden and Poland whose rivers debouch into the Baltic Sea, but these attempts were all unsuccessful. In 1868 the Southland Society acquired some Australian green tree frog spawn from their *confrères* in Hobart, Tasmania, which were placed in various waters within the Society's district.

The Hawke's Bay Acclimatisation Society[31]

At a meeting of the Hawke's Bay Agricultural Society held in Napier on 27 January 1868, it was resolved that 'as it is highly desirable to encourage the introduction of insectivorous birds, useful plants, and trees, an Acclimatisation Society be formed'.[32] The Society's foundation was marked by an editorial in the *Hawke's Bay Herald* on 4 February, which said:[33]

> For some time past there has been a growing desire on the part of the settlers to introduce the insectivorous birds of the mother country to protect the farmer from the ravages of the caterpillar and grasshopper.

Within a month of its formation, the Society was offering for sale to its members pheasants 'at £5 per pair', and in April and May 'a collection of valuable seeds', and 'choice vine-cuttings'.

For the next three years the Society seems, for reasons unknown, to have become quiescent. In mid-February 1871 it came to life again with a series of daily advertisements for six weeks in the *Herald* seeking new members. On 24 March the newspaper lent its weight to this campaign with a censorious editorial:[34]

> Is nothing going to be done towards forming an Acclimatisation Society; or rather towards revivifying the one already in existence? What between caterpillars, beetles, slugs, and other destructive insects, half the crops attempted to be grown in this Province are, year after year, swept off the face of the country. The cure, and only cure, is a supply of insectivorous birds. . . . We want, therefore, an Acclimatisation Society with money annually at its disposal.

The *Herald's* fervent wish was fulfilled on 17 October 1874, when the *Queen Bee* from England docked in Napier with a consignment of no fewer than 650 insectivorous birds, comprising 357 blackbirds and song thrushes, 206 skylarks, 72 rooks, and 15 grey or red-legged partridges. In February of the following year the barque *Hudson* arrived in Napier after a record-breaking run from England of eighty-four days with a shipment of 137 skylarks, 110 goldfinches and chaffinches, 60 European robins, and 44 partridges. In 1889, when acclimatisation societies were being attacked from all sides for the damage caused to agricultural, horticultural and fruit crops by house sparrows, the Hawke's Bay Society was provoked, somewhat incautiously, into declaring that 'the enormous increase of small birds and their damage upon all classes of settlers is viewed with alarm by the public, in general; but the Society takes the opportunity to remind the said public that the Acclimatisation Society is *not* responsible for the introduction of linnets, sparrows, larks, or Hares'.[35] In the case of the larks, the Society's memory was short indeed.

From then on the Society concentrated on the introduction of game fish and, especially, gamebirds.

California quail were imported first by the Hawke's Bay Provincial Council and subsequently, around 1876, by the Society; brown quail from Australia were introduced privately at Rissington, Hawke's Bay in 1866 by a Colonel Whitmore, and again after 1875 by the Society; mallard first imported in 1867, were not firmly established until the mid-1940s, as a result of further introductions; in 1958 the Society received 150 grey partridge eggs by air from Denmark, but the species is still not properly established in New Zealand.

From the early days of settlement, attempts were made to stock game fish in waters in the Hawke's Bay district. Many of the early pioneers raised brown trout in private hatcheries, from which the first stocking was made by Captain D. G. Hamilton in the Manawatu and Mangatoro rivers in 1872. Four years later 60,000 Chinook or quinnat salmon ova from San Francisco arrived at the Ahuriri Lagoon, west of Napier, on behalf of the Society. 20,000 were taken to Mr William Shrimpton's hatchery at Matapiro, while the remainder were sent to that of Mr F. W. Sturm at Clive. The water at Matapiro proved too warm, and none of the eggs survived. Some 30,000 of the 40,000 at Clive, however, hatched successfully, and the parr were released in the upper reaches of the Ngaruroro, Manawatu, and Tuki Tuki rivers. Unfortunately, none of these fish appears to have survived for long.

The Society first became actively involved in trout farming just before the First World War, when it took over management of a privately run hatchery at Mangatera. Originally, brown trout ova were obtained from the Otago and Southland Societies (whose stock had mostly come from England and Scotland via Australia), and later from Masterton, and the Hakataramea River in Marlborough. In recent years, the Society has obtained most of its ova from government hatcheries at Wanaka, Turangi, and Ngongataha. Since 1958 the Society has reared large numbers of both brown and rainbow trout—the latter coming mainly from Tongariro or Ngongataha and the former from Wanaka.

The first recorded introduction of red deer into the Hawke's Bay district was made at Matapiro on behalf of the Society in 1880 by Mr W. Shrimpton, who three years later turned them out in the Ruahine Ranges.

In 1905, six sika deer of the Manchurian subspecies *manchuricus* from the Duke of Bedford's herd at Woburn Abbey in Bedfordshire were presented to the Society and released on Mr W. N. Smith's sheep run, Taharua Station (now known as Poronui) near Rangitaiki. Unlike the red deer, which soon became widely distributed, the sika remained confined to a fairly small area until the outbreak of the Second World War. Today, however, they range over more than 11,000 square kilometres of country from the Tongariro National Park and the northern Ruahines to the Kaingaroa State Forest and the Moungaharura Range, the main concentrations being found in the northern Kaimanawa Mountains and in the Kaweka and Ahimanawa ranges.

Also in 1905, Mr T. E. Donne of the Tourist Department obtained some black-tailed or mule deer from Santa Fé, New Mexico, which were released on behalf of the Society at Runuanga, Tarawera; although a decade later the Society reported that they were increasing, they seem to have died out (or been killed) shortly thereafter.

The Wellington Acclimatisation Society[36]

The Wellington Acclimatisation Society was founded in 1871, with an initial membership of only thirty-three. Eleven years later, in 1882, an acclimatisation society was also formed in the Wairarapa which amalgamated with the Wellington Society in 1884, as is shown by the following extract from a letter[37] dated 1 October 1884 from Mr Alex Rutherfurd, the honorary secretary of the 'Wellington and Wairarapa District Acclimatization Society'—now known more simply as the Wellington Acclimatisation Society—to the Colonial Secretary:

> I have the honour to inform you that at a meeting held in the Colonial Museum on the 24th ultimo, it was resolved to form an Acclimatization Society to be called The Wellington and Wairarapa District Acclimatization Society, and Rules were then adopted stating the objects for which the Society was formed.

In the first decade after its original formation in 1871, the Society released a wide variety of birds; these included common or Indian mynahs, grouse, 'Bramble Finches' (probably bramblings), waxbills, quail (presumably *Lophortyx californicus*), skylarks, redpolls, Australian bronze-wing pigeons, 'Brown Doves' (possibly brown pigeons) from northeastern Australia), wonga pigeons from eastern Australia, Australian crested pigeons, 'Scrub Quail, Australian Quail' (? spp.), blackbirds (at £2 per pair), siskins, 'Butcher birds' (probably red-backed or great-grey shrikes), laughing jackasses or kookaburras, European starlings (from Dunedin in 1877), plovers, song thrushes, 'Aplonies', 'Jager birds', European robins, crested bellbirds from Australia, 'Bunting's Curl' (probably cirl buntings), 'Diamond Sparrows', and 'Main Geese' (presumably Australian maned geese).

In 1892 the introduction of nightingales and further insect-eating birds was proposed, but never fulfilled. Six 'orlolons' (probably ortolan buntings) were imported from southern France and released at Otaki in 1886; although at first they seem to have flourished, the arrival of poisoned grain put out for rabbits appears to have killed them all off.

The first gamebirds introduced to Wellington were common or ring-necked pheasants, costing £2 a pair, in 1872. Twelve years later a further twenty-four pheasants were freed in the Hutt and Horowhenua counties, where the first licences, at £1 each to run from 1 March to 10 May, were issued in 1886. In 1891 one Don Fredrigo Gobbold of Puan, Buenos Aires, offered to try to obtain some 'Tinamu' (Tinamidae) for the Society, but these apparently never materialised. In the same year the governor of Wellington, who was also the Society's patron, gave the Society three grey partridges from England, followed a year later by a further seventeen. These birds were all turned down at Masterton and at Bartons in the Hutt. In 1892 or 1893 California quail and thirteen 'Teneriffe Partridges' (Barbary partridges) were placed on Kapiti Island, where breeding was later reported. In 1898, twenty grey partridges and two years later either 100 or 240 bobwhite quail were released at Otaki, where according to contemporary reports the latter survived for several years. Subsequently, many more of these species were turned down with varying degrees of success in different parts of Wellington.

Three red deer from England were first introduced to Wellington in 1862—some nine years before the Society was founded—and were released in the Wairarapa, where within seven years they had increased to 'upwards of twenty'. The first three red deer imported by the Society, which came from Martinborough, were turned out at Greymouth in 1898. Later in the same year more were imported from Blackwood, Melbourne, and in 1906, 1909, and 1922 others were introduced from, respectively, Werribee Park, Victoria; Warnham Park, England; and the Otago Society, which had acquired its stock from the Earl of Dalhousie at Invermark in Scotland. The deer from Werribee were released in the Wairarapa and Wainuiomata; in 1898 or after 1908 an area of 6 hectares was fenced at Paraparaumu near Waikanae, enabling selected calves to be reared and released at various points in the Society's district and elsewhere, including Waikaremoana, Greymouth, Erewhon National Park, Bay of Islands, and Nelson. Further releases of red deer were banned by the government in 1926.

On 1 June 1875 Mr Falconer Larkworthy, on behalf of the Society, received from Ceylon (Sri Lanka) a pair of sambar at his property at Carnarvon, near the mouth of the Rangitikei River. Here the deer thrived, and before long had multiplied to over a hundred head. The Society's annual report for 1894, however, stated that 'The Ceylon Elk (Sambur [sic] Deer) . . . now number about thirty.' Following this decline, brought about largely, it is believed by poaching, the deer were given security by the government under the Animals' Protection Act. As a result, by 1898 the herd was reported to have increased to around a hundred again. By 1947 the population had further increased to between 400 and 500, and by the middle of the following decade had spread north-west to between the Waitotara River in the north and the Hokio River in the south.

Sambar in New Zealand are today established on the west coast between Otaki and Wanganui, on the southern side of Lake Taupo, to the south-east of Rotorua, and in the watershed of the Whakatane River. Although in their native range mainly a woodland species, in New Zealand sambar exhibit a more catholic choice of habitat, occurring in raupo swamps, with dense stands of manuka scrub, bracken, fern, lupin, flax, and giant bunch-grass (toetoe) near rough pastureland; they shelter in both native forests and exotic pine plantations, into which, however, they seldom penetrate very far. Their diet includes flax, grass, swedes, and the leaves and bark of some indigenous trees; their taste for the bark and young shoots of Californian Monterey pine saplings causes considerable silvicultural damage in some areas—though not to the same extent as in Sri Lanka, where they are regarded as a serious economic pest. Loss of habitat to agricultural development is likely to curtail their further dispersal in New Zealand.

In 1893 a pair of axis deer from Calcutta were released on Kapiti Island, where although at first they bred successfully they eventually died out.

The largest population of fallow deer in New Zealand, which has a high proportion of melanism, is found between the Whangaehu and Waitotara rivers north of Wanganui in Wellington. They are believed to be descended from ten animals from England which were liberated near the Wanganui River in 1877. In 1900 or 1901 a further pair was released on Kapiti Island, but was later shot when the island was declared a sanctuary.

Before importing brush-tailed possums from Australia, the Society received the following advice[38] from the animals' homeland: 'Damage done to fruit growers, etc. is very small and amply compensated by the commercial value of the skins' and 'In no respect can it become a pest like the rabbit. Let New Zealand cherish the opossum as a fertile source of revenue and therefore a most desirable colonist.'

Acting on these misleading recommendations, the Society released nineteen possums from Tasmania at Paraparaumu in 1892, and in the following year a further ten on Kapiti Island and a similar number at Wainui-o-mata. In 1922 some 17,000 animals were harvested, and revenue for licences and pelts amounted to £762. In the following year the latter figure almost doubled.

Brown hares, costing initially £6 each, were released by the Society as follows: a pair in 1874; fourteen in 1875; and forty-eight in 1876: by 1885 they were reported to be abundant around Wellington and at the lower end of the Wairarapa Valley.

Bumble bees were first introduced to Wellington from South Island in 1888 to help in the pollination of red clover.

Among game fish, brown trout were released in Wellington rivers as follows; first in 1872, purchased from the Canterbury Society; 400 in 1876 in the Waipoua River, a further 400 in the same year in the Hutt, and another 100 in the Wainuiomata. From the last named, 2,800 trout were transferred to the Hutt in 1883, and by 1885 some 18,000 ova had been stripped from the remainder.

Between 1880 and 1885 over 40,000 brown trout ova were placed in the Markara, Hutt and its feeders, together with those of Chinook or quinnat salmon, Atlantic salmon, Loch Leven trout, and American brook trout or charr. The Loch Leven trout came from Sir James Maitland's hatchery in Scotland in 1884. In 1897 brown trout were also stocked in Lake Waikaremoana. Shortly after the turn of the century, the Society began to strip ova from wild brown trout rather than from hatchery fish.

In the Wairarapa, 2000 brown trout ova were hatched out at Brancepeth and placed in the Wainuioru and Kaiwhara streams in 1876, and by 1882 some 15,000 fry from the Canterbury Society and ova from the Otago Society had been released in most of the suitable waters in Wellington. By 1886, 30,000 Loch Leven trout, brown trout, and both species of salmon had been freed in the same waters, and two years later 22,500 brook trout ova were placed in the Hutt.

In 1882 a fish hatchery was established at Masterton (which is still in operation) that supplied fish and ova throughout North Island and to the Nelson Society in South Island, and from which as early as 1887 ova were being despatched to Taranaki, Marlborough and Westland. Before the turn of the century, the hatchery consisted of thirty-one rearing ponds with an output capacity of 700,000 ova per annum.

In 1890 or 1891 the first twelve rainbow trout, from a consignment of 200 ova from the Auckland Society, were hatched at Masterton. In 1898, rainbows were first released in the Tongariro, the Mangatainoka, and the Moawhango; other waters in Wellington that were stocked with them included Moore's Creek (a tributary of the Makuri) and the Wainuiomata as early as 1895.

In 1928 the capacity of the Masterton hatchery was increased to 2 million ova and an output of 1,700,000 fry annually. The thriving state of brown trout fishing in Wellington is evidenced by the growth in the number of licences issued each year by the Society, which has risen from 739 in 1901 to 1400 in 1922, and to 3800 today.

The Taranaki Acclimatisation Society[39]

The Taranaki Acclimatisation Society was founded at a meeting held at the Taranaki Institute on 13 June 1874.

The early efforts of the Society were devoted largely to the attempted establishment in the district of various species of trout. At a meeting held on 6 February 1875 it was resolved that the Otago Society be thanked for its gift of an unspecified number of brown trout, and that it be asked to sell the Society a further 200 ova. In October 1884 a number of well-grown fish were obtained from the Nelson Society, and released in the Henui and Waiwakaiho rivers. In the same year a series of trout hatcheries was constructed on the Union Mills property of a member, Mr Honeyfield, in which a quantity of fry, also from Nelson, was successfully reared. In August of the following year these fish were placed in the Henui, Huatoki, and Mangatuku rivers, where they quickly became established. At around the same time American brook trout or brook charr were also introduced to the Society's hatchery; whether any were ever released is uncertain.

In February 1887 an unspecified number of brown trout ova was received by the Society from Otago; 120 of the resulting fish were despatched to the Stoney River, the balance being retained in the hatchery ponds; a year later these fish were liberated in various waters in the district.

In 1889 a supply of brown trout was acquired by the Society from the hatchery at Masterton, and these were turned out in the Tapuae, Oakura, Timaru, Henui and Waiwakaiho rivers.

In 1899–1900 the Society acquired from Masterton some 25,000 brown trout ova and 8000 rainbow trout ova, the hatched fish being released in the Waiwakaiho, Waiongona, and Mangaoraka rivers. In 1903 a further 5000 brook trout, 15,000 rainbows, and 20,000 brown trout arrived from the hatchery at Masterton, and were placed in rivers around Opunake, Sentry Hill, and New Plymouth. The rainbows released in the Waiwakaiho River were found to be well established, several fish of between 1.5 and 3.75 kilograms having been caught. Also in 1903 the Society constructed a second hatchery, in which were placed a further 5000 rainbow fry.

Between 1903 and 1910 a third hatchery must have been built, since in the latter year 7000 trout (of unrecorded species) from ponds at Pukekura were liberated in rivers in the Society's district. Later in the same year 40,000 more brown and rainbow trout fry were introduced to the Pukekura hatchery. From here in 1934, 210,000 brown and 40,000 rainbow fry were released in various Society waters. Today, the Society continues to stock such rivers as the Stoney and Mangamahoe with brown and rainbow trout, obtained from hatcheries at Hawke's Bay, Lake Wanaka, Rotorua, and elsewhere.

At the Society's annual meeting in 1887 it was reported that:

> On September 13th, our portion of the salmon fry, 1000 hatched at Christchurch from ova imported by the Government ex *Ionic* from London in March last, came to hand in fairly good order, with some 180 having died in transit. The young fish were kept in our ponds until the 17th November when 270 each were turned into the following rivers—Waiwakaiho, Waiongona and Waitara.[40]

This introduction of Atlantic salmon, as elsewhere in New Zealand apart from Southland, proved unsuccessful.

In 1876 the Society acquired and released an unspecified number of brown hares which in 1884 were reported to be thriving, especially in the Hua area. In the following year a further thirteen were liberated, mainly in the Waiongona district. In spite of poaching, the population increased to such an extent that the first shooting licences were able to be issued by the Society in 1887. Although the animals were by then well established, and were indeed reported to be causing agricultural damage, a few more were turned out in 1889.

In 1896, at a cost of £20, eighteen 'black opossums' (brush-tailed possums from Tasmania) were purchased from the Southland Society, of which nine were released in the Kaitake Ranges and four (the remainder having died in transit) at Inglewood. The first young were seen, at Inglewood, in 1904.

Although California quail first appeared in Taranaki in 1874, presumably having dispersed south from Auckland, the Society imported a further sixty birds from Nelson in about 1884, which were released at Mangorei. In 1894 they were reported to be abundant, and 'capital sport is anticipated'; a decade later they were said to be 'plentiful in all parts'.

In 1898 the Wellington Society imported 400 bobwhite quail from North America, of which 20 were released at Timaru and a like number at New Plymouth. A year later a further shipment of 756 arrived in Wellington, 44 of which were turned down at Stratford and 32 at New Plymouth. Although in 1902 the Society considered that they were 'steadily increasing and in a year or two should afford good sport',[41] two years later it was obliged to concede that the birds 'seem to have disappeared'.[42]

In 1894 four pairs of grey partridges were received from England, and a pair each was released at Waiwirenui, Tapaue, Brooklands, and Urenui. Four years later others were turned down at Okato, and by 1904 several coveys were reported in the Koru district. In 1959 the Department of Internal Affairs imported two shipments of grey partridge eggs from Denmark; these were hatched out at a game farm at Foxton, and a hundred of the birds released on a farm at Dorset Road in 1963. Although some persisted for several years, in spite of later liberations in Taranaki and elsewhere the grey partridge has been unsuccessful in colonising New Zealand. The reasons for this failure are believed to be a combination of contamination by herbicides and insecticides and predation by feral domestic cats, stoats, and black and brown rats.[43]

Common pheasants were said to be plentiful in Taranaki when the Society was founded in 1874, and they occur today mainly in coastal scrubland.

In 1898 several mallard were placed by the Society on Barrett's Lagoon, where before long they disappeared. Some time after 1906 more were liberated on Lake Okareka, where within a few years they had increased to around 200. Mallard have been released on many subsequent occasions in Taranaki, where they are now established.

In 1874 the Auckland Society was invited to supply its *confrères* in Taranaki with up to twenty pairs of European starlings; in 1888 twenty-four more birds were acquired from Nelson and released, and in 1894 a further forty-two from an unnamed source were freed.

House sparrows and skylarks were reported to be abundant in Taranaki by the time of the Society's formation in 1874, having probably spread south from Auckland where they were first introduced in 1865 and 1867 respectively.

A resolution at a meeting of the Society in 1878, 'that 5 pair of rooks be bought from Auckland'[44] was carried by a narrow majority of 6–4. Seventeen years later, presumably as the result of bitter experience, it was deemed 'inadvisable to have such a bird in our midst'.[45]

In 1874 and 1875, Australian black-backed magpies, and greenfinches, goldfinches, blackbirds, song thrushes, and dunnocks from England were approved for release in Taranaki; whether this recommendation was ever implemented is unknown.

The Tauranga Acclimatisation Society[46]

The Tauranga Acclimatisation Society evolved out of the Tauranga Farmers' Club, which met in Mr R. C. Jordon's auction market on Harrington Street, on 12 November 1881.

One of the earliest introductions made by the embryo Society was of an unrecorded number of brown trout received from the Trentdale Farm in Christchurch. In April 1882 ten pairs of mountain quail, part of a consignment of 400 birds imported by the Auckland and Otago societies from the western United States, were released near Tauranga, where they joined up with some bevies resulting from earlier liberations made, before the formation of the Society, in 1876. These birds eventually died out.

In 1883 some American brook trout or brook charr from Auckland were placed in the Waimapu, Waiorohi, Wairoa, Waitao, Kaitemako, Mangarewa, and Otamarakau rivers, and also at Rotorua, Te Puke, Katikati, and Whakatane.

In 1884 nine red deer calves were purchased by the Society for a total of £15.10s.0d. from Reid Brothers of Motutapu Island, which were released a few years later. A pair of emus from Australia were freed at around the same time at Poeke, but nothing more seems to have been heard of them.

In 1885 the Society constructed its first fish hatchery at Otamarakau, where in the initial year some 4000 ova were hatched.

Although there is no record of the release in Tauranga of brown hares and pheasants, in 1885 the Society took out prosecutions against poachers of both of these animals—for some reason seeking a lenient sentence in the case of the former and a more severe one for the latter.

Early in 1887 a shipment of brown trout was despatched to the Society from South Island, of which, however, only 640 arrived alive. This led to the construction of a second hatchery by the Society on nine hectares of land at Tamarua. Three thousand ova were placed in this hatchery in late 1887, from which in the following year 2806 fish were planted in waters around Rotorua. By the end of 1880 the Tamarua hatchery had raised a total of 21,000 brown trout, most of which were released in the Wairoa River.

The records of the Society are missing for the decade after 1888, but in about 1899 5000 rainbow trout fry arrived from Otamarakau, which were later released in the Waitahanui. By this time the red deer acquired by the Society in 1884 had increased sufficiently to allow the issue of a hunting licence for six stags. In 1901 the Society offered a bounty of 4d each for native hawks which, it was believed, preyed on native and introduced gamebirds. At around the same time enquiries were instituted to try to find an insect which would help to control the destructive codlin moth which, according to Thomson (1922), was probably introduced into New Zealand from Britain, America, or Australia.

The decade after 1903 was marked principally by determined attempts to enlarge the red deer herd and to increase the number of game species in the district. In 1907 a hundred common and ring-necked pheasants were ordered from the Winchester Game Farm in England, and in the following year fallow deer, obtained from the Fielding Society, were turned down on the north bank of the Wairoa River. More brown trout fry were purchased from the government hatchery at Rotorua, and released in waters in the Oropi and Cambridge Road regions and as far afield as the Katikati Riding. In 1912 further red deer were acquired, from the Wellington Society, and in the same year pheasants and Hungarian or grey partridges from England were unsuccessfully freed on the coast at Welcome Bay and at Otumoetai.

In 1913 the Society made a decision not to introduce the Australian black-backed magpie which, however, reached Tauranga naturally in the 1960s. In 1914 the first licence was issued for shooting fallow bucks, on the eastern side of the Waimpau, and in the following year two red deer stags and three hinds were turned out in the Minden area, which are believed to be the ancestors of the Whakamarama/Poripori herd. In about 1916 perch were acquired from the Hawera Society, and released in the Waimapu, Tautau, and Wairoa rivers.

Between 1923 and 1932, more than 500,000 brown trout fry were purchased by the Society from the Tourist Department's hatchery at Rotorua, and placed in local waters. As a result of the high rate of mortality of the released fry, a holding pond was built at Waimapu, where in 1928 6000 fry were reared to the yearling stage. A second pond was later constructed at Te Puke, and in 1930 6000 fry were placed in holding ponds at Otamarakau from where, in the same year, some yearlings were placed in the Wairohi.

During the decade under discussion the Kaimai rivers were dammed for hydro-electric schemes, considerably altering their flow. In 1924 and 1925, 30,000 rainbow trout fry were introduced to Lake McLaren, and an annual order of 40,000 rainbow fry was placed with the government's conservator of Fish and Game.

In 1923 the Society decided that an infusion of new blood from the record head-producing herd of red deer in Otago would be of benefit to the Tauranga population, and sought permission to import two stags from South Island. Unfortunately for them, their application coincided with the start of a Ministry of Internal Affairs programme of severely culling New Zealand's red deer herds, which were causing considerable agricultural and silvicultural damage, and permission to translocate these stags was refused.

In the late 1920s the Society began to take an interest in shellfish, requesting the Marine Department to establish oyster beds in Tauranga harbour, and between 1925 and 1930 translocating toheroas from Ohope to Omanu and Papamoa, where even today the occasional one is uncovered by people digging for tuatuas.

In the early 1930s the Society asked the Minister of Internal Affairs for permission, which was refused, to release brush-tailed possums on Major Island. Subsequently, however, these Australian marsupials must have been freed illicitly on the island, as there is today a thriving population.

From 1933 to 1942 between 40,000 and 50,000 trout fry were released annually in the Tauranga Society's waters, and in 1935–6 150,000 brown trout ova from the Greymouth hatchery were placed, not very successfully, in the Waimapu and other rivers in an attempt to augment naturally spawning fish. During this decade a total of 3463 pheasants—from local breeders and elsewhere—was turned down.

The first signs of damage by possums in the Tauranga district was observed towards the end of the Second World War, when it became apparent that these animals were going to prove grave economic pests rather than, as had been anticipated, the source of financial profit through their valuable furs.

In the late 1940s the duck population in Tauranga, as elsewhere in New Zealand, began to show signs of a serious decline; to combat this, the Society acquired large numbers of mallard eggs for artificial hatching. Between 1949 and 1952 1000 pheasants and nearly 600 mallard were turned down in the Society's district. In 1948, 80,000 rainbow trout fingerlings, which had been reared from ova and fry in holding ponds in Te Puke, Tauranga, and the Kaimais, were released in various of the Society's waters.

During the late 1950s the Society began to concern itself less with the control of so-called 'vermin' (hawks, mustelids, and spotted shags) and more with the conservation of the environment. Man was recognised as causing more harm than all other species combined, especially in his indiscriminating use of insecticides whose effects were felt to the top of the food chain. In 1959, in furtherance of this objective, the Society leased parts of the Kaikokopu and lower Kaituna wetlands on the Bay of Plenty as a waterfowl reserve, and in 1961–2 the Waiwaitutuki Block 8 was purchased. After 1963 more land was acquired in the Kaituna. Pollution, by herbicides, pesticides and sewage from such sources of factory waste, building contractors, quarries and outfalls, and farmers, continued to be a problem.

Between 1964 and 1972 some 6400 pheasants and 310,000 brown and rainbow trout were released on land and in waters under the Society's jurisdiction. In 1966 a proposal by the Society to the North Island Council for the introduction of several new species of wildfowl—wigeon, pochard, canvasback, eider, scoter, and goldeneye—and snipe and woodcock, was rejected.

It was becoming clear that the conservation of the environment, with self-maintaining and self-perpetuating 'naturalised' populations of species with a controlled harvest, was better game management than the continual augmenting of existing stocks by large-scale releases. To this end, such trees as swamp oak, persimmon, and fig, were planted to provide food for birds.

In 1977, with financial support from the Department of Internal Affairs and the North Island council, the Society spent $30,000 on the acquisition of a further 355 hectares of wetlands in the lower Kaituna as a game management reserve—the land to be designated as Crown property, but with day-to-day management under the control of the Society.

In 1980 the Society began releasing its first chukar partridges, at Oropi, Otamarakau, and Te Puke, but although some of the birds were reported to be nesting in the wild, the species has yet to become established in North Island. Brown and rainbow trout continued to be liberated, and some American brook trout were acquired by the Society for breeding purposes.

A century after its foundation, the Tauranga Acclimatisation Society, like other similar societies elsewhere in New Zealand, is no longer primarily interested in the introduction of new species, but rather in 'ensuring the survival and continuing high quality of habitat utilised by the fish and game resource upon which sport fish and hunting is based and funded'.[47]

15. The Imperial Russian Society for the Acclimatisation of Animals and Plants

AS part of a wider concept for agricultural regeneration and scientific progress, an interest in the acclimatisation and domestication of non-indigenous animals and plants existed in Russia from at least the early 1840s, and was in itself a manifestation of the direct rejection of Vladimir Odoevskii's narrow dictum that 'the goal of science is science itself—it has no other external goal.'[1]

In common with most zoological thought in Russia at the time, the idea of the acclimatisation of alien species was largely of French origin. So-called 'Westernisers' much admired contemporary French savants for their emphasis on empiricism, materialism, and a concern for the practical application and popularisation of science. It was precisely these attributes that attracted the acknowledged doyen of contemporary Russian zoology, Karl Frantsevich Rul'e (1814–58), to French scientific thinking, and subsequently characterised his own work.

A son of an impoverished immigrant survivor of Napoleon's *Grande Armée*, François Rouillier, Rul'e was born on 20 April 1814 (N.S.) in Nizhnyi Novgorod (now Gor'kii). In 1829 he entered the Moscow branch of the Medical-Surgical Academy, where he studied under Grigorii Ivanovich Fisher-fon-Val'dgeim [Fischer von Waldheim] (1771–1853) who, as founder in 1820 and first director of the Moscow Agricultural Society, had initiated the movement for science to show responsibility to the social requirements of Russia. Fisher, who had himself studied under the celebrated Georges Cuvier (1769–1832) in Paris where, among others, he became a friend of Etienne Geoffroy Saint-Hilaire (1772–1844; father of Isidore), was an admirer of French zoology and taught largely in that language, so Rul'e, who spoke French fluently, absorbed his scientific teaching directly from French thought.

The primary topic of the time among biologists was the question of the immutability versus the mutability of species. The dispute raged most furiously in France, where the evolutionist Etienne Geoffroy Saint-Hilaire, who was strongly supported by Rul'e, was opposed by the reactionary Cuvier, who not only maintained that species were immutable, but also that they were specifically designed by their Creator to live in similarly immutable environments, and that their morphological make-up had accordingly been pre-designed for life in these existing conditions.

Among the arguments employed by Rul'e to confound Cuvier and his fellow conservatives, was the transformation of animals and plants through acclimatisation and domestication, and through the development or abandonment of individual organs, brought about by their use or disuse. Rul'e propounded the theory that an organism is directly affected by its environment which stimulates it to make fundamental and heritable morphological adaptations, altering, for example, the density or coloration of pelt or plumage or body weight and size, by means of the direct action of sunlight, temperature and other climatic factors. (Bergmann's Rule, for example, states that the size of homoiothermic (warm-blooded) animals in a single, closely related evolutionary line increases along a gradient from warm to cold latitudes, i.e. that forms of species from cold climates are likely to consist of physically larger individuals than those forms from warm climates. This is because the surface-area-to-body-weight ratio decreases as body weight increases. Thus a larger body loses proportionately less heat than a smaller one. This is obviously an advantage in a cold climate but a disadvantage in a warm one.)

The acclimatisation of animals was to play a central role in solving the puzzles of evolution, as Rul'e emphasised in one of his lectures in 1851:[2]

> Science especially cries out for scrupulous observation of changes [in acclimatised animals] in response to new physical conditions. We are certain that science will gain enormously from such research; at the very least more than from dozens of ordinary expeditions or from the description of thousands of new genera and species of animals. Science will gain knowledge of laws and processes, although it will not add to its roll the name of one new animal.

As well as its relevance to the future development of the theory of evolution, acclimatisation also represented the practical application of that same evolutionary doctrine. Acclimatisation (in Russian *akklimatizatsiia* or *priurochivanie*, from *urok* = lesson) included the believed ability of animals and plants to undergo heritable adaptations to unfamiliar conditions—either natural or man-made—in a directed and ultimately predictable manner. For Rul'e and his fellow evolutionists the practical implications were important. 'What', wrote Rul'e in his *Obshchaia zoologiia* (Zoological Notebooks)[3] 'is the significance of the fact that, with a change in their way of life, climate or conditioning, animals, plants and people are also transformed? Is not agriculture based on that dream which strives to refashion both plants and animals—that is, to refashion that which according to [Cuvier's] theory is immutable?'

Rul'e had become interested in acclimatisation in the early 1840s, and in a lecture in 1845 had first suggested the domestication of wild Russian indigenous species. The source of this suggestion, as he later acknowledged, was Etienne Geoffroy St-Hilaire's son, Isidore, subsequently the driving force behind the establishment of the *Société Zoologique d'Acclimatation* in France.

Rul'e introduced his countrymen to the activities of the *Jardin des Plantes* in Paris, where Isidore was at the time the director, and where in the early 1840s a pair of wild Egyptian geese and some Asiatic asses or onagers had reportedly been domesticated.[4] At the same time, Rul'e suggested the possibility of acclimatising wild species to new habitats without domesticating them, which would 'enrich the forests with animals, remarkable either for their meat or for the quality of their fur, or for some other product'. This we would now term 'naturalisation' rather than 'acclimatisation' (see Introduction).

As time went by Rul'e's interest in acclimatisation and domestication (*priruchenie* or *odomashnenie*) increased, and in his syllabus on general zoology at Moscow University in the 1850s, where he was a lecturer, he gave evolutionism and acclimatisation an important place.

By the mid-1850s Rul'e felt that the time had come no longer to theorise but to act; the trigger that fired this decision was the formation in Paris in 1854 by his friend, Isidore Geoffroy Saint-Hilaire, of the *Société Zoologique d'Acclimatation*. Rul'e encouraged his disciples—Iakov Andreevich Borzenkov (1825–83), Andrei Nikolaevich Beketov (1825–1902), Nikolai Alekseevich Severtsov (1827–85), Sergei Alekseevich Usov (1827–86), and Anatolii Petrovich Bogdanov (1834–96)—to lay the foundations of an acclimatisation society in Russia, at the same time seeking organisational assistance from an old friend and colleague, Stepan Alekseevich Maslov (1793–1879), secretary of the Moscow Agricultural Society.

Maslov, a near-contemporary of Fisher-fon-Val'dgeim, who had visited the *Jardin des Plantes* when in Paris, was twenty-one years older than Rul'e. A dedicated agricultural reformer, he had refused academic and administrative advancement in favour of his present position. As editor of the *Zemledelcheskii zhurnal* (*Agricultural Journal*) he chose papers from the Western press that emphasised modern practices—including acclimatisation; he was a pioneer in Russian attempts to acclimatise silkworms, and chairman of the Moscow Sericulture Committee.

Maslov gave enthusiastic encouragement to Rul'e's proposal, and placed on the agenda of a meeting of the Moscow Agricultural Society on 17 November 1856 the subject of the formation of an acclimatisation society. At that meeting, Bogdanov pointed out that with the rapid growth in the human population and its spread to 'less felicitous climes', the science of agriculture was assuming increasing, and even crucial, importance. Nowhere was this more true than in Russia, where the serf economy was inert, the population was increasing, and where nature was at its harshest. 'To what,' Bogdanov enquired of his audience, 'if not to Science, can we turn for advice in such difficult circumstances?' Zoology was in a position 'to unite the science of animals with the world of praxis—Zoology with Agriculture' through acclimatisation:

> We may see that the field of action is great and majestic, that the results that can and will be attained in this field will not simply double but will increase the national wealth and well-being ten times over. Have we not waited long enough for the realization of this idea here in Russia, which has all the ingredients for success, unmatched by any nation? What can stop us? Can there really be an insufficiency of energy and old noble sentiment to do battle with failures and difficulties for the good of society?[5]

Bogdanov suggested that the new society should begin with the acclimatisation of herbivores, which were more amenable to domestication. His proposal was not only for the introduction of such alien species as the alpaca, llama, and vicugna from South America, the water buffalo from India and the yak from the Tibetan plateau, but also for the domestication of such native mammals as the saiga antelope, argali, red deer, elk, Siberian musk deer, roe deer, and Eurasian beaver.

Bogdanov fully accepted the existence of factors which limited instantly successful acclimatisation. Alien species would need to be conditioned to their new environments gradually, in order to accommodate the slow pace of environmental induction as it strove with conservative heredity. Subjects of experiments in the science of acclimatisation would be systematically subjected to varying and strictly controlled changes of specific factors of their environments, as Bogdanov explained:[6]

> If I know that the alteration of a factor, e.g. light intensity and quality, has a visible effect on the colour of a feather, I can then alter conditions in such a way as to create greater or lesser changes (in that feather) depending on need, or I can isolate the animal from the action of the factor altogether.

Thus, Bogdanov continued, 'the experiments of acclimatizers will provide data for the naturalist, who will derive from them laws for application by the agriculturist, and in that way science and practice will march arm in arm toward one objective: the common good.'

Citing experiments already carried out by Rul'e, Avgust Farenkol' with silkworms, Nikolai Ivanovich Annenkov with plants, and N. A. Varnek with fish, Bogdanov concluded his peroration by enquiring rhetorically whether any of his listeners could be in doubt 'that such a combination of persons united in this great goal of enriching The

Fatherland with a new branch of the economy will bring quick and brilliant results?'[7]

At the conclusion of the meeting, the members of the Moscow Agricultural Society enthusiastically voted in favour of the formation forthwith of an acclimatisation committee, whose founder members included Maslov and Rul'e, and the latter's protégés Bogdanov, Borzenkov and Usov; the doctors of medicine Farenkol' and E. E. Gro, who were amateur zoologists and friends of Rul'e; Varnek, the Professor of Zoology at Moscow University; Iakov Nikolaevich Kalinovskii (1814–1903), Professor of Agronomy at Moscow University; Annenkov, director of the Agricultural School of the Moscow Agricultural Society; the curator of the Moscow Society of Naturalists' Museum, I. S. Ber; V. V. Khlopov, N. G. Riumin, and D. F. Samarin.

The new committee held its inaugural meeting on 30 January 1857, when it was divided into two sub-committees—one, under Rul'e for animals and the other, under Annenkov, for plants. Until his death at the age of only forty-four on 10 August 1858, Rul'e's sub-committee profited by the great talent and prestige its chairman brought to the cause of acclimatisation. In May 1857 he despatched Bogdanov to Paris to study at first hand the activities of the *Société Zoologique d'Acclimatation*. In September, at a meeting of the Moscow Agricultural Society, he made a personal plea to N. M. Murav'ev, the Minister of State Lands, to convert him to the cause of acclimatisation. Only five months before his death, and already in poor health, Rul'e, with Borzenkov and Usov, paid a visit to V. N. Vrasskii's Nikol'skii Fish Hatchery to study his pioneering experimentation with the acclimatisation and artificial insemination of trout. Even after Rul'e's death, his sub-committee continued to expand, testifying both to its late chairman's influence and to its devotion to the cause of acclimatisation.

Rul'e was briefly succeeded by the dean of the Physics-Mathematics faculty of Moscow University, Mikhail Fedorovitch Spasskii, on whose death in January 1859 the chairmanship was assumed by S. A. Usov. Under his leadership the two sub-committees were amalgamated, and obtained the patronage of one of the brothers of the Tsar, the Ministers of State Lands and Education, and academicians F. B. Brandt, A. F. Middendorf and K. S. Veselovskii, all of whom became charter-members of the St Petersburg branch. Other branches were established in Khar'kov and Orel. On 3 January 1864 an official charter was granted to the infant society, and the Imperial Russian Society for the Acclimatisation of Animals and Plants embarked on its sixty-five-year long life with 1021 members, no fewer than eight of whom were also members of the imperial Russian family.

The late 1850s and early 1860s were the golden age of acclimatisation in imperial Russia, where support and publicity for the cause were provided by nearly a score of periodicals, including the Society's own *Izvestiia (News)*, *Zapiski (Notes)*, and monthly *Akklimatizatsiia*.

Rul'e's successors devoted themselves to the work of the Society with great dedication. In 1858 Bogdanov organised a successful acclimatisation fair in the Moscow School of Agriculture, and a second and much larger one, which lasted for ten days in April 1863, at the Manezh; the 10,000-rouble profits were allotted to the Society's principal project—the formation of a zoo in Moscow.

As early as 1856 Bogdanov and his colleagues had formulated the idea of establishing a zoo. Theirs, however, was to be no mere pleasure garden for the benefit of the gawping public—it was to be a strictly scientific institution modelled on the *Jardin des Plantes* in Paris, in which the hereditary changes, if any, in the animals acclimatising to their new environment could be closely studied. Due to the success of Bogdanov's two fairs, interest in acclimatisation was high, and donations of cash and promises of animals flowed in. E. M. Skvortsov, a rich St Petersburg merchant, and the government each contributed ten thousand roubles; Countess L. N. Panina donated a wolf and a monkey; Prince Obolenskii gave Russia's last pair of tarpans;[8] and from the Melbourne zoo in Australia came two dozen animals, including some wallabies and a kangaroo. The zoo was eventually established in the *Presnenskie prudy* (Fresh Ponds) area of Moscow.

Almost as soon as it was opened, however, trouble broke out; a group of academic zoologists, who gave the zoo's research programme priority over its applied research in domestication, acclimatisation and hybridisation, were opposed by some academic agronomists and practical agriculturalists who wished to give precedence to the applied research. The latter were led by two agronomists, Iosif Nikolaevich Shatilov (1824–89), who had been a member of the Society since 1858, and Professor Kalinovskii, who was the first director of the zoo, taught agronomy at Moscow University from 1853 to 1871, and besides also serving as secretary of the Society during this period was editor of the monthly journal *Akklimatizatsiia*. Shatilov, who had briefly studied under Rul'e before moving to Khar'kov University, had achieved notable success in breeding various species of silkworms on the Mokhovae estate in Tula Province, where he also won acclaim for developing new agricultural and silvicultural practices. With Annenkov and Maslov, Shatilov was a key member of the Moscow Agricultural Society, of which he was president for a quarter of a century from 1864 to 1889, and served on numerous government commissions.

Somewhat provocatively, the two dissidents and some of their colleagues—among whom was Bogdanov—started their own group on domesticated breeds within the Society. Shatilov claimed that instead of importing exotic species from abroad, the Society ought to have concentrated on gathering together a collection of the Russian breeds of sheep; should have been acquainting Russian farmers with relatively little-known varieties; and ought to have been extensively cross-breeding foreign breeds of domesticated animals to produce improved varieties. Maintaining animals for the entertainment of the public was not, Shatilov asserted, in keeping with the declared objects of the 'acclimatisation zoo', and even keeping native predators in captivity could only be justified if they were used in experimental cross-breeding with domestic dogs to produce 'improved' working breeds. 'It is clear from this', wrote Boris Evgen'evich Raikov, Usov's biographer,[9] 'that for the breeder-*praktik* Shatilov, the idea that a wolf or the fox could be interesting for their own sakes, or as subjects for zoological study, was completely alien.' To latter-day zoologists this seems an extraordinary proposition. By the 1860s, as Weiner says, attitudes had indeed moved far from the ideal of 'science for science's sake'.

Usov, on the other hand, maintained that the zoo possessed neither the funds nor the space for an experimental hybridisation farm, and that as it depended on admission fees to cover its expenses, it had no alternative other than to some extent to provide what the public demanded. In any case, the general study of living animals and the aim of educating the public were parts of the zoo's scientific research programme. Acclimatisation and hybridisation of domesticated species should not be the zoo's sole objectives, as the insurgents demanded. Usov was supported by N. A. Severtsov, a cerebral scientist who, as had Bogdanov, called for a programme of controlled experiments with a wide diversity of animals. While the science of acclimatisation promised great things for agriculture, the development of acclimatisation biology, both practical and theoretical, would have first to be developed systematically at the zoo, before its principles could be applied directly to agriculture. This could not be achieved by making a farm out of the zoo.

This controversy between the pure and applied researchers was soon overshadowed by the zoo's financial failure, and in 1871 it was let to an entrepreneur, A. A. Riabinin, in exchange for his undertaking to liquidate part of its debt of 66,000 roubles. The dispute rumbled on, however, well into the present century, and had a profound effect on a wide spectrum of Russian science.

Bogdanov reassumed an active role in the Society shortly before the zoo, wrecked by Riabinin's mismanagement and racketeering, was reacquired by the Society in 1878. With the profits from an acclimatisation exhibition held in the zoo grounds, Bogdanov undertook both the zoo's reconstruction and a programme of experimental hybridisation. Although physical restoration of the zoo was achieved, it proved impossible to place it on a sound financial footing; by 1893—three years before Bogdanov's death—its debt had reached 104,533 roubles, and a decade later it had to be leased out once more.

After the initial activity that followed Bogdanov's return, the Society began to stagnate. In the words of Grigorii Aleksandrovich Kozhevnikov (1866–1933), a pupil of Bogdanov and the Society's last president,[10] 'the zoo's troubled financial straits monopolised our attention, overshadowing questions of the zoo's very objectives and organization.'

Outside the ranks of the Society, however, the interest in acclimatisation was becoming increasingly evident. On the luxuriant steppes of Tavrida Province, north of the Perekop isthmus, a big landowner, Fridrikh Eduardovich Fal'ts-Fein (1863–1920), established the best-known acclimatisation and hybridisation park and gardens throughout Russia at Askania-Nova.

After the 1870s, there were many attempts to translocate such native fur-bearing species as Eurasian beavers, sable and rabbits. These efforts were given new impetus in 1903 by the publication of a treatise describing how best to acclimatise and breed native fur-bearing animals. Although Isidore Geoffroy Saint-Hilaire, Rul'e, and Bogdanov (who asserted that 'historically and practically speaking, the necessity for acclimatisation in Russia has been appreciated for a long time . . . but private efforts . . . have not and are not capable of achieving rich results') had some forty years previously emphasised the need for state support, it was only in the early twentieth century that the government began to take an active interest in acclimatisation. Even after the Minister of Agriculture, Aleksei Sergeevich Ermolov, who was sympathetic to the acclimatisation cause, left office in the early 1900s, the ministry continued to support acclimatisation projects.

The acclimatisation of plants, the concept of which had been brought to Russia from France by Rul'e, Bogdanov and Annenkov, also proceeded apace. By the 1880s, bamboo, lemons, oranges and tea were being cultivated in the Caucasus, and American cotton had been planted in Turkestan. Acclimatisation gardens began to germinate throughout the country: they included the Society's *sad* (gardens) in Ashkhabad; Nikitskii *sad* in the Crimea; Umanskii Tsaritsyn *sad* near Kiev, where both Annenkov and Kalinovskii were directors; the Orel Tree Nursery; the Botanical Acclimatisation Gardens at Sukhumi; the Siberian *sad* of A. I. Olonichenko at Krasnoiarsk, M. G. Nikiforov at Minusinsk, and Professor Nikolai Feofanivich Kashchenko at Tomsk (later Kiev); and, most important of them all, Fal'ts-Fein's *sad* at Askania-Nova. From its formation in 1858, the Imperial Horticultural Society of Russia, of which Bogdanov was an original member, also continued to support acclimatisation projects.

The Acclimatisation Society, now firmly under the control of academic zoologists, in 1892 sponsored the Botanico-Zoological Acclimatisation Congress in Moscow; this was by far the largest and most important biological conference in Russia in the nineteenth century, and the repercussions from it were felt well into the present century.

In the 1880s and 1890s three of Bogdanov's students held important positions in the Society: Vladimir Aleksandrovich Vagner (1849–1934) served as the Society's secretary; Nikolai Iur'evich Zograf (1851–?), a professor at Moscow University, was head of the ichthyological and later the invertebrate division, while Nikolai Mikhailovich Kulagin (1860–1940) was in charge of both ornithology and the Moscow zoo.

In pursuance of their policy of making zoology serve the interests of agriculture, both Vagner and Kulagin specialised in the control of injurious insects. The former visited the Nikitskii *sad* in the Crimea, to try to evaluate the possibility of introducing natural enemies of local agricultural insect pests which, together with rodents, were causing immense economic losses and periodic famines. This is an early example of an attempt at the biological control of a destructive native species by an introduced predator—a practice that has, all too frequently, had devastating consequences on other, and in many cases harmless, indigenous species of fauna and flora and their ecosystems throughout the world.

In the early 1900s it gradually began to dawn on at least some academic zoologists that their priorities had to change, and that the primary need now was not for the introduction and acclimatisation of exotic species, nor for the development of new varieties of domesticated species, but rather for the preservation or the restoration of what had once existed—in other words, for 'conservation'. This idea was not new—it had been propounded before by both Bogdanov and Maslov—but the Society's new president, Kozhevnikov, considered it of paramount importance. In his address at the jubilee conference of the Society in 1908, he made no mention whatever of acclimatisation, but instead spoke passionately of the urgent necessity of preserving, in a system of state reserves, what remained of virgin habitats and native animals.

Under Kozhevnikov's presidency, the Society moved away from the previous interventionist, utilitarian concepts of its founders, and by 1917 the agronomists and their academic confederates had largely deserted the Society in favour of other organisations. In the 1920s and 1930s, Zhitkov, Kashchenko and Manteifel' successfully persuaded important Soviet agricultural bodies actively to support the waning cause of acclimatisation. In the meantime, under Kozhevnikov, the conservation movement was finding other organisations to further its own cause, and the need for an Acclimatisation Society had virtually disappeared.

What finally caused the Society's demise was the growing acceptance of the theory of 'community ecology'—the value and importance of the complete ecosystems and the biosphere—as being taught by Kozhevnikov and his colleagues. Not only were Bogdanov's dicta on acclimatisation refuted, but the acclimatisation of exotic species of fauna and flora in virgin habitats was realised as positively harmful—indeed, seriously so—to the conservation of native species and their environment. By 1930, the Acclimatisation Society, no longer Imperial, had passed into oblivion.

What, then, did the Society achieve? The acclimatisation movement in Russia in the mid-nineteenth century, inspired by Isidore Geoffroy Saint-Hilaire's French society and by definite ideas, also derived from France, about the role and responsibility of science to society, was joined by academic scientists, agriculturalists, agronomists, and zoologists, based on the Moscow Agricultural Society. Later, the movement became more clearly defined with the formation of the Acclimatisation Society. Although it failed directly to initiate extensive attempts to introduce alien species to Russia, particularly via the Moscow zoo, it did help to spread the theory of acclimatisation in scientific and agricultural circles and, by so doing, encouraged local attempts to acclimatise a wide variety of fauna and flora, many of which, as with the British society, were totally unsuited to the purpose. The school of thought among Russian biologists, associated with Karl Frantsevich Rul'e and Anatolii Petrovich Bogdanov, that believed in the environmental induction of hereditary adaptations, itself drawn from the doctrine of Etienne and Isidore Geoffroy Saint-Hilaire and Jean-Baptiste Lamarck, derives from the early days of the acclimatisation movement. Although they have been almost completely ignored by Soviet and other scientific historians, members of this school (who were in all probability inspired by the same inductionist theories of heredity and idealistic ideas concerning the rôle of science in society that stimulated their masters), as well as upholding the cause of acclimatisation under the Soviets, played an important part in Soviet life sciences generally throughout the 1920s and 1930s.

'The history of the acclimatisation movement in Russia reads', as Weiner says, 'like a Marxian dialectic in reverse motion.'[11] Originally, the movement for acclimatisation, in its attempt to instil greater rationality into Russian agriculture, represented a progressive synthesis. It endeavoured to maximise the economic potential of the state by the acclimatisation of introduced species, while at the same time seeking to prevent the further irresponsible rape of the country's natural resources through intelligent usage and, ultimately, by what is sometimes wrongly regarded as the 'modern' tool of conservation. As a consequence of internal developments in biological thinking and social and institutional changes, however, the synthesis disintegrated, and by the

1930s the acclimatisers had become divided from the so-called 'conservationists' by a profound disagreement that was as much philosophical as scientific.

Acclimatisation, once hailed as a 'Westernising' example of increasing rationality, had come to be regarded as representing an irrational approach to the sensible management of natural resources, in particular during the Stalinist drive to introduce and naturalise in the wild large numbers of exotic (especially fur-bearing) economic species which, as they have all too frequently done elsewhere, had a serious impact on the native biota.

When the acclimatisation movement in Russia was in its infancy, its endorsement of the biological teaching of Geoffroy Saint-Hilaire and Lamarck was regarded as progressive and enlightened. In ignorance about chromosomes, genes and mutations, let alone DNA[12], it seemed at the time the best way to explain scientifically the growing evidence of the evolution of life forms on earth—later propounded by Charles Darwin (1809–82) in his *On the Origin of Species by Means of Natural Selection* (1859), and *Variation of Animals and Plants under Domestication* (1868), in which he developed the theory of pangenesis. It was, as Weiner says, 'a defence of Science against troglodytic Creationists'.

In the late 1920s, acclimatisation was on the one hand adopted by regime-supported radicals as a technological and agronomic panacea (i.e. as a precursor of the 'Stalin Plan for the Great Transformation of Nature'), while at the same time eliciting vigorous opposition from scientists and the intelligentsia, who correctly perceived in it a symbol and first step in the destruction of the integrity not only of Russian nature, but also of existing social relations, and in particular the autonomy of scientists.[13] By the mid-1930s, and quite possibly much earlier, the acceptance by academics, agriculturalists, agronomists, biologists, scientists and zoologists of these now outmoded beliefs, ran contrary to new evidence and more informed hypotheses. 'As such', Weiner concludes, 'it constituted an antiscientific defence of pseudoscientific ideas', and for this, if for no other reason, it was condemned to disappear.

16. Acclimatisation Societies in the United States and the Hawaiian Islands

AS early as 1846 the Natural History Society of America imported songbirds from Europe which were released near Brooklyn, New York. Others (including the first house sparrows—usually known in the United States as English sparrows—to be introduced to North America) were brought in between 1850 and 1853 by the Brooklyn Institute (under the direction of Mr Nicholas Pike), while the trustees of the Greenwood Cemetery on Long Island introduced several species late in 1852. The house sparrows (fifty-eight pairs) were introduced in the hope that they would control a plague of 'measuring-worms' or 'span-worms' (*Eunomos subsignarius*) that was defoliating trees in the state of New York. Until at least well into the 1880s many more were subsequently released in over one hundred urban centres in thirty-nine states and four Canadian provinces. B. F. Craig (1860), in the *Report of the Commissioner of Patents* for 1859 to the House of Representatives, states,[1] somewhat enigmatically, that

> The naturalization of foreign domestic animals is at the present day by no means an entirely neglected subject in this country; for, not to speak of other instances of progress, it is well known that Dr Davis, of South Carolina, has introduced into his native State more than one valuable animal, and, in fact, may be said to have commenced there a system of acclimation.

Who Dr Davis was, and which species he was attempting to acclimatise in South Carolina, we are unfortunately not informed.

In its 14 April 1860 edition, the British periodical the *Saturday Review* reported[2] that

> On the other side of the Atlantic, the citizens of New York, under the salutary impression that their teeming population requires space for recreation and amusement, as well as for material development, have decided that a portion of the tract of Central Park shall be devoted to the establishment of the 'Zoological and Botanical Gardens'. The able author, Mr F. L. Olinsted, who now holds the office of Surveyor to the New York Board of Works, has lately paid a visit to Europe for the purpose of collecting information as to the best method of carrying out these enlightened views.

Central Park was not only the proposed site for zoological and botanical gardens in New York—it was also the first place in the United States where exotic birds from Europe were released by an acclimatisation society.

The founding father of the movement for the acclimatisation of mammals and birds within the United States was an eccentric New York pharmaceutical chemist, amateur ornithologist, and Shakesperian devotee, Eugene Schieffelin, who conceived the whimsical notion of introducing to the United States all the birds mentioned by the Bard. To this end he founded the Friends of Shakespeare movement. He also formed, jointly with John Avery, and originally for the purpose of introducing the European starling to New York, the American Acclimatisation Society, of which he was the first president; with the stated objects in its charter and by-laws of 'the introduction and acclimatization of such foreign varieties of the animal and vegetable kingdoms as may be useful or interesting' and 'the discovery and development of valuable properties in species not hitherto brought into the service of man'. With a council consisting of Joshua Jones, Alfred Edwards, Edward L. Ludlow, William N. Clark, Joseph H. Westerfield, and Schieffelin, the Society was incorporated in New York on 20 April 1871. In July 1877 an unrecorded number of starlings and some 'Japanese finches' were released by the Society in Central Park, and at around the same time possibly also in Tuxedo Park. In 1890 forty pairs of starlings imported from England were again freed in Central Park, and a similar number in the following year. Breeding began almost immediately, the first nest being discovered, most appropriately, under the eaves of the American Museum of Natural History; by 1893–4 flocks up to fifty strong were being reported, and by the following year starlings were common in many districts of New York City, and had spread to Long Island, where three years later they were said to be abundant.

In 1873, a German immigrant to Cincinnati, Ohio, Andrew Erkenbrecher, who had emigrated from his native country at the age of fifteen and eventually amassed a considerable fortune in his adopted land, founded the Cincinnati Acclimatisation Society, the objects of which were defined in the Society's constitution and by-laws as being

> To introduce to this country all useful, insect eating European birds, as well as the best singers, and to see to it that the imported, as well as domestic birds, have a better protection against the attacks of heartless men, and thoughtless boys, that the shooting of useful birds be prevented and the destruction of birds nests be stopped, with all legal means at the disposal of the society.

Membership of the society was open to 'all persons bearing a good reputation, and who agree to further the objects of the Society to the best of their power', and it was 'the duty of every member to advance the object explained in the Constitution . . . and always to maintain a good understanding with his fellow members, as well as the good reputation of the Society.'

In the year of its foundation, the Cincinnati Acclimatisation Society published a notice entitled *The Protection of Birds,* under the names of the president, Erkenbrecher, and the secretary, Armin Tenner, which stated that

THE CINCINNATI SOCIETY OF ACCLIMATIZATION, encouraged by the successful attempts made in the introduction of foreign birds, will expend this spring a sum of $5,000 for the importation of 15 new varieties of European birds, particularly singing birds and insect eaters. The object of the society in introducing these birds is to obtain some remedy against the encroachment of insects, as well as to enliven our parks, woods and meadows, which in comparison with European countries, are so bare of feathered songsters. It must be confessed, that the introduction of insect eating birds will prove highly beneficial to our orchard and shade trees, and we may also expect that the ennobling influences of the song of birds will be felt by the inhabitants. But now arises the question: Have the birds here that protection which is indispensable to make them stay with us, and to promote their increase? Even in Europe boys could not be prevented by fines and punishments alone from shooting and disturbing the birds, and particularly in cities it became necessary to accomplish with the assistance of teachers and the clergy, what could not be done by the severest police regulations. Experience teaches us that it is much easier to impress upon children, by timely reproaches, the great moral wrong of this offense, and awaken their love for the merry songsters, than to attempt to cow them with threats. In consequence the society addresses to all clergymen, teachers, parents, and lovers of nature and birds the request, to aid it in the above indicated manner in its efforts.

Erkenbrecher subsequently reported to the Cincinnati Society of Natural History that in 1873–4 his society had spent some $9000 in purchasing and importing to Ohio 4000 European songbirds and other species, at an average price of $4.50 a pair. According to the *Journal of the Cincinnati Society of Natural History* for 1881 (which described Erkenbrecher as the *late* president of the acclimatisation society), the species introduced were robins, wagtails, skylarks, starlings, hedge sparrows—now known as dunnocks—song thrushes, mistle thrushes, blackbirds, redwings, 'Hungarian Thrushes', nightingales, goldfinches, siskins, bullfinches, great tits, 'Dutch tits', dippers, corncrakes, parrot crossbills, house sparrows, and 'Cherry Birds'.

To acclimatise these foreign importations before their release into the wild, they were housed in a mansion in that part of Cincinnati known as Burnet Woods. From here, on a morning in May, they were set free *en masse*; 'a cloud of beautiful plumage', Erkenbrecher later rhapsodised, 'burst through the open window, and a moment later Burnet Woods was resonate with a melody of thanksgiving never heard before and probably never heard since.' Most of these birds, with the exception of the house sparrows, were never seen again.

At around the same time, a Society for the Acclimatisation of Foreign Birds was formed at Cambridge, Massachusetts, which between 1872 and 1874 released large numbers of goldfinches in Mount Auburn Cemetery, 'some of which were reported at various places in New England for many years afterwards.'[3] In the 1880s and 1890s they were said to be breeding freely, and were reported in eastern Massachusetts, at New Haven, Connecticut, and north to Toronto, Ontario, in Canada, where four were seen in 1887. Goldfinches seem to have survived in New England until at least the turn of the century. Climatic factors, rather than a lack of suitable habitat, are likely to have been the species' controlling factor in the eastern United States.

In Portland, Oregon, in 1880, another German immigrant, C. F. Pfluger, founded the Society for the Introduction of Useful Song Birds into Oregon (commonly known as the Portland Song Bird Club), initially to introduce house sparrows and starlings. In 1889 and again in 1892, at a cost of some $2000, the following 'Imported and Acclimated German Song Birds' were released in Oregon:

Species	Number	Status in 1896–1897
Song thrush	35 pairs	'they have increased remarkably well.'
Parrot crossbill	20 pairs	—
Siskin	40 pairs	—
Bullfinch	20 pairs	—
European starling	35 pairs	'turned loose in the city of Portland . . . and have since increased remarkably well.'
European robin	5 pairs	'there were many more of them when they first arrived, but unfortunately they died.'
Linnet	35 pairs	—
Goldfinch	40 pairs	'they have become very plentiful throughout the State, and can be seen quite often on the east side of the city.'
Goldfinch	20 or 40 pairs	[Released in 1907.]
Greenfinch	15 pairs	—
Chaffinch	40 pairs	—
Chaffinch	20 pairs	[Released in 1907.]
Skylark	50 pairs	'they were let loose . . . in East Portland; . . . near McMinnville; near Milwaukee and Molalla . . . and in the Waldo Hills. They have increased

wonderfully.' Numerous in Umpqua Valley, Douglas County, and in Marion and Washington counties. Survived for 20–25 years in neighbourhood of Portland, Salem, and Gresham.

Woodlark	10 pairs	—
Northern mockingbird	3 pairs	'set free . . . at Milwaukee . . . said to have returned to breed the following season.'
Northern mockingbird	nearly 40 pairs	in 1895 'set free from the Aviary' in Portland.
Nightingale	?	—
Blackcap	20 pairs	[in 1900 and 1907]

Of these fifteen species only one, the European starling, has become successfully established in the United States.

Other birds unsuccessfully released by the Portland Song Bird Club included grosbeaks (or, according to Phillips (1928) possibly haw-finches), 'singing quail', and yellowhammers.

The formation of the American and Cincinnati acclimatisation societies and the Portland Song Bird Club encouraged the founding of similar organisations in various states. Palmer (1899) reported that:

> Acclimatisation of plants and animals has attracted attention in all parts of the world. Useful or curious species have been introduced from one country to another with varying degrees of success. . . . During the last fifty years a number of acclimatisation societies have been organized for the purpose of introducing animals and plants from foreign countries. Private individuals, too, have devoted both time and money to importing birds or mammals which they consider necessary or desirable additions to the native fauna. Four or five societies exist in New Zealand and several have been formed in the United States.

One of the latter, the Country Club of San Francisco, was founded mainly to introduce the brown trout from Europe to the streams of California. It also despatched several large shipments of Chinook salmon ova to the acclimatisation societies of Australia and New Zealand; in the latter country, under the name of quinnat salmon, they are now well established and a popular and sought-after game fish in several South Island rivers.

In 1891, the Country Club of San Francisco released sixty-seven pairs of northern mockingbirds from Louisiana and five or six species of English song-birds (including goldfinches, and a hundred nightingales sent out in 1887 to be 'turned loose in a gentleman's park') in California, none of which survived for long.

In its annual *Bulletin* for 1884, under the heading of 'Zoological Miscellany', a correspondent to the Cincinnati Society of Natural History
listed the birds introduced to Ohio by Andrew Erkenbrecher. 'While
we deem the above facts of sufficient ornithological importance to merit
a record in permanent form', the editor concluded, 'and cannot but
admire the sentiment which promoted the introduction of these birds,
we may properly at the same time express the opinion that the general
principle is, zoologically speaking, a wrong one, and that its application
is, in many instances, absolutely harmful, economically considered.'

Notwithstanding this condemnation, a group of bird-lovers in the
Hawaiian Islands (then a Territory of the United States) banded
together to form, on 30 March 1930 under the presidentship of Mrs
Frederick J. Lowrey, the Hui Manu (Hawaiian for 'Bird Society'), whose
objectives included 'the importation and appreciation of birds [and] to
increase the number of song birds in the islands'. This could only be
achieved with the cooperation of the Board of Agriculture, which was
responsible for excluding from the islands any species that might be
injurious to the indigenous fauna and flora.

Prior to the formation of the Hui Manu, however, private individuals
had introduced several exotic birds to the Hawaiian Islands. As early
as 1865 Dr William Hillebrand, for example, had imported nutmeg
mannikins, Java sparrows and also the common mynah from India
to combat a plague of army worms (*Laphygma exempta* or *Cirphis
unipuncta*) and cutworms (*Spondoptera* spp.)—locally known collectively as *poko*—that was ravaging the islands. Between 1928 and 1931
Mr William H. McInerny had imported to Oahu between 300 and 350
red-crested cardinals and common cardinals, and more of these species
and barred doves, the red-billed leiothrix, and varied tits were released
at around the same time on Kaui by Mrs Dora R. Isenberg. Other species
liberated by McInerny included eighty-four northern mockingbirds on
Oahu, and Japanese white-eyes. Gambel's quails were planted on
Kahoolawe by Mr H. A. Baldwin in 1928; peafowl on Kauai by Mrs
Frances Sinclair in or about 1860; skylarks on Oahu by the Hon. A. S.
Cleghorn in 1870, and on Kauai by Mrs Sinclair, while canaries were
freed on the Midway group by Mr Daniel Morrison in 1909. Several
other species were introduced prior to the formation of the Hui Manu
by the Hawaiian Division of Fish and Game and private organisations.

Among the species introduced by the Hui Manu to the Hawaiian
Islands, where they have subsequently become successfully established, were northern mockingbirds from the American mainland,
which were released on the island of Oahu in 1931, 1932 and 1933,
and on Maui in 1933; white-rumped shamas from India, freed in the
Nu'u-anu Valley and on the Makiki Heights on Oahu in 1940, in the

Upper Manoa Valley in 1948, and at Tantalus in 1950; Japanese bush warblers (*Uguisu*), 116 of which were liberated on Oahu between 1930 and 1941 by the Honolulu Mejiro[4] Club—some in the Nu'u-anu Valley and others 'in bushes of gardens of the F. J. Lowrey residence, Old Pali Road'; varied tits from Japan (Oahu, 1930 and 1931); Japanese white-eyes on Oahu, Maui, Molokai, Lanai and Hawaii; red-crested cardinals from Brazil (Oahu, 1931); common cardinals from the United States mainland (Oahu, 1931); red avadavats from the Far East (Oahu, probably between 1930 and 1968); and black-headed mannikins from India (Oahu, 1936–41).[5] According to Pleadwell (1942), several other species were introduced unsuccessfully; these included Japanese flycatchers or *oruri*; Japanese robins or *komadori*; Japanese hill robins; Japanese tits or *yamagara*; Mongolian larks; yellow-breasted buntings; narcissus flycatchers; pope cardinals; dayal thrushes; sunbirds; mandarin ducks; indigo buntings; nonpareil buntings; butterfly or Mexican buntings; and Japanese tumblers (presumably pigeons or doves).

The Hui Manu placed considerable importance on the education of the young in wildlife conservation—a concept that was well in advance of the times. With the cooperation of the Hawaiian Humane Society, the Hui Manu initiated a campaign whereby for every gun surrendered by a boy a new camera was given in exchange. The cameras were supplied by the Hui Manu and the Humane Society, Mr and Mrs Wade Warren Thayer provided the films, and the Eastman Kodak Company processed the first film for each boy free of charge. A local radio station broadcast the sound of ninety-six guns being destroyed as they were handed in—an effect somewhat spoiled by the voice of a small boy announcing over the air 'I don't care—I'm getting a new one for Christmas!' Large paintings of the more familiar Hawaiian birds were circulated among the schools on the various islands where a junior Hui Manu was formed, and members of the adult society gave talks about the importance of wildlife conservation. For tourists visiting the Hawaiian Islands the Hui Manu organised tours of many of the most beautiful gardens in Honolulu, which were extremely popular and provided a valuable source of income to the Society.

In 1968, after a life-span of only thirty-eight years, members of the Hui Manu received a letter from the vice-president, Mr James A. H. Wilder, informing them that the executive board had unanimously decided to disband the society. 'This action', Mr Wilder explained, 'was precipitated by several factors such as: increasingly strict regulations to control the importation of birds for deliberate liberation; the lack of younger members; diminishing funds; and the feeling that, since its founding, the Hui Manu has served its purpose.' One suspects that the first of these reasons was the prime consideration.

It will be apparent that acclimatisation societies in the United States, like those in Australia and New Zealand, were concerned not with acclimatisation but rather with naturalisation. Unlike those in the anti-podes, however, American societies were almost exclusively interested in assuaging the feelings of nostalgia of recently arrived immigrants, with little thought being given to the provision of additional sources of food or sport, or to the control of insect pests. Like the United Kingdom society and, to a lesser extent, Australian and New Zealand societies, those in the United States were generally not scientifically orientated.

17. Is there a Rôle for Exotic Species?

'UNLESS one is a fisherman, hunter, or member of an acclimatisation society', wrote J. H. Brown (1989),[1] 'there is a tendency to view all exotic vertebrates as "bad" and all native species as "good".' Most people, for example, view with disapproval the introduction of small Indian mongooses to the West Indies, European starlings to North America, muskrats to Europe and Asia, American mink to Britain, rabbits to Australia, and brush-tailed possums to New Zealand—all of which have become unmitigated pests in their adopted homes.

Brown further suggests that there is a a kind of irrational xenophobia in the case of invading animals and plants, which he compares to the inherent intolerance and fear of alien human races, cultures and religions. There is, however, an important difference between invading animals and plants and foreign peoples, in that the former all too often cause real, and the latter only imagined, problems in their new homes. Furthermore, invasive animals and plants seldom confer any real and lasting benefits on their adopted lands, whereas alien human races are frequently of much service to their host countries.

Nevertheless, a result of the destruction by man of natural habitats and the concomitant extinction of indigenous species, is that there is increasingly an ecological rôle for exotics to play. If, as seems probable, present growth in the world's human population and the reclamation of land for agricultural purposes or urbanisation continue, the increasing homogenisation of the world's biota seems, as Brown says, inevitable. Invasions by biological organisms will continue, in spite of attempts to prevent them, and some at least will succeed. Some species will be natural invaders, while others will be accidentally or deliberately introduced by man. Localised indigenous species with specialised habitat and other requirements will gradually disappear, while broadly based life-forms which can tolerate man and even in some cases benefit from human disturbance—of which the commensal house sparrow is a typical example—will extend their range (as the house sparrow has done notably in South America) and become increasingly predominant.

Furthermore, exotics will sometimes be among the few species able to live in habitats transformed by man which are becoming increasingly common throughout the world. In Australia, for example, several alien birds have become established in man-made habitats which are totally inimical to indigenous species. The proportion of the earth's natural resources which supports nature and wildlife will progressively

191

diminish as mankind rapaciously grasps an increasingly large share to support his own growing population. Developed land, whether urban, agricultural or silvicultural, is managed primarily to serve the human population and its associated domestic stock and cultivated plants, and only occasionally and as a secondary consideration to benefit wildlife. Sometimes the last-named will be indigenes, but all too frequently the choice may have to be made between alien species or virtually no wildlife at all. Unfortunately, many of these aliens are commonly looked upon as 'pests'—a term which encompasses any organism which is, in the broadest sense, harmful to man.

On the other hand, no effort should be spared to preserve undisturbed landscapes and the native animals and plants they contain, including precautions to inhibit the intrusion of potentially damaging exotics. Almost invariably, given the choice, natives are to be preferred to aliens, if only because the former are less likely than the latter to prove harmful in 'managed' (and therefore disturbed) ecosystems or in adjacent marginally transformed areas. More and more, however, broadly tolerant and common natives will become invaders by extending their habitat and geographical ranges into greatly altered environments.

We must learn to accept the various consequences attendant upon the growth of the world's human population and the impact that has on the environment, and rather than attempt the impossible—the preservation of the *status quo ante*—we should try to accept the altered habitats we have created and attempt to utilise them both for ourselves and for wildlife. That in some, if not many, instances, the latter will be exotic rather than native species, is a fact of life we must learn to accept.

Appendix
Chronological List of Principal Acclimatisation Societies

1854 La Société Zoologique d'Acclimatation (Paris)

c.1855 La Société Zoologique d'Acclimatation pour la Région des Alpes (Grenoble)

c.1856 La Société Régionale d'Acclimatation d'Encouragement et de Progrès (Nancy)

1858 Akklimatisations-verein (Berlin)

1859 Comité d'Acclimatation de l'Algérie (Algiers)

1860 Acclimatisation Society of the United Kingdom (London)

1860 Glasgow Acclimatisation Society (Scotland)

1861 Guernsey Acclimatisation Society (Channel Islands)

1861 Società di Acclimazione (Palermo, Sicily)

1861 Acclimatisation Society of Victoria (Melbourne)

1862 Acclimatisation Society of South Australia (Adelaide)

1862 Queensland Acclimatisation Society (Brisbane)

1863 Nelson Acclimatisation Society (New Zealand)

1864 Imperial Russian Society for the Acclimatisation of Animals and Plants (Moscow)

1864 (North) Canterbury Acclimatisation Society (Christchurch, New Zealand)

1864 Otago Acclimatisation Society (Dunedin, New Zealand)

1867 Auckland Acclimatisation Society (New Zealand)

1867 Southland Acclimatisation Society (Invercargill, New Zealand)

1868 Wanganui Acclimatisation Society (New Zealand)

1868 Hawke's Bay Acclimatisation Society (Napier, New Zealand)

1860s Ballarat Acclimatisation Society (Victoria, Australia)

1860s Beechworth Acclimatisation Society (Victoria, Australia)

1860s Portland Acclimatisation Society (Victoria, Australia)

1871 American Acclimatisation Society (New York)

1871 Wellington Acclimatisation Society (New Zealand)

1873 Cincinnati Acclimatisation Society (Ohio)

c.1873 Society for the Acclimatisation of Foreign Birds (Cambridge, Massachusetts)

1874 Taranaki Acclimatisation Society (New Zealand)

1877 Waitaki Acclimatisation Society (New Zealand)

1879 New South Wales Zoological (Acclimatisation) Society (Sydney)

1879 Hawera Acclimatisation Society (New Zealand)

1880 Society for the Introduction of Useful Song Birds into Oregon (Portland)

1880 Marlborough Acclimatisation Society (New Zealand)

1881 Tauranga Acclimatisation Society (New Zealand)

1882 Wairarapa Acclimatisation Society (New Zealand)

c.1885 Country Club of San Francisco (California)

1886 Ashburton Acclimatisation Society (New Zealand)

1888 Waimate Acclimatisation Society (New Zealand)

1888 Westland Acclimatisation Society (New Zealand)

1894 Stratford Acclimatisation Society (New Zealand)

1895 Bay of Islands Acclimatisation Society (New Zealand)

1895 Tasmanian Game Protection and Acclimatisation Society (Hobart)

1895 South Canterbury Acclimatisation Society (Opotiki, New Zealand

1896 Western Australia Acclimatisation Society (Perth)

1896 Whangarei Acclimatisation Society (New Zealand)

1899 Northern Tasmania Acclimatisation Society (Launceston)

1900 Mangonui-Whangaroa Acclimatisation Society (New Zealand)

1901 Hobson Acclimatisation Society (New Zealand)

1903 Waimarino Acclimatisation Society (New Zealand)

1930 Hui Manu (Hawaiian Islands)

1936 New England Trout Acclimatisation Society (Inverell, New South Wales)

1930s Central Acclimatisation Society (Bathurst, New South Wales)

1930s Monaro Acclimatisation Society (Tumut, New South Wales)

1930s Orange Trout Acclimatisation Society (Orange, New South Wales)

Bibliography

Acclimatisation Society of America. 1871. Charter and By-Laws. American Acclimatisation Society, New York: 15 pp.

Acclimatisation Societies of Australia: Annual Reports.

Acclimatisation Society of Cincinnati, Ohio. Constitution and By-Laws, 1873.

Acclimatisation Societies of New Zealand: Annual Reports.

Acclimatisation Society of the United Kingdom. Annual Reports, 1861–65 and with Ornithological Society of London, 1866–67.

Acclimatisation Society of the United Kingdom. n.d. A collection of reports, newspaper cuttings etc., largely on the Guernsey branch, compiled by Mrs J. Balfour Cockburn (daughter of Dr S. E. Hoskins, secretary of the Guernsey branch) and presented to 'F.J.C.' in 1888. (Presented to the Priaulx Library, Guernsey, by Mrs Edith Carey in 1935).

Acclimatisation (and Zoological) Society of Victoria. 1861–1951. Papers (mostly minutes and reports), vols 1–13. (Copies in Library of Monash University, Clayton, Victoria, and the La Trobe Library, State Library of Victoria).

Acclimatisation Society of Victoria, Australia. 1864. Answers furnished by the Acclimatisation Society of Victoria to the enquiries addressed to it by His Excellency the Governor of Victoria at the instance of The Right Hon. the Secretary of State for the Colonies. Acclimatisation Society of Victoria.

Aflalo, F. G. 1900. *A Walk Through the Zoological Gardens*; Sands, London.

Anon. 1851. *Catalogue of the Menagerie and Aviary at Knowsley, formed by the late Earl of Derby*. Privately printed, Liverpool.

———. 1856. Report from the Select Committee of the Legislative Council on the Alpaca. Government Printer, Melbourne.

———. 1860. Acclimatisation of animals. *Edinburgh Review* 111 (226): 161–88. (Believed to be by the late D. W. Mitchell, secretary of the Zoological Society of London.)

———. 1860. Zoological Gardens. *Saturday Review* 14 April: 466.

———. 1861. Acclimatisation. *All the Year Round* 5: 492–6.

———. 1863 (July). Acclimatisation and preservation of animals. *National Review*.

———. 1881. Introduction of European birds. *Journal of the Cincinnati Society of Natural History* 4: 342–3.

———. 1903. Buckland, F. T. *Dictionary of National Biography* 3: 204–5. Oxford University Press, Oxford.

———. (n.d.) *Tracts: Acclimatisation* (Zoology Library, Natural History Museum, London).

———. (n.d.) *Gleanings from the Menagerie and Aviary at Knowsley Hall*. 2 vols.

———. 1989. Export prospects for Emu meat. *South Western Times* (Australia) 8 June.

———. 1989. Old man Emu à la carte. *Financial Review* (Australia) 2 June.

Argus, The 1853 (15 March); 1854 (18 February, 19 August, 26 and 28 October, 8 and 14 November); 1855 (9 July, 7 September, 22 October); 1856 (23 January, 26 February, 2 April); 1857 (1 January, 14 July, 23 and 31 October, 3 November, 7 December); 1858 (15 January, 21 October, 9 November, 20 December); 1859 (21 January, 17 February, 2 and 30 March). Australia.

Ashby, C. R. 1967. *The Centenary History of the Auckland Acclimatisation Society, 1867–1967*. Auckland Acclimatisation Society, Auckland.

195

Bacon, F. 1857–9. *Works* (ed.) J. Spedding, R. S. Ellis & D. D. Heath. Longman, London.

Balmford, R. 1978. Early introductions of birds to Victoria. *Australian Bird Watcher* 7: 237–48. Reprinted in *Victorian Naturalist* 98: 96–105 (1981) .

———. 1985. Newspapers as a source of information about natural history. *Victorian Naturalist* 102: 20–27.

Bathgate, A. 1897. Notes on acclimatisation in New Zealand. *Transactions of the New Zealand Institution*: 266–79.

Bennett, G. 1862. Acclimatisation: its eminent adaptation to Australia. Acclimatisation Society of Victoria; 40 pp.

Berkeley, G. F. 1863. In: *Dorset County Chronicle*, 27 September.

Blunt, W. 1976. *The Ark in the Park; the Zoo in the Nineteenth Century*. Hamish Hamilton/Tryon Gallery, London.

Bogdanov, A. P. 1852. Ob akklimatizatsii. *Zhurnal Sel'skogo Khoziaistva* 12: 192–224.

———. 1857. Uspekhi estestvennykh nauk i ikh prilozheniia. *Otechestvennye Zapiski* 113(4): 18–21.

———. 1860 and 1862. *Obshchaia Biologiia Izidora Zhoffrua Sent-Ilera*. 2 vols. Moscow. [Translation of Geoffroy Saint Hilaire's *General Biology*].

Bompas, G. C. 1885. *Life of Frank Buckland*. Thomas Nelson & Sons, London.

Bray, W. (ed.) 1911. *The Diary of John Evelyn*. Dent, London; and Dutton, New York.

Brereton, W. 1844. *Travels in Holland . . . England, Scotland and Ireland* (ed. E. Hawkins). Chetham Society.

Brown, D. 1989. The Emu is coming for dinner. *Sunday Telegraph* (9 August).

Brown, J. H. 1989. Patterns, Modes and Extents of Invasions by Vertebrates. In: Drake, J. A. *et al.* (eds) *Biological Invasions—a Global Perspective*: 85–109. John Wiley & Sons, Chichester, for Scientific Committee on Problems of the Environment of the International Council of Scientific Unions.

Buckland, F. T. 1857–72. *Curiosities of Natural History*, 4 vols. Richard Bentley, London.

———. 1861. On the acclimatisation of animals. (Paper read on 30 November 1860 to the Society of Arts). *Journal of the Society of Arts* 9: 19–34, (see also pp. 46–8, 92). Republished by the Acclimatisation Society of Victoria in Victorian pamphlets No. 32, La Trobe Library, State Library of Victoria, Australia: William Goodhugh & Co., Melbourne.

———. 1864. *Manual of Salmon and Trout Hatching: An Explanation of the Fish-Hatching Apparatus at the Royal Horticultural Gardens, the South Kensington Museum, Zoological Gardens*. Tinsley, London.

———. 1876. *Land and Water* 21: 12.

———. 1881. *Natural History of British Fishes*. S.P.C.K., London.

———. Personal papers in the library of the Royal College of Surgeons of England (deposited by Professor M. Gordon).

Bulletin de la Société Zoologique d'Acclimatation. 1854–59. 4 volumes. Paris. (Continued as *Bulletin de la Société Impériale Zoologique d'Acclimatation*, and *Bulletin de la Société d'Acclimatation*.)

Burgess, G. H. O. 1967. *The Curious World of Frank Buckland*. John Baker, London.

Clark, A. H. 1949. *The Invasion of New Zealand by People, Plants and Animals: the South Island*. Rutgers University Press, New Brunswick.

Clements, J. n.d. *Salmon at the Antipodes: a history and review of trout, salmon and char and introduced coarse fish in Australasia*. Author, Victoria.

Collins Baker, C. H. 1949. *James Brydges; First Duke of Chandos*. Clarendon Press, Oxford.

Craig, B. F. 1860. Acclimation and domestication of animals. In: Report of the Commissioner of Patents for 1859. Agriculture. House of Representatives, 36th Congress, 1st Session: 207–17. Washington.

De Sausmarez, R. 1963. Acclimatization in Guernsey. *Quarterly Review of Guernsey Society*: 10–11.

Druett, J. 1983. *Exotic Intruders: the Introduction of plants and animals into New Zealand*. Heinemann, New Zealand.

Egerton, J. 1976. *George Stubbs; Anatomist and Animal Painter*. Tate Gallery, London.

Erkenbrecher, A. and Tenner, A. 1873. *The Protection of birds*. Cincinnati Acclimatisation Society; 1 p.

Festing, S. 1987. Animal Crackers. *Country Life*: 124–5.

———. 1988. Menageries and the landscape garden. *Journal of Garden History* 8 (4): 104–17.

Field, The. 1860–65. vol. XV (382)–XXVI: *passim* (mostly under the heading of Naturalist). See also issue of 29 February 1868.

Finley, W. L. 1925. Unpublished letter to J. C. Phillips *re* the Portland Song Bird Club.

Fitter, R. S. R. 1959. *The Ark in Our Midst*. Collins, London.

Forge, J. L. 1972. *Oatlands House*. Walton and Weybridge Local Historical Society.

Fox, F. E. E. 1970. Appendix (*St James's Park Lake—Waterfowl Collection*) to *Bird Life in the Royal Parks, 1967–68*. Report of the Committee on Bird Sanctuaries in the Royal Parks for 1967–68. Her Majesty's Stationery Office, London.

Francis, G. W. 1862. The Acclimatisation of harmless, useful, interesting and ornamental animals and plants. *Philosophical Society of Adelaide*, South Australia: 22 pages.

Galton, F. 1863. *The First Steps towards the Domestication of Animals*. Privately printed.

Geoffroy Saint-Hilaire, I. 1861. *Acclimatation et Domestication des Animaux Utiles*. 4th ed. Librairie Agricole de la Maison Rustique, Paris.

Gillbank, L. R. 1980. The Acclimatisation Society of Victoria. *Victorian Historical Journal* 51: 255–70.

———. 1986. The origins of the Acclimatisation Society of Victoria: practical science in the wake of the gold rush. *Historical Records of Australian Science* 6 (3): 359–74.

Gray, J. E. 1864a. On museums, their use and improvement, and on the acclimatization of animals. *Annals and Magazine of Natural History* 3rd ser. 14: 283–97.

———. 1864b. Address by the President of the Botany and Zoology Section of the British Association for the Advancement of Science. In: *Report of the British Association for the Advancement of Science, 1864*: 75–86. See also *The Field*, 12 and 19 July 1862, and 4 and 18 July 1863.

Grimard, E. 1876. *Le Jardin d'Acclimatation: Le Tour du Monde d'un Naturaliste*. J. Hetzel, Paris.

Groves, R. H. & Burdon, J. J. 1986. *Ecology of Biological Invasions: an Australian Perspective*. Australian Academy of Science, Canberra.

Guerin-Meneville, F. E. n.d. *The Ailanthus Silkworm and the Ailanthus Tree*. (Abridged and translated by Lady Dorothy Nevill, *c.*1862).

Guthrie-Smith, H. 1921. *Tutira: the story of a New Zealand sheep station*. London.

Hall, A. F. B. 1929. Royal Zoological Society of New South Wales' Jubilee. *Australian Zoologist* 5: 263–4.

Hardy, A. 1860. Importance de l'Algérie comme station d'acclimatation. [Extrait de *L'Algérie Agricole, Commerciale, Industrielle*.] Paris.

Hayes, W. 1779–86. *Birds in the Collection at Osterley Park*. London.

———. 1794–99. *Rare and Curious Birds from Osterley Park*. London.

Head, A. 1902. Nightingales in California. *Condor* 4 (1): 94–5.

Hornaday, W. T. 1913. *Our Vanishing Wildlife: its extermination and preservation*. Charles Scribner's Sons, New York.

Hunt, J. 1862. On ethno-climatology, or the acclimatisation of man. *Transactions of the Ethnological Society of London* 2: 50–83.

Jenkins, C. F. H. 1977. *The Noah's Ark Syndrome; one hundred years of acclimatization and zoo development in Australia.* Zoological Gardens Board of Western Australia, Perth.

Jewett, S. G. & Gabrielson, I. N. 1929. Birds of the Portland Area, Oregon. *Cooper Ornithological Club* 19: 47–9.

Jousset, A. 1884. *Traité de l'acclimatement et de l'acclimatation.* Octave Doin, Paris.

Kerry, Earl of. 1922. King's Bowood Park. *Wiltshire Archaeological & Natural History Society* 137 (92): 26.

Kyle, R. 1987. *A Feast in the Wild.* Kudu, Oxford.

Lamb, R. C. 1964. *Birds, Beasts & Fishes: the first hundred years of the North Canterbury Acclimatisation Society.* North Canterbury Acclimatisation Society, Christchurch.

Lambton, L. 1986. *Beastly Buildings.* Collins, London. (List of animals in auctioneer's catalogue of 8th Earl of Northampton's sale at Castle Ashby on 30 May, 1774.)

Land and Water. 1865–68; *passim.*

Lauder Lindsay, W. 1867. On plant acclimatisation in Scotland with special reference to Tussac Grass. *Transactions of the British Association for the Advancement of Science*: 88.

Laycock, G. 1966. *The Alien Animals: the story of imported wildlife.* Ballantine Books, New York.

Ledger, C. 1861. The alpaca: its introduction into Australia and the probabilities of its acclimatisation there. *Journal of the Society of Arts* 9: 212–24; 10: 213–14; see also 8: 198; 9: 547.

Lefevre, M. 1977. The Little Queen of Oatlands. *Surrey Life* (January).

Le Souef, J. C. 1965. Acclimatisation in Victoria. *The Victorian Historical Magazine* 36 (1): 8–29.

———. 1966. The development of a zoological garden at Royal Park. *The Victorian Historical Magazine* 37: 221–52.

Le Souef, W. H. D. 1890. Acclimatisation in Victoria. In: *Report of the Second Meeting of the Australian Association for the Advancement of Science*, Melbourne 1890: 476–82.

Lever, C. 1977. *The Naturalized Animals of the British Isles.* Hutchinson, London. (Paladin-Granada, London, 1979).

———. 1985. *Naturalized Mammals of the World.* Longman, London.

———. 1987. *Naturalized Birds of the World.* Longman Scientific & Technical, London.

———. 1988. The Naturalization of Birds: Causes and Consequences. *Natural History Book Reviews* 9 (1): 1–10.

Livingstone, D. N. 1987. Human acclimatization: perspectives on a contested field of inquiry in science, medicine and geography. *History of Science* 25: 359–94.

Llanover, Lady (ed.) 1861–2. *The Autobiography and Correspondence of Mary Granville, Mrs Delany.* London.

Loisel, G. 1912. *Histoire des Ménageries de l'Antiquité à nos Jours.* 3 vols. Octave Doin, Paris.

McCoy, F. S. 1862. Acclimatisation: its nature and applicability to Victoria. Anniversary address at First Annual General Meeting of the Acclimatisation Society of Victoria. Victoria Acclimatisation Society, Melbourne.

McCulloch, D. A. 1985. Over the last 100 Years. In: *Wellington Acclimatisation Society 100th Annual Report*: 2–5. (Reprinted from the *Centennial Year Annual Report and Financial Statement* 1971: 21–6.)

McDowall, R. M. 1983. When it all began . . . 1983. *Freshwater Catch* 19: 2–4.

———. 1984. Acclimatisation Societies: then and now. *Freshwater Catch* 22: 4–6.

———. 1989. *New Zealand Freshwater Fishes: a guide and natural history.* Heinemann, Auckland.

Macray, W. D. 1894. *Register of the Members of St Mary Magdalen College.* Oxford.

March, Earl of. 1911. *A Duke and his Friends: the life and letters of the second Duke of Richmond.* London.

Marr, L. J. 1984. *Guernsey People.* Phillimore, St Peter Port.

Marshall, F. 1946. The Society: the Past and the Future. *Proceedings of the Royal Zoological Society of New South Wales 1945–6*: 6–7.

Mearns, B. and Mearns, R. 1988. *Biographies for Birdwatchers.* Academic Press, London.

Mitchell, D. W. & Sclater, P. L. 1859. *Guide to the Gardens of the Zoological Society of London.* Zoological Society of London, London.

Mitchell, P. C. 1929. *Centenary History of the Zoological Society of London.* Zoological Society of London, London.

Moyal, A. M. 1976. *Scientists in Nineteenth-Century Australia.* Cassell, Melbourne.

Naudin, C. V. & von Mueller, F. 1887. *Manuel de l'Acclimateur ou choix de plantes recommandées pour l'agriculture, l'industrie et la médicine.* J. Marchand, Antibes.

Nicols, A. 1882. *The Acclimatisation of the Salmonidae at the Antipodes.* Sampson Low, Marston, Shearle and Rivington, London.

O'Malley, P. 1988. Commercial Emu Farming. *Western Australian Department of Agriculture.*

Oppler, A. 1887. On acclimatisation. *Proceedings of the Royal Geographical Society* 9: 690–1.

Osborne, M. A. 1987. *The Société Zoologique d'Acclimatation and the New French Empire: the Science and Political Economy of Economic Zoology during the Second Empire.* Unpublished doctoral thesis, University of Wisconsin-Madison: 428pp. In press as: *The Societe Zoologique d'Acclimatation and the New French Empire: Science and Political Economy during the Second Empire and the Third Republic.* Indiana University Press, Bloomington.

———. 1988. A Collaborative Dimension of the European Empires: Australian and French Acclimatization Societies and Intercolonial Scientific Cooperation. In: Home, R. W. & Kohlstedt, S. G. eds. 1991. *International Science and National Scientific Identity.* Klumer Academic Publishers.

———. 1989. Zoos in the Family: the Geoffroy Saint-Hilaire clan and the three zoos of Paris. Paper delivered at a conference on The History and Evolution of Modern Zoos at the National Zoological Park, Washington, D.C., U.S.A., 13–14 October, 1989.

Owen, R. 1859. 21 January. Letter to *The Times* (on the quality of eland meat).

Owen, Revd R. 1894. *The Life of Richard Owen* (2 vols). John Murray, London.

Palmer, T. S. 1899. The dangers of introducing noxious animals and birds. *US Department of Agriculture Yearbook 1898*: 87–110.

Pfluger, C. F. 1896–97. The Imported and Acclimated German Song Birds in Oregon. *The Oregon Naturalist*, 3 (4): 32; 59; 3 (7): 103–5; 3 (8): 109–11; 3 (11): 141–2; 3 (12): 153–5 (1896); 4 (5): 29–31 (1897).

Phillips, J. C. 1928. Wild birds introduced or transplanted in North America. *U.S. Department of Agriculture Technical Bulletin* No. 61: 1–63.

Pleadwell, L. M. S. 1942. The Hui Manu: Bird Society. *Paradise of the Pacific* 54 (11): 13–15.

Powis, W. G. 1968. The organized movement for acclimatization in Victoria 1857–84. Bachelor of Arts (Hons) thesis, Department of History, Monash University, Victoria: 82pp.

Pratt, A. 1934. *Centenary History of Victoria,* Melbourne.

Prest, J. 1981. *The Garden of Eden.* Yale University Press, New Haven and London.

Prince, J. H. n.d. *The First One Hundred Years of the Royal Zoological Society of New South Wales 1879–1979.* R.Z.S.N.S.W., Sydney.

Quickfall, B. R. 1974. Taranaki Acclimatisation Society. In: *Centennial Report and Balance Sheet, 1974*: 24–36.

Ritchie, C. I. A. 1981. *The British Dog*. Hale, London.

Ritchie, J. D. 1975. *Australia As We Once Were*. Heinemann, Melbourne.

Ritchie, J. G. 1988. *The Australian Trout: its introduction and acclimatisation in Victorian waters*. The Victorian Fly-Fishers Association, Melbourne.

Ritvo, H. 1987. *The Animal Estate: the English and other creatures in the Victorian age*. Harvard University Press, Cambridge, USA.

Rolfe, W. D. I. William Hunter (1718–83) on Irish 'elk' and Stubbs's 'Moose'. *Archives of Natural History* II (2): 263–90.

Rolls, E. C. 1969. *They All Ran Wild: the story of pests on the land in Australia*. Angus & Robertson, London.

Rose, R. N. 1953. *The Field, 1853–1953*. Michael Joseph, London.

Ruskin, J. 1908. *Praeterita* (ed. E. T. Cook & A. Wedderburn). George Allen, London.

Sachs, T. R. 1878. Transportation of live Pike-Perch. *Land & Water* 25 May: 476.

Scherren, H. 1905. *The Zoological Society of London*. Cassell & Co., London.

Scott, P. 1982. *Tauranga Acclimatisation Society*. 1882–1982: 26pp.

Serventy, D. L. 1928. The menace of acclimatization. *Emu* 27.

Smith, J. 1864. England's debt to acclimatisers. Acclimatisation Society of Victoria, Third Annual Report: 49.

Snell, W. E. 1967. Frank Buckland, medical naturalist. *Proceedings of the Royal Society of Medicine* 60: 291–6.

Sowman, W. C. R. 1981. *Meadow, Mountain, Forest and Stream: the Provincial History of the Nelson Acclimatisation Society 1863–1968*. Nelson Acclimatisation Society, Nelson.

Stock, A. H. 1915. *History of the Southland Acclimatisation Society* (New Zealand). Southland Acclimatisation Society; 48pp.

Taylor, G. 1973. *Ham House Guide*. Victoria & Albert Museum, London.

Taylor, L. 1968. About People [The Hui Manu (Bird Society)]. *Honolulu Star-Bulletin* (9 July).

Times, The. Letters: 1859 (21 January, 18 October); 1860 (6 April, 10 August, 22 September, 27 December).

Teagle, W. G. 1988. *The Times*; letter, 4 January.

Thomson, G. M. 1922. *The Naturalisation of Animals and Plants in New Zealand*. Cambridge University Press, Cambridge.

Tuckwell, W. 1907. *Reminiscences of Oxford*. Smith, Elder & Co., London.

Vevers, G. 1976. *London's Zoo*. The Bodley Head, London.

Walker, T. E. C. 1968. *The Clives at Claremont*. Surrey Archaeological Society.

Wallace, A. R. & Finn, F. 1910. Acclimatization. In: *The Encyclopaedia Britannica* 11th edn: 114–21. Encyclopaedia Britannica, London and New York. (See also 15th edn, 1988.)

Walpole, H. 1928. *Journal of Visits to Country Seats*: vol. VII (ed. J. T. Paget). Walpole Society.

Weiner, D. R. 1985. The roots of 'Michurinism': transformist biology and acclimatisation as currents in the Russian life science. *Annals of Science* 42: 243–60.

———. 1988. *Models of Nature: Ecology, Conservation and Cultural Revolution in Soviet Russia*. Indiana University Press, Bloomington.

Wellwood, J. M. (ed.) 1968. *Hawke's Bay Acclimatisation Society Centenary 1868–1968*. Hawke's Bay Acclimatisation Society.

Wheelwright, H. W. ('An Old Bushman'). 1861. *Bush Wanderings of a Naturalist*. Routledge, Warne and Routledge, London.

Whitley, G. P. 1960. Presidential Address: Eighty Years Young. *Proceedings of the Royal Zoological Society of New South Wales 1960–64*: 24–9.

Wilson, E. 1859. *Rambles at the Antipodes: a series of sketches*. London.

———. 1860. 22 September. Letter to *The Times*.

———. 1875. Acclimatisation. Paper read before the Royal Colonial Institute, London.

Wilson, S. 1863. *The Angora Goat: with an account of its introduction into Victoria.*
    Stillwell & Knight, Melbourne.
Westgarth, W. 1864. *The Colony of Victoria.* London.
Wolf, J. 1858. *Zoological Sketches.* London.
Wood, J. G. 1886. Acclimatisation. *Longman's Magazine* 8 (48): 656–71.
Wotton, H. 1903. *Elements of Architecture.* Longman, Green & Co., London.
Zeitschrift Für Acclimatisation: Organ Das Acclimatisations-Vereins Für Die Königlich
    Preussischen Staaten. 1858–74. Gustav Bosselman (Berlin) and La Librairie de Victor
    Masson, Paris.
Zoological Society of London. 1859. Annual Report.
Zuckerman, Lord (ed.) 1976. *The Zoological Society of London 1826–1976 and Beyond.*
    Academic Press, for the Zoological Society of London.

NOTES

Preface

1 Wallace, 1910: 114 (11th edition).
2 Fitter, 1959: 14–15.
3 Lever, 1977: 17.
4 *Oxford English Dictionary*.
5 Lever, 1985: xii. 1987: xiv.
6 Fifteenth edition, 1988: 55.
7 'The establishment of self-regenerating populations [unsupported by and independent of man] of an introduced species or race in a free-living state in the wild.' Linn, I. L., ed., 1979. *Wildlife Introductions to Great Britain. Report by the Working Group on Introductions of the UK Committee for International Nature Conservation*, 32 pp. Nature Conservancy Council. Derived from Boitani, L., ed., 1976. *Reintroductions: Techniques and Ethics*. World Wildlife Fund, Rome. (Quoted by Lever, 1985: xi. 1987: xiii).
8 'An animal that has lapsed into a wild from a domesticated condition'. (Lever, 1985: xii. 1987: xiv).

Introduction

1 For parts of the Introduction, I have drawn on the entries under 'acclimatisation' in *The Encyclopaedia Britannica*, 11th edition; Wallace, 1910: 114–21, and 15th edition, 1988: 55.
2 See note 7 of Preface. In Australia and New Zealand, the term 'acclimatisation'—as in 'Acclimatisation Society'—was regarded as synonymous with 'naturalisation'.
3 See note 8 of Preface.
4 *The Oxford Dictionary of Natural History*. M. Allaby, ed., 1985.
5 McCoy, 1862: 36.

Chapter 1

1 For events in France leading up to the formation of the *Société Zoologique d'Acclimatation*, I am indebted to Osborne, 1987.
2 This seems a curious error on the part of Geoffroy Saint-Hilaire, for the common turkey—from which the domesticated variety is derived—was introduced to Europe from North America in the first half of the sixteenth century.
3 From its foundation on 10 February 1854 until 10 December 1958 the *Société* retained its original title. From the latter date until 25 March 1960 it was

known as the *Société Nationale d'Acclimatation de France et de Protection de la Nature*. Thereafter, reflecting a change of emphasis in its activities, it has been called the *Société Nationale de Protection de la Nature et d'Acclimatation de France*. As a leading organisation in the French nature conservation movement, it is a member of the *Fédération Française des Sociétés de Protection de la Nature*. From its offices in the *Muséum National d'Histoire Naturelle* in Paris it publishes, *inter alia*, the scientific journal *La Terre et La Vie*. (M. A. Osborne and N. Yavercovski, personal communications 1989 and 1990.)

4 *The Edinburgh Review*, 1860: 163.
5 *The Saturday Review*, 1860: 466.
6 Louisiana was acquired by the United States from the French in 1803.
7 See Lever, 1985.
8 For a summary of the activities and achievements of the *Société Zoologique d'Acclimatation*, I am indebted to Osborne, 1987.

Chapter 2

1 For much of the history of and references to menageries and aviaries in Britain, I am indebted to Ritvo, 1987, and Festing, 1988, from whom most of the quotations are taken.
2 Prest, 1981: 24.
3 Macray, 1894: 24–25, 64.
4 Prest, *op. cit.*, 23.
5 Brereton, 1844: 33.
6 Wotton, 1903: 87.
7 Bray, 1911. Volume I: 87.
8 Prest, *op. cit.*, 52.
9 Bacon, 1857–59. Volume VII: 492.
10 Llanover, 1861–62. Volume III, series I: 241. According to a drawing from life by Mrs Delany, probably a zebu.
11 Adapted from Festing, personal communication and 1988.
12 Taylor, 1973: 65.
13 Collins Baker, 1949: xvi, 39, 45, 64, 127, 185, 270.
14 March, 1911: 139, 216.
15 Portland Papers, Nottingham University Library, MS PWF 722, 724, 725, 741, 751. See also Festing, S. *The Duchess of Portland* (unpub. MS).
16 Walpole, 1928: 53.
17 Ritchie, 1981: 123.
18 Hayes; 1779–86 and 1794–99.
19 Egerton, 1976: 30.
20 Lambton, 1986: 94.
21 Kerry, 1922: 26.
22 Lambton, 1986: 142.
23 Rolfe, 263, 279, note 8.
24 *Ibid.*
25 Walker, 1968: 92–93.
26 See note 18; Forge, 1972: 23, and Lefevre, 1977: 8–9.

Chapter 3

1 *Land and Water*. 1 January 1876. Volume 21.
2 Francis Leggatt Chantrey (1781–1841) was one of the foremost sculptors of his day, as well as being an accomplished artist who exhibited at the Royal Academy from 1804–07. He was knighted in 1835.
3 Pages 202–203.
4 Buckland, 1857.
5 *Ibid*, 1860.
6 Rose, 1953: 69.
7 Owen, 1894; volume I.
8 Ruskin, 1908.
9 Tuckwell, 1907.
10 See note 7.
11 *Temple Bar Magazine*, 1873.
12 Buckland, 1861.
13 Scherren, 1905: 10, and Mitchell, P. C., 1929: 7–8.
14 Mitchell, P. C., 1929: 10.
15 *Ibid*, page 12.
16 Pages 232–33.
17 Bompas, 1885: 95–96, and Buckland, 1861: 19–20. Although Bompas gives the date as 21 January and Buckland himself says it was 22 January, it was in fact Wednesday 19 January, since Owen, in his letter to *The Times* dated 20 January (published on 21 January) refers to 'yesterday's' dinner.
18 Quoted by Mitchell and Sclater in *The Edinburgh Review*, 1860. Volume 16: 161–80.
19 Buckland's personal papers in the library of the Royal College of Surgeons of England.
20 Volume 15 (382): 309. 21 April 1860.
21 An adult eland can easily leap over a motor-car.
22 This has since been increased to six, by the introduction of the Japanese sika, the Chinese water deer, and the Chinese muntjac (see Lever, 1977 and 1985).
23 Since the early 1950s reindeer have been acclimatised near Aviemore in the Cairngorm Mountains of Inverness-shire in Scotland (see Lever, 1977 and 1985).
24 This species has been naturalised in England in the north Midlands (and formerly in Sussex) since 1939 (see Lever, 1977 and 1985).
25 See Lever, 1977 and 1985.
26 Elands, though large, are actually exceptionally timid and wary of man.

Chapter 4

1 Several attempts have since been made to establish bobwhite quail in England, but none has met with lasting success (see Lever, 1977).
2 In expressing this wish Buckland was unconsciously prophetic, for a salmon reintroduction programme is currently being attempted by the Thames Salmon Trust.

3 It is somewhat ironic that just twenty years later Buckland was to say that 'many attempts have been made to transport this fish alive to England', where it was first introduced more than a century ago and is now naturalised in many eastern Midland and East Anglian waters (see Lever, 1977).

4 The wels of European catfish is now naturalised in Britain in several eastern Midland and East Anglian water systems (see Lever, 1977).

Chapter 5

1 The progeny of these four deer were subsequently used to stock a number of parks in England and Scotland, the first of which were probably at Waddesdon in Buckinghamshire in about 1874 and at Tulliallan in Fife around 1870. Since then, some thirty estates have preserved Japanese sika, many of which have escaped to form naturalised herds in the surrounding countryside (see Lever, 1977 and 1985).

2 Marked with a spot of colour encircled by a band of another colour, resembling an eye.

3 The cheer pheasant is now officially classified as 'endangered' in the International Council for Bird Preservation's *Red Data Book*.

4 Introduced to Piedmont in north-western Italy from China in 1856.

Chapter 6

1 Not in fact a swallow (*Hirundinidae*) but a swift (*Apodidae*), the edible-nest swiftlet, from Indonesia.

2 Also known as the spotted deer or chital.

3 'Praised by some, disliked by others.'

4 'With good reason'.

5 A flavouring agent made in the West Indies by boiling the juice of the bitter cassava to a thick syrup.

6 *The Field* was, of course, correct in rejecting 'the theory of the hybrid', since hares and rabbits cannot interbreed.

Chapter 7

1 This questionnaire, and the answer received to it from the Acclimatisation Society of Victoria in Australia, are discussed in chapter 9.

2 In 1989 it was announced that farmers in Western Australia were planning to export to Europe (including Britain) emu meat, skins (which make into high-quality leather), feathers, and oil for cooking purposes. It was anticipated that by 1992 between 19,000 and 20,000 emu carcases per annum would be ready for this trade.

3 Quoted by Burgess, 1967: 105.

4 The dingo or warrigal—the wild dog of Australia—is not a native of that country, but was introduced as a domestic animal by Aboriginal voyagers from south-eastern Asia, perhaps some 3000–7000 years ago, and subsequently became feral (see Lever, 1985).
5 Trout that live in lakes in Britain are now regarded as conspecific with those inhabiting rivers, and are known collectively as brown trout. The lake trout lives in lakes and rivers in North America.

Chapter 8

1 Red-necked or Bennett's wallabies are currently naturalised in Britain in the Peak District of Derbyshire and Staffordshire, and formerly occurred in Ashdown and St Leonard's forests in north-central Sussex (see Lever, 1977 and 1985).
2 The silver pheasant has been introduced to parts of England and Scotland, but has failed to become established (see Lever, 1977).
3 The golden pheasant is currently naturalised in Britain in parts of East Anglia, Galloway, and on the Isle of Anglesey off the coast of Gwynedd (see Lever, 1977 and 1987).
4 John Reeves (1774–1856) was in 1812 appointed assistant inspector— later rising to chief inspector—of tea for the East India Company in Canton (see Mearns and Mearns, 1988). From time to time Reeves's Pheasants have become temporarily established in the wild in Britain (see Lever, 1977 and 1987).
5 All these four species are now naturalised in parts of Australia, though not, ironically, in Queensland (see Lever, 1987).
6 Plant-like animals, such as sponges, corals, jelly-fish and sea anemones.
7 Shell-fish with a hard continuous brick-red shell.

Chapter 9

1 In 1858 British Columbia was declared an independent colony; in 1872 it became part of the Dominion of Canada.

Chapter 10

1 A large form of aviary.
2 Serious cases of cholera were treated by enemata of starch (and laudanum, tincture of opium), such as that produced in the tuberous roots of arrowroot.

Chapter 11

1 In the mid-nineteenth century the eider in Britain was confined mainly to the northern and western isles of Scotland, with lesser numbers on the east coast. Since then it has been steadily increasing in numbers and expanding its range, and it is now Britain's most abundant and widespread sea duck.
2 Mandarin ducks are now naturalised in Britain (see Lever, 1977 and 1987).
3 Egyptian geese are now naturalised in Britain (see Lever, 1977 and 1987).
4 Volume 5: 154.

Chapter 12

1 1864b: 80.
2 1887. Volume 36: 188. Quoted by Ritvo, 1987: 242.
3 1861: 495.
4 12 August 1865. Volume XXIV: 128.

Chapter 13

1 1987: 364–65; 1988: 15.
2 For much of the information on the history and activities of Australian acclimatisation societies, I am indebted to Jenkins, 1977. For further details see also Lever, 1985 and 1987.
3 *Sydney Empire*, 28 June 1852. Quoted by Whitley, 1960: 24.
4 Quoted by Jenkins, 1977: 99.
5 *Ibid.*
6 Quoted by Rolls, 1969: 217.
7 Quoted by Jenkins, 1977: 100.
8 *Proceedings of the Royal Zoological Society of New South Wales*, 1960–4: 24.
9 The name 'Taronga' is derived from an Aboriginal word meaning 'Waterview' (see Jenkins, 1977: 101).
10 The full story of Ledger's introduction of alpacas from Peru to Australia is described by Rolls, 1969: 258–62.
11 *Sydney Morning Herald*, 14 November 1883.
12 See under Queensland.
13 Quoted by Rolls, 1969: 227.
14 For information on the history of the Acclimatisation Society of Victoria, I am principally indebted to Jenkins, 1977 and Gillbank, 1980 and 1986.
15 Quoted by Balmford, 1978: 237.
16 Quoted by Gillbank, 1986: 369.
17 *The Age*, 2 April 1858. Quoted by Gillbank, 1986: 370, from *The Australian Thunderer—The Age after the Gold Rush 1854–1859*, Melbourne (n.d.): 67–8.
18 *The Argus*, 9 March 1858: 4. Quoted by Gillbank, 1986: 370.
19 Quoted by Gillbank, 1986: 369.
20 *Ibid.*

21 *First Annual Report of the Acclimatisation Society of Victoria, 1862:* 9. Quoted by Gillbank, 1986: 372.
22 See under Queensland.
23 *Journal of the Philosophical Society of South Australia*, 1862. Quoted by Jenkins, 1977: 46.
24 In this, he displayed considerably greater knowledge than Rolls, 1969 (page 273), who claimed that 'acclimatization is really a misnomer for a simple transference of plant or animal from one country to another.'
25 These and other quotes in the account of the South Australia Society are taken from Jenkins, 1977: 46–59.
26 *Brisbane Courier*, 20 April 1870.
27 *Ibid*, 25 August 1870.
28 *Daily Herald*, 1 March 1873.
29 *The Australasian*, 27 August 1870.
30 *Brisbane Courier*, 20 April 1870.
31 *Proceedings of the Royal Society of Queensland*, 1960.
32 *Transactions of the Queensland Acclimatisation Society for 1892*; 1893: 17.
33 Quoted by Rolls, 1969: 354–5.
34 *Transactions of the Queensland Acclimatisation Society for 1892*; 1893: 17.
35 *Brisbane Courier*, 1 August 1872.
36 *Ibid*, 16 July 1872. A reference to the support, in the form of grants of land and money (the latter amounting to £250 in 1872), received by the Society from the government of Queensland.
37 *Brisbane Courier*, 14 October 1872.
38 *Ibid*, 23 June 1874.
39 *The Telegraph*, 9 May 1875.
40 *Ibid*, 26 April 1875.
41 Quoted by Jenkins, 1977: 115.
42 *Brisbane Courier*, 20 July 1871.
43 Quoted by Jenkins, 1977: 115.
44 *Ibid*.
45 Quoted by Jenkins, 1977: 114.
46 *Ibid*.
47 Quoted by Jenkins, 1977: 115.
48 Quoted by Jenkins, 1977: 112.
49 Quoted by Jenkins, 1977: 117.
50 *Ibid*.
51 *Ibid*.
52 Quoted by Jenkins, 1977: 118.
53 Quoted by Jenkins, 1977: 120.
54 Quoted by Jenkins, 1977: 94.
55 Quoted by Jenkins, 1977: 92.
56 See, e.g., *Emu* 28: 61.
57 Quoted by Jenkins, 1977: 20.
58 Quoted by Jenkins, 1977: 21.
59 Where some still survive.
60 Quoted by Jenkins, 1977: 22.
61 *West Australian Naturalist*, 1968: 1.
62 *West Australian Yearbook*, 1902–4: 138.
63 Quoted by Jenkins, 1977: 23.
64 *West Australian Naturalist*, 1976: 136.
65 Quoted by Jenkins, 1977: 42.
66 *Ibid*, page 45.

67 Oyster spawn.
68 *Sunday Times*, 19 June 1960. Quoted by Jenkins, 1977: 26.

Chapter 14

1 For much of the history of the acclimatisation movement in New Zealand I am indebted to Thomson, 1922 and Druett, 1983.
2 1922: 21–22.
3 This sentence is repeated almost verbatim but without quotes by Carolyn King in *Immigrant Killers*. Oxford University Press, 1984: 64.
4 As in Australia, the activities of acclimatisation societies in New Zealand were in fact 'naturalisation' rather than 'acclimatisation'. These activities had been carried out by private individuals for many years before the formation of the societies, which in both countries would have been more appropriately called 'naturalisation' societies.
5 Druett, 1983: 92.
6 *Ibid*: 95–6.
7 *Ibid*: 88.
8 *Ibid*: 96.
9 *Ibid*: 96.
10 *Ibid*: 99.
11 *Ibid*: 100.
12 McDowall, 1989: 406.
13 For further details on New Zealand acclimatisation societies and their activities, see Lever, 1985 and 1987.
14 For much of the history of the Nelson Acclimatisation Society I am indebted to Sowman, 1981.
15 Quoted by Sowman, 1981: 10.
16 *Ibid*.
17 Pages 140–1.
18 Damage to a tree caused by deer rubbing 'velvet' (the protective covering of skin) from their new-grown antlers.
19 For much of the history of the (North) Canterbury Acclimatisation Society I am indebted to Lamb, 1964 and Druett, 1983.
20 Von Haast, H. F. 1948. *The Life and Times of Sir Julius von Haast*: 224. Quoted by Lamb, 1964: 16.
21 Quoted by Lamb, 1964: 16.
22 *Ibid*.
23 Page 149.
24 Page 138.
25 For the present range of sika in New Zealand see pp 160–1.
26 Page 195. According to Druett, 1983 (page 137) who may have misread Thomson, the number was 10,000.
27 For much of the history of the Auckland Acclimatisation Society, I am indebted to Ashby, 1967 and Douglas C. Emmett, personal communication, 1990.
28 Quoted by Thomson, 1922: 152.
29 For much of the history of the Southland Acclimatisation Society, I am indebted to Stock, 1915.

30　Page 51.

31　For much of the history of the Hawke's Bay Acclimatisation Society, I am indebted to Wellwood, 1968.

32　Quoted by Wellwood, 1968: 20.

33　*Ibid.*

34　Quoted by Wellwood, 1968: 22.

35　Quoted by Druett, 1983: 114.

36　For much of the history of the Wellington Acclimatisation Society, I am indebted to McCulloch, 1985.

37　Reproduced as a frontispiece to McCulloch, 1985.

38　Quoted by McCulloch, 1985: 4.

39　For much of the history of the Taranaki Acclimatisation Society, I am indebted to Quickfall, 1974.

40　Quoted by Quickfall, 1974: 29.

41　Quoted by Quickfall, 1974: 25.

42　*Ibid.*

43　Lever, 1985.

44　Quoted by Quickfall, 1974: 29.

45　*Ibid.*

46　For much of the history of the Tauranga Acclimatisation Society, I am indebted to Scott, 1982.

47　B. Parkes (National Executive of Acclimatisation Societies), personal communication, 1989.

Chapter 15

1　Quoted by Weiner, 1985 (page 245), to whom I am indebted for much of the information on the acclimatisation movement in Russia.

2　Quoted by Weiner, 1985: 247.

3　Quoted by Weiner, 1985: 248.

4　Egyptian geese were first domesticated by the ancient Egyptians, by whom they were regarded as sacred.

5　Quoted by Weiner, 1985: 250–1.

6　Quoted by Weiner, 1985: 251.

7　*Ibid.*

8　The tarpan, the European wild steppe horse, which was at one time widespread throughout central Europe, became extinct in the wild in 1851, when the last ones were killed in the Ukraine.

9　Quoted by Weiner, 1985: 254.

10　Quoted by Weiner, 1985: 256.

11　Quoted by Weiner, 1985: footnote to page 257.

12　Deoxyribose nucleic (deoxyribonucleic) acid is the genetic material of organisms, whose sequence of paired bases constitutes the genetic 'make-up' or code.

13　Douglas R. Weiner, personal communication, 1989.

Chapter 16

1 Page 216.
2 Page 466.
3 Phillips, 1928: 49.
4 Mejiro is a name sometimes given to the Japanese White-eye.
5 See Lever, 1987.

Chapter 17

1 Page 105.

Index

Principal Animals and Plants

MAMMALS

Acuchi *Myoprocta* sp. 7
Agouti *Dasyprocta* sp. 7, 103, 110
Alpaca *'Lama pacos'* 4, 5, 30, 38, 65, 96, 103, 110, 175
Argali *Ovis ammon* 175
Armadillo, Dasypodidae 16, 31
Ass, Asiatic *Equus hemionus* 174
Aurochs *Bos primigenius* 25, 30

Bandicoot, Peramelidae 75
Beaver, Eurasian *Castor fiber* 30, 175, 179
Bison, American *Bison bison* 30
Bison, European *Bison bonasus* 13, 25
Blackbuck *Antilope cervicapra* 125–6
Boar, Wild *Sus scrofa* 12, 16, 17, 44, 126
Buffalo, Water *Bubalus bubalis* 175

Camel, Arabian *Camelus dromedarius* 5
Cat, Domestic *'Felis catus'* viii, 155
Chinchilla *Chinchilla brevicaudata / laniger* 77, 118

Deer, Axis *Cervus axis* 18, 30, 45–6, 48, 77, 111, 119–20, 163
Deer, Barasingha see Deer, Swamp
Deer, Black-tailed *Odocoileus hemionus* 151, 161
Deer, Chital see Deer, Axis
Deer, Fallow *Cervus dama* 12, 30, 32, 54, 103, 111–12, 119, 125, 139, 143, 146, 151, 163, 168–9
Deer, Hog *Cervus porcinus* 18, 77, 111, 125
Deer, Japanese Sika *Cervus nippon* 39, 48, 56, 65, 82, 146, 160–1
Deer, Mule see Deer, Black-tailed
Deer, Musk *Moschus moschiferus* 175
Deer, Red *Cervus elaphus* 30, 39, 48, 54–5, 103–4, 112, 120, 125, 138–9, 143, 146, 152, 156–8, 160, 162, 168–9, 175
Deer, Roe *Capreolus capreolus* 30, 48, 77, 141, 175
Deer, Rusa see Deer, Timor
Deer, Sambar *Cervus unicolor* 30, 39, 48, 56, 65, 82, 111, 151–2, 162–3
Deer, Spotted see Deer, Axis
Deer, Swamp *Cervus duvauceli* 30

Deer, Timor *Cervus timorensis* 77, 104, 111, 120, 125
Deer, Virginia see Deer, White-tailed
Deer, White-tailed *Odocoileus virginianus* 16, 30, 139, 157
Dingo *Canis familiaris dingo* 58
Dormouse, Edible *Glis glis* viii, 7
Dromedary see Camel, Arabian

Echidna, Short-nosed *Tachyglossus aculeatus* 75
Eland *Tragelaphus oryx* viii, 26–30, 32, 36, 38–9, 44, 48, 56, 77, 96–7, 110, 126
Elk see Moose

Ferret *'Mustela furo'* 22, 143, 146
Fox, Red *Vulpes vulpes* 113

Gazelle, Dorcas *Gasella dorcas* 77
Gemsbok see Oryx, Beisa
Giraffe *Giraffa camelopardalis* 22, 96
Gnu see Wildebeest
Goat, Angora 5, 18, 103, 110, 121–2, 126
Goat, Cashmere 110
Goat, Tibetan 130
Goat, Wild *Capra hircus* viii
Guanaco *Lama guanicoe* 30, 66

Hare, Brown *Lepus capensis* 77, 103, 111, 124, 139–40, 143, 152, 158, 163, 166, 168
Hare, Snowshoe *Lepus americanus* 77
Hedgehog, European *Erinaceus europaes* 7, 143
Hyrax, Rock *Procavia capensis* 77

Kangaroo, Western Grey *Macropus fuliginosus* 4
Kiang *Equus kiang* 4
Koala *Phascolarctus cinereus* 129
Kudu *Tragelaphus imberis / strepsiceros* viii, 30, 77

Lemur, Lemuridae 90
Llama *'Lama glama'* 4, 30, 96, 100–1, 110, 121–2, 175

Mongoose, Small Indian *Herpestes auropunctatus* 7, 113, 191
Moose *Alces alces* 16, 18, 157

Mouflon *Ovis musimon* 17, 48, 56

Nilgai *Bos tragocamelus* 13, 17, 30, 48

Onager see Ass, Asiatic
Oribi *Ourebia ourebia* 77
Oryx, Arabian *Oryx leucoryx* 30, 77
Oryx, Beisa *Oryx gazella* 77

Peetsi see Quagga
Possum, Brush-tailed *Trichosurus
    vulpecula* 110, 139, 143, 146, 152, 158,
    163, 166, 169, 191

Quagga *Equus quagga* 4

Rabbit, European *Oryctolagus
    cuniculus* viii
Rat, Black *Rattus rattus* 155, 167
Rat, Brown *Rattus norvegicus* 155, 167
Rat, House see Rat, Black
Rat, Ship see Rat, Black
Reindeer *Rangifer tarandus* 30

Sable *Martes zibellina* 179
Saiga *Saiga tatarica* 175
Sheep, Chinese 34, 39, 44, 46–8, 56, 65, 82
Sheep, Diminutive (Brittany) 34–5, 47
Sheep, Kalmuch 66
Sheep, Oxfordshire Downs 47, 82
Sheep, Purik 31, 36
Sheep, Rocky Mountain Bighorn *Ovis
    canadensis* 77
Sheep, Soay '*Ovis aries*' viii
Sheep, Somali 18
Sheep, Southdown 47
Sheep, Wexford 47
Springhare *Pedetes capensis* 77
Stoat *Mustela erminea* 17, 143, 146, 155–6,
    167

Tapir *Tapirus* sp. 7, 14
Tarpan *Equus caballus* 177

Vicugna *Vicugna vicugna* 30, 66, 175

Wallaby, Bennett's *Macropus rufogriseus
    bennetti* 30, 66, 82, 143
Wallaby, Brush-tailed Rock *Petrogale
    penicillata* 152
Wallaby, Parma *Macropus parma* 152
Wallaby, Red-necked *see* Wallaby,
    Bennett's
Wallaby, Tammar *Macropus eugenii* 152
Wapiti *Cervus elaphus canadensis* 30, 39,
    48, 56, 65, 77, 82, 157–8
Weasel *Mustela nivalis* 143, 146, 155–6
Wildebeest *Connochaetes taurinus* 14, 30
Wisent see Bison, European
Wolf *Canis lupus* 12, 14, 16, 177–8

Wombat, Common *Vombatus ursinus* 31

Yak *Bos mutus* 5, 30, 96, 175

Zebu *Bos indicus* 15, 17–18, 34, 96

BIRDS

Ant-thrush, Formicariidae 77
Avadavat, Red *Amandava amandava* 17,
    189

Bellbird, Crested *Oreoica gutturalis* 161
Blackbird *Turdus merula* 18, 68, 78,
    110–11, 114, 121, 123, 135–6, 141, 145,
    148–9, 159, 161, 167, 185
Blackcap *Sylvia atricapilla* 187
Brambling *Fringilla montifringilla* 113,
    161
Brolga *Grus rubicunda* 31, 57, 67, 149
Brush Turkey *Alectura lathami* 31, 38, 49,
    57–8, 67–8, 75, 83, 103, 149–50
Budgerigar *Melopsittacus undulatus* 31
Bulbul, Red-whiskered *Pycnonotus
    jocosus* 104, 105–6
Bullfinch *Pyrrhula pyrrhula* 18, 113, 136,
    185–6
Bunting, Butterfly *Passerina* sp. 189
Bunting, Cirl *Emberiza cirlus* 145, 161
Bunting, Indigo *Passerina cyanea* 189
Bunting, Mexican see Bunting, Butterfly
Bunting, Ortolan *Emberiza
    hortulana* 110, 161–2
Bunting, Yellow-breasted *Emberiza
    aureola* 189
Bush Quail, Painted *Perdicula
    erythrorhyncha* 90
Bustard, Australian *Choriotis australis* 38
Bustard, Great *Otis tarda* 4, 17, 31
Bustard, Great Indian *Choriotis
    nigriceps* 90
Bustard, Houbara *Chlamydotis
    undulata* 90
Button Quail *Turnix* sp. 90

Canary *Serinus canaria* 15, 18, 110, 135,
    148, 188
Canvasback *Aythya valisineria* 41, 170
Capercaillie *Tetrao urogallus* 6
Cardinal, Common *Cardinalis
    cardinalis* 188, 189
Cardinal, Red-crested *Paroaria
    coronata* 188, 189
Cassowary, Double-wattled *Casuarius
    casuarius* 148
Chaffinch *Fringilla coelebs* 18, 110, 113,
    121–2, 135–6, 141–2, 145, 148–9, 159, 186
Cockatoo, Black *Calyptorhynchus
    funereus* 90

Cormorant, Common *Phalacrocorax
carbo* 80, 81, 93
Corncrake *Crex crex* 185
Crane, Demoiselle *Anthropoides virgo*
67
Crane, Manchurian *Grus japonica* 31
Crane, Wattled *Bugeranus
carunculatus* 90
Crossbill, Parrot *Loxia
pytyopsittacus* 185, 186
Cuckoo, Pallid *Cuculus pallidus* 106
Curassow, Black *Crax alector* 78
Curassow, Blue-bellied *Crax alberti* 78

Dipper *Cinclus cinclus* 185
Dove, Barred *Geopelia striata* 188
Dove, Crested *Ocyphaps lophotes* 31
Dove, Laughing *Streptopelia
senegalensis* 127
Dove, Spotted *Streptopelia chinensis* 111,
113–14, 123, 127, 144
Dove, Zebra *Geopelia striata* 90
Duck, Australian Black *Anas superciliosa
rogersi* 41, 46, 48, 128
Duck, Australian Grey *Anas superciliosa
superciliosa* 138
Duck, Carolina see Duck, Wood
Duck, Eider *Somateria mollissima* 90,
170
Duck, Mandarin *Aix galericulata* 90, 189
Duck, Muscovy *Cairina moschata* 16, 18,
41, 48, 130
Duck, North American Black *Anas
rubripes* 41
Duck, Red-billed *Anas
erythrorhynchos* 31
Duck, Summer see Duck, Wood
Duck, Tufted *Aythya fuligula* 81, 90
Duck, Whistling *Dendrocygna* sp. 16, 90
Duck, Wood *Aix sponsa* 18, 31, 41, 48, 81,
90, 151
Dunnock *Prunella modularis* 77, 121–2,
141–2, 145, 148–9, 167, 185

Emu *Dromaius novaehollandiae* 4, 52, 55,
58, 67, 75, 83, 148, 168

Finch, Firetail *Emblema* sp. 149
Flycatcher, Narcissus *Ficedula
narcissina* 189
Francolin, Black *Francolinus
francolinus* 78
Francolin, Cape see Partridge, Cape
Francolin, Grey *Francolinus
pondicerianus* 78

Gadwall *Anas strepera* 41, 81
Garganey *Anas querquedula* 90
Goldeneye *Bucephala clangula* 81, 170
Goldfinch *Carduelis carduelis* 18, 104–5,
111, 113–14, 121, 123, 127, 135, 142, 145,
148–9, 159, 167, 185–6
Goose, Ashy-headed *Chloephaga
poliocephala* 31
Goose, Bar-headed *Anser indicus* 90
Goose, Barnacle *Branta leucopsis* 81
Goose, Bean *Anser fabalis* 16, 26, 31, 81
Goose, Brent *Branta bernicula* 46, 81
Goose, Canada *Branta canadensis* 12, 18,
46, 81, 128, 138, 142, 144, 156
Goose, Cereopsis *Cereopsis
novaehollandiae* 31, 90
Goose, Egyptian *Alopochen
aegyptiacus* 12, 90, 110, 138, 174
Goose, Hawaiian *Branta sandvicensis* 31
Goose, Magellan see Goose, Upland
Goose, Magpie *Anseranas
semipalmata* 31
Goose, Maned *Chenonetta jubata* 161
Goose, Orinoco *Neochen jubatus* 48
Goose, Spur-winged *Plectropterus
gambensis* 128
Goose, Upland *Chloephaga picta* 31, 90
Goose, White-fronted *Anser albifrons* 81
Greenfinch *Carduelis chloris* 104, 105,
111, 113–14, 135, 137, 142, 145, 148, 167,
186
Grouse, Black *Tetrao tetrix* 40
Grouse, Hazel *Bonasa bonasia* 49, 57, 91
Grouse, Red *Lagopus lagopus* 150
Grouse, Ruffed *Bonasa umbellus* 40, 45,
91
Grouse, Sharp-tailed *Tympanchus
phasianellus* 150
Grouse, Spruce *Dendragapus
canadensis* 91
Guan *Penelope* sp. 33, 34, 36, 40, 45–6,
66–7, 78, 83
Guineafowl, Helmeted *Numida
meleagris* 110, 118, 128

Hawfinch *Coccothraustes
coccothraustes* 187
Hedge Sparrow see Dunnock

Jackdaw *Corvus monedula* 22, 135
Java Sparrow *Padda oryzivora* 17, 110,
148, 188
Jungle Fowl, Grey *Gallus sonneratii* 82
Jungle Fowl, Red *Gallus gallus* 90, 110,
125

Kookaburra, Laughing *Dacelo
novaeguineae* 31, 76, 124, 125, 126–7,
145, 161

Lapwing *Vanellus vanellus* 149
Lark, Mongolian *Melanocorypha
mongolica* 189
Leiothrix, Red-billed *Leiothrix lutea* 188

Linnet *Acanthis cannabina* 18, 110, 135, 148, 159, 186
Lyrebird, Superb *Menura superba* 102, 123

Magpie, Black-backed *Gymnorhina tibicen* 76, 142, 145, 148, 167
Mallard *Anas platyrhynchos* 41, 81, 111, 123, 127–8, 138, 142, 144, 151, 156, 167, 170
Mallee Fowl *Leipoa ocellata* 76
Mannikin, Black-headed *Lonchura malacca* 189
Mannikin, Chestnut-breasted *Lonchura castaneothorax* 149
Mannikin, Nutmeg *Lonchura punctulata* 149, 188
Mockingbird, Northern *Mimus polyglottos* 187, 188
Morepork, see Owl, Boobook
Mynah, Common *Acridotheres tristis* 77, 78, 110, 111, 145, 161, 188
Mynah, Indian see Mynah, Common

Nene see Goose, Hawaiian
Nightingale *Erithacus megarhynchos* 108, 161, 185, 187
Nuthatch, European *Sitta europaea* 149

Ostrich *Struthio camelus* 4, 6–7, 14, 16, 18, 21, 67, 78, 110, 112, 114–15, 128
Owl, Barn *Tyto alba* 145
Owl, Boobook *Ninox novaeseelandiae* 155
Owl, Little *Athene noctua* 145–6

Parakeet, Alexandrine *Psittacula eupatria* 17
Parrot, Blue-headed *Pionus menstruus* 17
Partridge, Barbary *Alectoris barbara* 17, 149, 162
Partridge, Black see Francolin, Black
Partridge, Cape *Francolinus capensis* 90
Partridge, Chukar *Alectoris chukar* 90, 123, 142, 145, 150, 171
Partridge, French see Partridge, Red-legged
Partridge, Grey *Perdix perdix* 78, 138, 141, 149–50, 156, 159–60, 162, 166–7, 169
Partridge, Hungarian see Partridge, Grey
Partridge, Painted *Francolinus pictus* 90
Partridge, Red-legged *Alectoris rufa* 17, 32, 78, 138, 150, 155–6, 159
Partridge, Rock *Alectoris graeca* 5–6
Peacock-Pheasant, Malay *Polyplectron malacense* 90
Peacock-Pheasant, Rothschild's *Polyplectron inopinatum* 90
Peafowl, Common *Pavo cristatus* 90, 123, 145

Peafowl, Green *Pavo muticus* 90
Pelican, White *Pelecanus onocrotalus* 91
Pheasant, Cheer *Catreus wallichii* 30, 41, 90
Pheasant, Chinese Monal *Lophophorus lhuysii* 78
Pheasant, Common *Phasianus colchicus* 3, 18, 41, 57, 68, 78, 82, 111, 118, 125, 127, 138, 142, 144, 149–50, 151, 167
Pheasant, Fire-back *Lophura* sp. 55, 57, 67, 90
Pheasant, Golden *Chrysolophus pictus* 17, 18, 68, 78, 90, 113, 151
Pheasant, Great Argus *Argusianus argus* 90
Pheasant, Himalayan Monal *Lophophorus impeyanus* 30–1, 78, 90
Pheasant, Japanese *Phasianus colchicus versicolor* 31, 57, 68, 82
Pheasant, Kalij *Lophura leucomelana* 41, 82, 90
Pheasant, Mongolian *Phasianus colchicus mongolicus* 128
Pheasant, Reeves's *Syrmaticus reevesii* 82, 87–9
Pheasant, Ring-necked *Phasianus colchicus torquatus* 31, 68, 78, 138, 144, 150–1, 156, 168
Pheasant, Silver *Lophura nycthemera* 17, 68, 78, 90, 151
Pigeon, Bronzewing *Phaps chalcoptera* 49, 55, 57, 66, 83, 148–9, 161
Pigeon, Crested *Ocyphaps lophotes* 90, 161
Pigeon, Crowned *Goura* sp. 78
Pigeon, Feral *Columba livia* 123
Pigeon, New Caledonia *Ducula goliath* 148
Pigeon, Wonga *Leucosarcia melanoleuca* 31, 38, 49, 54, 57, 61, 66, 70, 76, 83, 161
Pintail *Anas acuta* 41, 46, 48, 78, 81
Pintail, Bahama *Anas bahamensis* 48, 90
Plover, Golden *Pluvialis apricaria* 149
Pochard *Aythya ferina* 81, 170
Prairie Chicken *Tympanuchus cupido* 31, 34, 35, 40, 45, 48, 65, 67, 82, 90–1, 150
Ptarmigan, Rock *Lagopus mutus* 41, 49, 57

Quail, Black-breasted *Coturnix coromandelica* 150
Quail, Bobwhite *Colinus virginianus* 35, 40–1, 48–9, 91, 138, 145, 150, 162, 166
Quail, Brown *Synoicus ypsilophorus* 138, 145, 149, 150, 156, 160
Quail, California *Lophortyx californica* 31, 49, 82, 104–5, 111, 113, 125, 128–9, 138, 142, 144, 149–50, 156, 160–1, 162, 166

Quail, Common *Coturnix coturnix* 90
Quail, Gambel's *Lophortyx gambelii* 188
Quail, Mountain *Oreortyx picta* 82, 138,
   167–8
Quail, Pectoral *Coturnix pectoralis* 138,
   149–50
Quail, Stubble see Quail, Pectoral
Quail, Virginia see Quail, Bobwhite

Redpoll *Acanthis flammea* 136, 137, 142,
   145, 149, 161
Redwing *Turdus iliacus* 185
Rhea, Greater *Rhea americana* 4
Robin, European *Erithacus rubecula* 110,
   135, 148, 159, 161, 186
Robin, Japanese *Erithacus akahige* 189
Robin, Pekin see Leiothrix, Red-billed
Rook *Corvus frugilegus* 110, 121, 135, 137,
   142, 148–9, 159, 167
Rosella, Crimson *Platycercus elegans* 145
Rosella, Eastern *Platycercus eximius* 145

Sandgrouse, Black-bellied *Pterocles*
   orientalis 90
Sandgrouse, Pintailed *Pterocles*
   alchata 90
Sandgrouse, Pallas's *Syrrhaptes*
   paradoxus 40
Scaup *Aythya marila* 41, 48–9
Scoter *Melanitta nigra* 170
Secretary Bird *Saggitarius*
   serpentarius 7, 78, 104
Shag, Spotted *Phalacrocorax*
   punctatus 155, 170
Shama, White-rumped *Copsychus*
   malabaricus 188–9
Shoveller *Anas clypeata* 81, 90
Shrike, Great-grey *Lanius excubitor* 161
Shrike, Red-backed *Lanius collurio* 161
Siskin *Carduelis spinus* 110, 161, 185, 186
Skylark *Alauda arvensis* 68, 78, 104, 111,
   113–14, 121–2, 128, 135–6, 141, 145, 148,
   149, 159, 161, 167, 185–6, 188
Snipe, Common *Gallinago gallinago* 170
Snowcock, Himalayan *Tetraogallus*
   himalayensis 90
Sparrow, Chestnut *Sorella eminibey* 148
Sparrow, House *Passer domesticus* 77,
   104, 110–11, 112, 121, 123, 135–6, 142,
   145, 148–9, 159, 167, 183, 185–6, 191
Sparrow, Tree *Passer montanus* 77, 111,
   122, 149
Starling, Common *Sturnus vulgaris* 78,
   104, 105, 110–11, 113–14, 121, 123–4,
   135–6, 145, 148–9, 156, 161, 167, 184–7,
   191
Stork, Adjutant *Leptotilos*
   javanicus/dubius 78
Stork, White *Ciconia ciconia* 17, 31
Sunbird, Nectarinidae 17, 189

Swan, Black *Cygnus atratus* 31, 76, 81, 90,
   127, 136, 138, 142, 144, 151, 156
Swan, Black-necked *Cygnus*
   melanocoryphus 31, 78
Swan, Mute *Cygnus olor* 110, 123, 124,
   127, 142, 144, 151
Swan-Goose *Anser cygnoides* 81

Teal, Blue-winged *Anas discors* 41
Thrush, Mistle *Turdus viscivorus* 185
Thrush, Song *Turdus philomelos* 68, 77–8,
   110–11, 113, 121, 135–6, 141, 145, 148,
   159, 161, 167, 185–6
Tit, Great *Parus major* 185
Tit, Long-tailed *Aegithalos caudatus* 149
Tragopan, Horned *Tragopan*
   melanocephalus 77
Tragopan, Satyr *Tragopan satyra* 77
Tragopan, Temminck's *Tragopan*
   temminckii 151
Trumpeter, Common *Psophia*
   crepitans 49, 57
Turkey, Common *Meleagris gallopavo* 40,
   67
Turkey, Ocellated *Agriocharis*
   ocellata 31, 40, 48–9, 56, 67

Wagtail, Grey *Motacilla cinerea* 149
Wagtail, Pied *Motacilla alba* 149
Wagtail, Yellow *Motacilla flava* 149
Warbler, Bush *Cettia diphone* 189
Wattle Bird, Little *Anthochaera*
   chrysoptera 123
Wattle Bird, Yellow *Anthochaera*
   paradoxa 123
Waxbill, Red-browed *Aegintha*
   temporalis 149
Weka *Gallirallus australis* 148
White-eye, Japanese *Zosterops*
   japonica 188, 189
Whitethroat *Sylvia nana* 148
Wigeon *Anas penelope* 17, 81, 151, 170
Wonga Wonga see Pigeon, Wonga
Woodcock *Scolopax rusticola* 170
Woodlark *Lullula arborea* 149, 187
Woodpecker, Picidae 77, 149

Yellowhammer *Emberiza citrinella* 104,
   110, 136–8, 141, 145, 148–9, 187

REPTILES AND AMPHIBIANS

Frog, Australian Green Tree *Litoria*
   sp. 144, 147
Snake, Tiger *Notechis ater/scutatus* 127

FISH

Bass, Black see Bass, Largemouth
Bass, Largemouth *Micropterus salmoides* 91, 152, 154
Bass, Silver *Pomoxis annularis* 152
Burbot *Lota lota* 59

Carp, Common *Cyprinus carpio* viii, 128
Carp, Crucian *Carassius carassius* viii
Catfish, Channel *Ictalurus punctatus* 153
Catfish, European *Silurus glanis* 34, 36, 49, 55, 58, 65, 68–70, 84
Char(r) *Salvelinus alpinus* 50, 59, 78, 83
Char(r), American Brook see Trout, American Brook
Cod, Murray *Maccullochella macquariensis* 33, 42, 49, 58, 76
Cod, Perch see Cod, Murray

Eel, Common *Anguilla anguilla* 71, 128
Eel, Conger *Conger conger* 53

Flounder *Platichthys flesus* 71

Gouramie *Osphromenus gorami* 78
Grayling *Thymallus thymallus* 50, 59, 78
Gudgeon *Gobio gobio* 53, 78

Loach, Pond *Cobitis fossilis* 70

Mullet, Grey *Crenimugil labrosus* 71, 78

Perch *Perca fluviatilis* 50, 128, 153
Pike-Perch see Zander
Pilchard see Sardine
Plaice *Pleuronectes platessa* 71

Roach *Rutilus rutilus* 110

Salmon, Atlantic *Salmo salar* 31, 35, 50, 53, 58–9, 68, 78, 83, 91, 93, 108, 110, 128, 140–1, 147, 152, 158, 164, 166
Salmon, Chinook *Oncorhynchus tshawytscha* 140, 144, 147, 152–3, 158, 160, 164, 187
Salmon, Danube *Hucho hucho* 50
Salmon, Quinnat see Salmon, Chinook
Salmon, Sockeye *Oncorhynchus nerka* 147
Sardine *Sardina pilchardus* 84
Smelt *Osmerus eperlanus* 153–4

Tench *Tinca tinca* 55, 58, 110, 128
Thunderfish, European see Loach, Pond
Trout, American Brook *Salvelinus fontinalis* 147, 154–5, 158, 164–5, 168, 171
Trout, Brown *Salmo trutta* 50, 59, 68, 78, 83, 91, 93, 103, 106, 111, 124, 128–9, 132, 140–1, 144, 146, 152, 154, 155, 158, 160, 164–71, 176, 187
Trout, Lake *Salvelinus namaycush* 91
Trout, Loch Leven *'Salmo levensis'* 164
Trout, Rainbow *Salmo gairdneri* 140, 144, 146–7, 155, 158, 160, 164, 165–6, 168–71
Trout, Sea see Trout, Brown

Wels see Catfish, European
Whitefish *Coregonus albulus* 153

Zander *Stizostedion lucioperca* 31, 36, 42, 45, 83–4

INSECTS

Bees, Bumble *Bombus* sp. 136, 142, 143, 164
Bee, Egyptian see Bee, Honey
Bee, Hive see Bee, Honey
Bee, Honey *Apis mellifera* 85, 110, 137
Bee, Ligurian see Bee, Honey
Bee, Syrian see Bee, Honey
Blowfly, Golden-haired *Calliphora laemica* 145

Cochineal Insect *Coccus cacti / Dactylopius coccus* 78, 110, 116, 117

Moth, Codlin *Laspeyresia pomonella* 168

Silkworm, Ailanthus *Samia cynthia* 42, 50, 55, 59, 61–2, 70, 72, 78, 85, 110
Silkworm, Common see Silkworm, Mulberry
Silkworm, Cynthia see Silkworm, Ailanthus
Silkworm, Mulberry *Bombyx mori* 62, 84–5, 91
Silkworm, Yamma Mai *Antheraea yammamai* 59, 70, 84–5

CRUSTACEANS

Crab, Edible *Cancer pagurus / Scylla serrata* 78, 153
Crayfish, Freshwater *Astacus pallipes* 35, 42, 58
Lobster, Blue *Homarus vulgaris* 78
Prawn, Freshwater *Macrobrachium* sp. 153

MOLLUSCS

Mussel, Pearl *Margaritifer margaritifer* 34, 42

Oyster, Flat *Ostrea edulis* 62
Oyster, Native see Oyster, Flat
Snail, Garden *Helix aspersa* 21

PLANTS

Argan *Argania spinosa* 79
Arrowroot, Brazilian *Ipomoea batatus* 43,
   50, 85
Avocado Pear *Monstera deliciosa* 117

Bean, Lima *Phaseolus lunatus* 50, 63, 73
Bilberry *Vaccinium myrtillus* 79
Blackberry *Rubus fruticosus* 106, 142
Blackwood *Acacia* sp. 76
Bramble *Rubus* sp. 79

Cactus, Prickly Pear *Opuntia*
   cochinellifer 110, 116–17
Cassava, American *Manihot esculenta* 78
Clover, Red *Trifolium pratense* 164
Cotton, American *Gossypium*
   barbadense/hirsutum 179
Crocus *Crocus nudiflorus* 79

Ebony *Diospyrus ebenus* 60

Fig *Ficus* sp. 105, 170
Fir, Douglas *Pseudotsuga douglasii/*
   menziesii 144
Fir, Silver *Albies alba* 78
Flax *Phormium* sp. 76, 163

Gentian, Great Yellow *Gentiana lutea* 79
Glasswort *Salicornia* sp. 137
Grass, Buffalo *Buchloe dactyloides* 78
Grass, Elephant *Pennisetum*
   purpureum 63, 73
Grass, Tussock (Tussac) *Poa*
   flabellata 78, 95, 138
Grenadilla *Cyphomandra* sp. 63
Gum, Blue *Eucalyptus*
   globulus/saligna 76
Gum, Red *Eucalyptus camalduleasis/*
   Angophora castata 76, 116

Ironbark *Eucalyptus paniculata/creba* 76

Larch *Larix decidua/kaempferi* 78
Lupin, Tree *Lupinus arboreus* 137

Maize, Peruvian *Zea mays* 60
Manuka *Leptospermum* sp. 163
Monkswood *Aconitum napellus* 79
Mulberry *Morus* sp. 108, 116, 121, 144
Mustard, Black *Brassica nigra* 78

Nardoo *Marsilea drummondii* 73

Oak, Cork *Quercus suber* 79, 85, 108
Oak, Pedunculate *Quercus robur* 84
Oak, Turkey *Quercus cerris* 84
Oak, Valonea *Quercus macrolepis* 79
Osier *Salix viminalis* 79

Palm, Date *Phoenix dactylifera* 6
Palmetto *Sabal* sp. 6
Pea, Jamaican Hook-podded *Dolichos*
   unguiculatus 50, 60, 63, 73
Pea, Wild *Nauclea latifolia* 155
Persimmon *Diospyros virginiana* 170
Pine, Austrian *Pinus laricio* 71
Pine, Monterey *Pinus radiata* 163
Pine, Norfolk Island *Araucaria*
   heterophylla 144

Rice, Canadian see Rice, Wild
Rice, Wild *Zizania aquatica* 60, 65, 155

Saffron, Meadow *Colchicum*
   autumnale 79
Sassafras *Sassafras* sp. 76
Spruce, Norway *Picea abies* 78
Stringy Bark *Eucalyptus* sp. 76
Swamp Oak *Casuarina* sp. 170

Thistle *Carduus/Cirsium* spp. 137

Valerian, Common *Valeriana*
   officinalis 79

Walnut *Juglans regia* 79, 137
Wellingtonia *Sequoiadendron*
   giganteum 79

Yam, Chinese *Dioscorea batatas* 4, 33, 36,
   42–3, 47, 50, 63

Index

People and Organisations

Aarmanston, Viscount 122
Abinger, Lord 60
Acclimatisation societies
    in Algeria: *Comité d'Acclimatation de*
        l'Algérie 9, 99, 100
    in Australia 99–129, 190
        Ballarat 109, 128
        Beechworth 109
        Central 103
        Monaro 103
        New England Trout 103
        New South Wales (Sydney) 38, 51, 99,
            101–6
        Orange Trout 103
        Portland 109
        Queensland (Brisbane) 39, 51, 52, 55,
            58, 66, 68, 90, 99, 115–22
        South Australia (Adelaide) 99, 111–15
        Northern Tasmanian (Launceston) 99,
            122–4
        Tasmanian Game Protection and
            Acclimatisation Society (Hobart) 99,
            122–4, 158
        Victoria (Melbourne) 31, 37, 48, 49, 51,
            52, 57, 58, 65, 75–9, 84, 99, 103, 104,
            106–111, 131, 152, 158
        Western Australia Avicultural
            Society 129
        Western Australia (Perth) 99, 124–9
    in Ceylon (Sri Lanka) 10
    in Channel Islands (Guernsey) 39, 43, 50,
        53, 60-3, 71–3
    in China 10
    in Egypt 10
    in France
        Société Régionale d'Acclimatation
            d'Encouragement et de Progrès
            (Nancy) 4
        Société Zoologique d'Acclimatation
            pour la Région des Alpes
            (Grenoble) 4, 94
        Société Zoologique
            d'Acclimatation vii, 1–10, 20, 26, 29,
            33, 35, 36, 42–3, 44, 47, 51, 52, 60, 83,
            84, 95, 96–7, 98, 174, 176, 181
    in Holland 10
    in India (Lahore and Calcutta) 10, 90
    in Italy 10
    in Madeira 10
    in New Zealand 99, 130–71, 190

Ashburton 134
Auckland 38, 147–55
Bay of Islands 134
(North) Canterbury 140–4, 147, 152
South Canterbury 134, 141
Hawera 134, 135
Hawke's Bay 159–61
Hobson 134
Mangonui-Whangaroa 134
Marlborough 134
Nelson 135–40, 147
Otago 144–7, 154
Southland 156–8, 166
Stratford 134, 135
Taranaki 165–7
Tauranga 167–71
Waimarino 134
Waimate 134
Wairarapa 134
Wairoa 132, 134
Waitaki 134
Wanganui 134, 135, 152
Wellington 131, 134, 146, 161–4, 166
West Coast 134
Westland 134
Whangarei 134
    in Prussia: *Akklimatisations–verein*
        (Berlin and Cologne) 10
    in Russia: Imperial Russian
        Acclimatisation Society of
        Moscow 65, 66, 172–82
    in Sicily: *Società di Acclimazione*
        (Palermo) 10, 51, 52
    in South Africa (Natal) 90
    in Spain (Madrid) 10
    in Switzerland 10
    in United Kingdom
        Acclimatisation Society of the United
            Kingdom vii, viii, 20–98; *passim*
        Glasgow (Scotland) 35, 37, 39
    in United States and Hawaiian
        Islands 183–90
        American Acclimatisation Society 184
        Cincinnati Acclimatisation
            Society 184–5
        Cincinnati Society of Natural
            History 185, 188
        Country Club of San Francisco 152,
            154, 187
        Honolulu Mejiro Club 189

220 THEY DINED ON ELAND

Acclimatisation societies, in United States and Hawaiian Islands (*contd.*)
    Hui Manu (Bird Society) 188–9
    Society for the Acclimatisation of Foreign Birds (Cambridge, Massachusetts) 186
    Society for the Introduction of Useful Song Birds into Oregon (Portland Song Bird Club) 186, 187
Adams, G. G. 85
Ailesbury, (sic) Lady 16, 19
Albert, Prince Consort 40, 81
Allan (Allen), John 41, 55
Anne, Queen (wife of James I) 12
Annenkov, Nikolai Ivanovich 175, 176, 177, 179
Arden, R. E. 92
Argyle, (sic), Duke of 35
Astley, Philip 13
Augusta, Princess 15, 17–18
Austin, T. A. 34
Australia *see* acclimatisation societies
Avery, John 184

Bacon, Francis 13
Bailey, F. M. 117–18
Baldwin, H. A. 188
Balfour, F. R. S. ix
Banks, Sir Joseph 94
Barkley, Sir Henry 108, 109, 115
Barnard, Revd R. 41
Barracluff, J. T. 104
Bartlett, A. D. 49
Basstian, Christopher 158
Becquerel, Alexander Edmond 95
Becquerel, Antoine César 95
Becquerel, Antoine Henri 95
Bedford, Dukes of ix
Beketov, Andrei Nikolaevich 174
Bennett, Dr George 101–2, 106
Bennett, William 52
Bentham, Jeremy 18
Ber, I. S. 176
Berkeley, the Hon. George Charles Grantley F. 28, 29, 35, 40–1, 42, 48, 53–4, 90
Bernays, Lewis 117, 119
Berney, G. D. 55, 58
Bicidor, Samuel H. 33
Bisdee, John 119
Black, Dr Thomas 107
Black, J. 103
Blackburrow, W. E. 35, 38, 39
Blackwell, Thomas 28
Blyth, E. S. 35
Bogdanov, Anatolii Petrovich 174–6, 177, 178–9, 180, 181
Borzenkov, Iakov Andreevich 174, 176
Bowen, Sir George 38, 49, 115
Brandt, F. B. 176

Breadalbane, Marquess of viii, 26, 28, 29, 30, 36, 42, 44
Brereton, R. M. 33, 36
Brereton, Sir William 12
British Association for the Advancement of Science 33, 95, 98
Brocklehurst, Capt. Henry ix
Brosse, Guy de la 1
Broughton, J. L. 68
Brown, J. H. 191
Brown, Lancelot ('Capability') 13
Buccleuch, Duke of 35
Buchan, Earl of 35
Buckland, Frank (Francis Trevelyan) 20–32, 33, 35, 38, 40, 41, 42, 44, 45, 46–7, 50, 52, 53, 54, 55, 64, 65, 66, 68, 70, 83, 84, 92, 95, 96, 98
Buckland, J. W. 66, 68
Buckland, Mary (née Morland: wife of Frank) 20, 22–3
Buckland, the Very Revd Dr William 20, 21–2, 96
Buffon, Georges Louis Leclerc, Comte de 1–2
Bull, Dr Henry 57, 66, 83
Burckhardt, Jacob 12
Burdett Coutts, Miss Angela 33, 34, 35, 65, 84, 85
Burlington, Lord 15
Burr, Higford 35, 40, 50–1, 54, 55, 58, 60, 65, 68, 70, 84
Bush, J. 40, 41, 42, 44, 49, 56, 59, 65, 66, 70, 82, 84, 85
Buxton, Sir Thomas Fowell, Bt viii

Caesar, Julius 11
Carey, Peter Stafford 39
Caroline, Queen (wife of George IV) 13
Carré, H. O. 47, 55, 61, 63, 71, 82–3
Carrington, Lord 102
Ceylon (Sri Lanka), *see* acclimatisation societies
Chamberlayne, Thomas 60
Chandos, James Brydges, Duke of 15, 16, 19
Chantrey, Sir Francis 20
Charles I, King of England 12, 80
Charles II, King of England 12, 80–1
Charlotte, Queen (wife of George III) 15, 17–18, 19
Cheater, Harry 92
Child, Sarah, Mrs Robert 15, 19
China, *see* acclimatisation societies
Chirnside, Audrey 157
Chirnside, Thomas 120
Clanricarde, Marquis of 28
Clark, William N. 184
Clarke, Sir Rupert 156–7
Cleghorn, the Hon. A. S. 188
Clifford, G. P. 146

Clive, Lord and Lady 16, 18
Cobham, Lord 16
Colebrooke, John 63
Collings, Dr Adolphus 72
Collings, Edward 71
Collings, Revd W. T. ('Seigneur of
    Serk') 54, 57, 61, 71, 73, 84
Comité d'Acclimatation de l'Algérie 9, 99,
    100
Conyngham, Marquis of 28
Cook, Capt 94
Cooper, Col. Edward ix
Costeker, J. 90
Cox, Edward (of Mulgoa) 103
Cox, Edward William 28
Craig, B. F. 183
Crauford, J. A. 55
Craven, Earl of 16, 28, 41, 48
Crawford, Col 57
Crichton, A. W. 52
Crockford, John 23, 28
Cross, Edward 14
Crowe, John Rice 55
Crystal Palace 68
Cumberland, Duke of 16
Cunard, E. 34, 35
Cuvier, Georges 172–3

Damer, Capt. S. Dawson 34, 36, 65
Darling, Governor 50
Darwin, Charles 95, 182
Daubenton, Louis Jean Marie 2
Davidson, W. J. 34
Davis, Dr 183
Dawson, T. Pilkington 28
Dear, H. C. 34
Delany, Mary, Mrs Patrick 15, 17
Denison, Col. 55, 56–7
Derby, Earl of 25–6, 29
Dickens, Charles 97–8
Dobree, Mr 63
Dolmatoff, Dimitri de 25
Doncaster, W. C. 128
Donne, Thomas Edward 131, 132
Drummond, Andrew 28
Dry, Sir Richard 122
Duff, James, 4th Earl of Fife viii
Dyce, J. 40

Early, Henry 42, 68
Eastman Kodak Company 189
Edgar, Mr 125
Edwards, Alfred 184
Egerton, Lord 26, 29–30
Egypt, see acclimatisation societies
Elliott, Charles 135
Embling, Dr Thomas 107
Erkenbrecher, Andrew 184, 185–6, 188
Ermolov, Aleksei Sergeevich 179
Erskine, Lord 18

Evelyn, John 12, 81
Eyre, Lieut. Governor, of Jamaica 60
Ezra, Alfred ix

Fal'ts-Fein, Fridrikh Eduardovich 179
Farenkol', Avgust 175, 176
Fischer von Waldheim, Grigorii
    Ivanovich 172, 174
Fortescue, Lord 15
France see acclimatisation societies
Francis, Francis 53, 58–9, 64–5, 68–70, 70–1
Francis, G. W. 111, 112
Frederick II, King of Denmark 12
Friedrich-Wilhelm, King of Prussia 6

Gage, Viscount 60
Galway, Lady Brigit 16
Garnett, Thomas 34
Genczik, Dr 55
Geoffroy Saint-Hilaire, Albert 8–9
Geoffroy Saint-Hilaire, Etienne 2, 172, 171,
    181
Geoffroy Saint-Hilaire, Isidore 2–4, 7, 20,
    33, 35, 43, 95, 172, 174, 179, 181, 182
George IV, King of England 81
George VI, King of England 113
Gillbanks, Jackson 55, 60, 85
Gobbold, Don Fredrigo 162
Gordon, Adam Lindsay 107
Graham, J. Maxtone 42
Grant, Mackenzie 125
Gray, Dr John 95–6, 98
Grey, Sir George (governor of New
    Zealand) 106, 143, 152
Grey, Viscount ix
Gro, E. E. 176
Guerin-Meneville, M. 55
Günther, Dr A. 34, 36, 96
Gurney, J. H. ix
Gurney, S. 34, 49, 59, 60, 67

Haast, Dr (later Sir) Julius von 130–1,
    140–1
Hackett, the Hon. J. W. (later Sir
    Winthrop) 124–5
Halifax, Lord 15, 17
Hambro, Charles 92
Hamilton, Capt. D. G. 160
Hamilton, Duke of 35
Hancock, Henry 57, 70, 84
Hann, William 119–20
Harcourt, Lord 22
Hardy, Capt. 33–4, 40
Harewood, Lord 16
Hawaiian Islands see acclimatisation
    societies, United States and
    Hawaiian Islands
Hawkins, Waterhouse 64, 81, 85, 87, 88, 91,
    96
Henderson, Thomas 150

Henry I, King of England 11
Henry III, King of England 11–12
Henry IV, King of England 11
Henry VII, King of England 12
Hepburn, Mr 55
Hill, Mr 117
Hill, Sir Richard 16
Hill, Viscount 26, 29, 36
Hillebrand, Dr William 188
Hockings, H. N. 120
Hockings, R. A. C. 120
Holford, R. S. 68
Holland, see acclimatisation societies
Honeyfield, Mr 165
Hooker, Sir Joseph 94, 95
Hooker, Sir William 94, 95
Hoskins, Dr S. Elliott 53, 60, 63, 71, 72
Howell, Capt. John 158
Hudson, Col. 92
Hudson's Bay Company 65
Hunt, James 95
Hunter, John 16
Hursthouse, Charles 131
Huyshe, Revd J. 47

India see acclimatisation societies
Isabella II, Queen of Spain 5
Isenberg, Dora R. 188
Italy see acclimatisation societies
Iveagh, Earl of ix

Jackson, C. W. 156
Jager, Dr. 55
James I, King of England 12, 80
Jamrach, Carl 39
Jardin des Plantes due Roi (later Muséum
    National d'Histoire Naturelle) 1, 2,
    174, 177
Jervois, Sir William 112, 114
Johnson, A. M. 146
Jones, Joshua 184
Jongh, M. de 61
Jordon, R. C. 167

Kalinovskii, Iakov Nikolaevich 176, 177,
    179
Kashchenko, Nikolai Feofanivich 179, 180
Kaye, J. 92
Kennion, Bishop of Adelaide 113
Kent, Saville 129
Khartoum, Emir of 6
Khlopov, V. V. 176
Kidd, Dr 21
Kozhevnikov, Grigorii
    Aleksandrovich 179, 180, 181
Kulagin, Nikolai Mikhailovich 180

L'Abbé Incarville 61
Lakeman, Sir Stephen 65, 68–70
Lamarck, Jean-Baptiste 181, 182

Lamington, Lord 120
Larkworthy, Falconer 151, 162
Lauderdale, Bess Dysart, Duchess of 15, 16
Le Souef, Lieut-Col. E. A. 126
Learoyd, Mr 128–9
Ledger, Charles 103
Leicester, Earl of ix
Lichtenstein, Prince 48, 55
Lindsay, W. Lauder 95
Linnean Society 96
Lippe, Count 18
Lichfield, Earl of 15
Loder, Sir Giles and Sir Edmund, Bts ix
Logan, J. R. 104
London Zoo 66
Lord, J. K. 90–1
Louis IX, King of France 12
Louis XIV, King of France 1, 22
Lowe, James 38, 40, 41, 43, 52, 53, 57, 60–1,
    62, 63, 64, 68, 71
Lowrey, Mrs Frederick J. 188, 189
Ludlow, Edward L. 184
Lumsden, David 47

Macansh, the Hon. J. D. 117
McClarty (ranch) 125
McConnell, David 120
McCoy, Prof. Frederick S. xv–xvi, 75, 109
McGowan, W. 122–3
McInerny, William H. 188
Maclean (McLean), A. C. 54, 57
Madden, Dr 75
Madeira, see acclimatisation societies
Maitland, Sir James 164
Malcolm, J. Wingfield 56, 60, 70, 90
Malcomb, W. 34
Malmesbury, Earl of 28, 35, 40
Mansell, Mr 15
Marchand, André 62
Marlborough, Duke of 16, 65, 66, 67, 82
Marshall, Lieut. C. H. J. 89–90
Marshall, Robert 49, 56
Martin, Peter 43
Marx, Karl 181
Maslov, Stepan Alekseevich 174, 176, 177,
    180
Matheson & Co. 39, 47, 57
Maxtone, J. 34
Maxwell, Mr 125
Meade–Waldo, Lieut.-Col. E. G. B. ix
Medhurst, W. 87–8, 89
Melbourne Botanic Gardens 75, 107, 108,
    111
Melbourne Zoological Gardens 109, 110
Merivale, Herman 57
Middendorf, A. F. 176
Miller, Dr 55, 57
Miller, Dr W. Harte 55
Milne-Edwards, Henri 8
Minchin, R. E. 112, 113